Intermediate Algebra

SECOND EDITION

Intermediate Algebra

John H. Minnick

De Anza College
Cupertino, California

PRENTICE-HALL, INC.
ENGLEWOOD CLIFFS, NEW JERSEY 07632

Library of Congress Cataloging in Publication Data

MINNICK, JOHN HARPER (date)
    Intermediate algebra.

    1. Algebra. I. Title.
QA154.M68 1978   512.9   77-14559
ISBN   0-13-469569-0

10   9   8   7   6   5   4   3

Printed in the United States of America

PRENTICE-HALL INTERNATIONAL, INC., *London*
PRENTICE-HALL OF AUSTRALIA PTY. LIMITED, *Sydney*
PRENTICE-HALL OF CANADA, LTD., *Toronto*
PRENTICE-HALL OF INDIA PRIVATE LIMITED, *New Delhi*
PRENTICE-HALL OF JAPAN, INC., *Tokyo*
PRENTICE-HALL OF SOUTHEAST ASIA PTE. LTD., *Singapore*
WHITEHALL BOOKS LIMITED, *Wellington, New Zealand*

contents

preface

This is a textbook for a one-semester course for college students who have studied algebra before, but who are not yet ready for the study of trigonometry. One of the major objectives of such a course is to strengthen the student's understanding of the topics introduced in a first course in algebra. Thus, the first three chapters of this book contain a complete review of the beginning concepts. However, as each topic is reviewed the student is required to go beyond what was given in a first course. For example, when the factoring formula for the difference of two squares is reviewed in Chapter 1, the formula for factoring the sum or difference of two cubes is also presented. When division with polynomials of one variable is reviewed in Chapter 2, the technique is extended to division with polynomials that contain two variables. After reviewing the use of factoring to solve second degree equations in Chapter 3, factoring is then used to solve certain third and fourth degree equations. Thus, the first three chapters should not be skipped even by those students who have just completed a first course in algebra.

Although sets are introduced in Chapter 1, and the solution sets for equations and inequalities are defined in Chapter 3, set notation is not used extensively and the special notation for an interval has been omitted from this edition of the book. In Chapter 4 the solution set for an equation or inequality in two variables and the graph of the solution set are presented. In Chapter 5 the solution set for a system of equations that contains more than one variable is given. Functional notation, $f(x)$, is introduced in Chapter 1 as a means of specifying that certain replacements should be made for the variables in an expression. The concept of domain and range and the correspondence between these two sets is not given until Chapter 6, however. Variation and sequences are treated as special types of functions in that chapter. Logarithmic functions are defined as the inverses of exponential functions in Chapter 7. It is assumed that many students will soon have access to an electronic calculator, and thus a presentation of common logarithms and natural logarithms is given that does not include the use of logarithm tables. For those who do not yet have a calculator there is also the standard presentation that includes tables, linear interpolation, and calculations using logarithms.

The set of real numbers is the universal set in the book, and imaginary solutions for equations are ignored. However, Chapter 8 introduces arithmetic with complex numbers and imaginary square roots and cube roots. This may be covered any time after the completion of Chapter 3, if desired.

The use of formulas in problem solving is treated extensively in the book, and there are many problems stated verbally that require the student to translate first into an algebraic equation. Many students lack confidence in their ability to solve such problems and are apprehensive when they encounter a whole section of word problems. Therefore, I have included some word problems in each section that gives techniques for solving equations, but there are no sections consisting entirely of word problems.

Axioms, definitions, and theorems are always carefully stated and identified as such. Some theorems are proved so that the reader may be introduced to the nature of a mathematical proof, but the student is not asked to write proofs in the exercises. Answers to most of the exercises, including graphs, are given in the back of the book. Additional problems that can be used for testing are available in a separate teacher's manual.

If all sections of the book are covered, including the set of review exercises for each chapter, there is enough for a semester course that meets four hours per week. Several sections are designated as optional, and these sections may be omitted without interrupting the continuity of the presentation, if a shorter course is desired.

JHM

Intermediate Algebra

1

polynomial expressions

1.1 Sets of Real Numbers

Sometimes we represent a set by listing its members within braces. For example, $\{1, 2\}$ is the set whose members are 1 and 2. If two sets have the same members, we say that they are equal sets. Repetition of the members and the order in which the members are listed are ignored. Thus, $\{2, 2, 1\} = \{1, 2\}$ because the sets contain the same members. However, $\{2, 3\} \neq \{1, 2\}$ because these sets do not have the same members.

The symbol $\in$ means "is a member of," and the symbol $\notin$ means "is not a member of." Thus, if

$$S = \{1, 2\}$$

then $1 \in S$, $2 \in S$, and $3 \notin S$, because 1 and 2 are the only members of S. Let

$$T = \{1, 2, 3\}$$

Because every member of S is also a member of T, we say that S is a **subset** of T. On the other hand, if

$$V = \{2, 3, 4\}$$

then S is not a subset of V because S contains a member, namely 1, that is not a member of V. The symbol $\subseteq$ means "is a subset of" and the symbol $\nsubseteq$ means "is not a subset of." Thus, $\{1, 2\} \subseteq \{1, 2, 3\}$ and $\{1, 2\} \nsubseteq \{2, 3, 4\}$.

1.1.1   Definition: **Subset**

If every member of set A is also a member of set B, then $A \subseteq B$.

Note the distinction between the *members* of a set and the *subsets* of that set. If $S = \{1, 2\}$, then 1 and 2 are members of S, whereas $\{1\}$ and $\{2\}$ are subsets of S. The entire set S is also a subset of S, because every member of $\{1, 2\}$ is also a member of $\{1, 2\}$. Moreover, the empty set $\{ \ \}$ is a subset of S. We say that every member of $\{ \ \}$ is a member of $\{1, 2\}$ because we cannot find a member of $\{ \ \}$ that is not a member of $\{1, 2\}$. Indeed, $\{ \ \}$ is a subset of every set!

Example 1:   List each member of $\{1, 2, 3\}$ and list each subset of $\{1, 2, 3\}$.

Solution: The only members of $\{1, 2, 3\}$ are 1, 2, and 3. The subsets of $\{1, 2, 3\}$ are $\{ \ \}, \{1\}, \{2\}, \{3\}, \{1, 2\}, \{1, 3\}, \{2, 3\}$, and $\{1, 2, 3\}$.

The set that contains exactly those members which are either in set A, in set B, or in both sets A and B is called the **union** of A and B and is represented by $A \cup B$. The set that contains exactly those members which are common to both sets A and B is called the **intersection** of A and B and is represented by $A \cap B$.

Example 2:   Represent each of the following sets by listing its members within braces.

(a) $\{2, 3\} \cup \{2, 4\}$ (b) $\{2, 4\} \cap \{3, 4\}$

Solution:

(a) This represents the union of the two sets. Thus,

$$\{2, 3\} \cup \{2, 4\} = \{2, 3, 4\}$$

(b) This represents the intersection of the two sets. Thus,

$$\{2, 4\} \cap \{3, 4\} = \{4\}$$

We use set-builder notation to define formally the union and intersection of two sets. In this notation, which follows, the colon is read "such that."

1.1.2 *Definition:* **Union**

$$A \cup B = \{x : x \in A \quad \text{or} \quad x \in B\}$$

1.1.3 *Definition:* **Intersection**

$$A \cap B = \{x : x \in A \quad \text{and} \quad x \in B\}$$

Example 3: Let $A = \{1, 2, 3\}$ and $B = \{2, 3, 4\}$. Represent each of the following sets by listing its members within braces.

(a) $\{x : x \in A \quad \text{or} \quad x \in B\}$ (b) $\{x : x \in A \quad \text{and} \quad x \in B\}$

Solution:

(a) This represents the union of sets A and B. Thus,

$$\{x : x \in A \quad \text{or} \quad x \in B\} = \{1, 2, 3\} \cup \{2, 3, 4\}$$
$$= \{1, 2, 3, 4\}$$

(b) This represents the intersection of sets A and B. Thus,

$$\{x : x \in A \quad \text{and} \quad x \in B\} = \{1, 2, 3\} \cap \{2, 3, 4\}$$
$$= \{2, 3\}$$

The numbers that we use for counting are called **natural numbers**, and the set of all such numbers is represented by N. Any number that is either a natural number, the opposite of a natural number, or zero is called an **integer**. The set of all integers is represented by I.

1.1.4 *Definition:* **Natural Number**

$$N = \{1, 2, 3, \ldots\}$$

1.1.5 *Definition:* **Integer**

$$I = \{\ldots, -2, -1, 0, 1, 2, \ldots\}$$

The three dots . . . in Definitions 1.1.4 and 1.1.5 mean "and so forth." Note that N is a subset of I. Indeed, N is the set of all positive integers.

Example 4: Let $S = \{-4, 0, \frac{1}{2}, 3\}$. Represent each of the following sets by listing its members within braces.

(a) $S \cap I$ (b) $\{x : x \in S \text{ and } x \in N\}$

Solution:

(a) This is the set of all integers that are in set S.

$$S \cap I = \{-4, 0, 3\}$$

(b) This is the set of all natural numbers that are in set S. Thus,

$$\{x : x \in S \text{ and } x \in N\} = \{3\}$$

Any number that may be represented exactly by a common fraction a/b, where a and b represent integers and $b \neq 0$, is called a **rational number**. The set of all rational numbers is represented by F. Because $a = a/1$, every integer is also a rational number. Thus, both I and N are subsets of F.

1.1.6   *Definition:* **Rational Number** F

$$F = \left\{ x : x = \frac{a}{b}, \quad a \in I, b \in I, b \neq 0 \right\}$$

Rational numbers may also be represented by decimal numerals. Some rational numbers, such as $\frac{1}{2} = 0.5$ and $\frac{3}{4} = 0.75$, have exact decimal forms that terminate. Other rational numbers, such as $\frac{1}{3} = 0.333\cdots$ and $\frac{5}{11} = 0.454545\cdots$, have decimal forms that do not terminate, but that contain a repeating sequence of digits. Any number with a decimal form that is nonterminating and nonrepeating, such as $\sqrt{2} = 1.41421\cdots$ and $\pi = 3.14159\cdots$, is called an **irrational number**. Any number that has a decimal form, either terminating or nonterminating, is called a **real number**, and the set of all real numbers is represented by R. Each real number is either rational or irrational. Thus R is the union of the set of all rational numbers and the set of all irrational numbers. Furthermore, the sets N, I, and F are all subsets of R.

1.1.7   *Definition:* **Real Number**

$$R = \{x : x \text{ has a decimal form}\}$$

Example 5: Let $S = \{-3/4, 0, \sqrt{3}, 2.5, 7\}$. Represent each of the following sets by listing its members within braces.

(a) $S \cap F$ (b) $\{x : x \in S \text{ and } x \notin R\}$

Solution:

(a) This is the set of all rational numbers that are in set *S*. Each of the members of *S*, except $\sqrt{3}$, may be represented exactly by a common fraction and thus is a rational number. Therefore,

$$S \cap F = \left\{ \frac{-3}{4}, 0, 2.5, 7 \right\}$$

(b) Every member of set *S* has a decimal form, and thus every member of *S* is a real number. That is, if $x \in S$, then $x \in R$. Therefore,

$$\{x : x \in S \quad \text{and} \quad x \notin R\} = \{ \quad \}$$

There are numbers, such as $\sqrt{-1}$, that do not have a decimal form and hence are not real numbers. In fact, each square root of any negative number is a nonreal number. An introduction to such numbers is given in Chapter 8. For now, however, set *R* is our universal set. Every number we consider is a real number, and every set of numbers we consider is a subset of *R*.

For each point on a line it is possible to designate a unique real number called the **coordinate** of the point, as illustrated in Figure 1.1.1. The coordinates are chosen in such a way that the numbers are in increasing order from left to right.

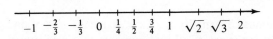

Figure 1.1.1

The symbol $>$ means "is greater than," and the symbol $<$ means "is less than." Thus, $\{x : x > a\}$ is the set of all real numbers that are greater than the real number *a*. This set is called an **interval**, and its graph is shown in Figure 1.1.2. The empty circle at the point *a* indicates that the number *a* is not a member of the set. The symbol $\geq$ means "is greater than or equal to," and the symbol $\leq$ means "is less than or equal to." Hence, $\{x : x \leq b\}$ is the set of all real numbers that are either less than or equal to the real number *b*. The graph of this interval is shown in Figure 1.1.3. The filled circle at the point *b* indicates that the number *b* is a member of the set.

Figure 1.1.2   **Figure 1.1.3**

Example 6: Sketch the graph for each of the following sets.

(a) $\{x : x < -2 \quad \text{or} \quad x \geq 1\}$ **(b)** $\{x : x \geq -1 \quad \text{and} \quad x < 3\}$

Solution:

(a) This set is the union of two intervals.

$$\{x : x < -2 \quad \text{or} \quad x \geq 1\} = \{x : x < -2\} \cup \{x : x \geq 1\}$$

The graph is shown in Figure 1.1.4. Note that -2 is not a member of the set, whereas 1 is a member of the set.

Figure 1.1.4

(b) This set is the intersection of two intervals.

$$\{x : x \geq -1 \quad \text{and} \quad x < 3\} = \{x : x \geq -1\} \cap \{x : x < 3\}$$

The graph is shown in Figure 1.1.5.

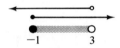

Figure 1.1.5

The **continued inequality** $a < x < b$ means $a < x$ and $x < b$. Thus, $\{x : a < x < b\}$ is the set of all real numbers that are between a and b. The interval of Example 6(*b*), shown in Figure 1.1.5, may be represented by a continued inequality. That is,

$$\{x : x \geq -1 \quad \text{and} \quad x < 3\} = \{x : -1 \leq x < 3\}$$

EXERCISES 1.1

For Exercises 1–12 let $A = \{2, 3\}$, $B = \{1, 2, 3\}$, $C = \{2, 3, 4, 5\}$, and $\varnothing = \{\ \}$. Answer true or false.

1. $1 \in A$ **2.** $4 \in C$ **3.** $A \subseteq B$ **4.** $B \subseteq A$

5. $C \subseteq C$ **6.** $B \subseteq C$ **7.** $\varnothing \subseteq A$ **8.** $\varnothing \subseteq \varnothing$

9. $\varnothing \in B$ **10.** $A \in C$ **11.** $2 \subseteq A$ **12.** $1 \subseteq B$

For Exercises 13–24 let $P = \{1, 2, 4\}$, $Q = \{3, 4\}$, $S = \{2, 4\}$, $T = \{1, 2\}$, and $\varnothing = \{\ \}$. Represent each set by listing its members within braces.

13. $P \cup Q$ **14.** $P \cap T$

15. $P \cap Q$ **16.** $P \cup T$

17. $\{x : x \in Q \quad \text{and} \quad x \in S\}$ **18.** $\{x : x \in S \quad \text{or} \quad x \in T\}$

19. $\{x : x \in Q \ \text{ or } \ x \in S\}$ **20.** $\{x : x \in S \ \text{ and } \ x \in T\}$

21. $\{x : x \in Q \ \text{ and } \ x \in T\}$ **22.** $\{x : x \in Q \ \text{ or } \ x \in T\}$

23. $T \cup \varnothing$ **24.** $T \cap \varnothing$

For Exercises 25–32 let N, I, F, and R be the sets of natural numbers, integers, rational numbers, and real numbers as defined in the text. Let

$$D = \{5, 0, -2, -\tfrac{1}{2}, 0.7, \sqrt{3}\}$$
$$E = \{3, 0, -5, \tfrac{3}{5}, -1.3, \sqrt{5}\}$$

Represent each set by listing its members within braces.

CD
√5

25. $\{x : x \in D \ \text{ and } \ x \in I\}$ **26.** $\{x : x \in E \ \text{ and } \ x \in F\}$

27. $\{x : x \in D \ \text{ and } \ x \notin F\}$ √3   **28.** $\{x : x \in E \ \text{ and } \ x \notin I\}$

29. $E \cap N$ **30.** $D \cap R$

31. $E \cap R$ **32.** $D \cap N$

For Exercises 33–42 sketch the graph of the indicated set.

33. $\{x : x > -3\}$ **34.** $\{x : x < 1\}$

35. $\{x : x \le -1\}$ **36.** $\{x : x \ge 2\}$

37. $\{x : -1 < x < 4\}$ **38.** $\{x : -2 \le x \le 3\}$

39. $\{x : x > 2 \ \text{ or } \ x \le 0\}$ **40.** $\{x : x \le 2 \ \text{ and } \ x > -3\}$

41. $\{x : -2 \le x \le 3\} \cup \{x : 1 \le x \le 4\}$

42. $\{x : -2 \le x \le 3\} \cap \{x : 1 \le x \le 4\}$

For Exercises 43–48 represent each of the indicated sets by using one of the symbols N, I, F, R, or $\varnothing$, as defined above.

43. $N \cup I$ **44.** $N \cap I$ CD √8 **45.** $F \cap R$

46. $I \cup F$ **47.** $I \cap \varnothing$ **48.** $R \cup \varnothing$

1.2 The Axioms for Real Numbers

An **expression** is any symbol used to represent a number. If the expression must always represent the same number, it is called a **constant**. An expression that may represent more than one number is called a **variable**. If the variable x in the expression $3x + 2$ is replaced by the constant 4, the result is $3 \cdot 4 + 2 = 14$. We say that 14 is the **value** of the expression $3x + 2$ when x is replaced by 4. The set of all real replacements for a variable that result in a real value for the expression in which the variable appears is called the **replacement set** for the expression. Because the expression $3x + 2$ has a real value for every real replacement of x, its replacement set is R.

If x is replaced by 4 in the expression $2 + 3x$, the resulting value is $2 + 3 \cdot 4 = 2 + 12 = 14$. Thus, the value of the expression $3x + 2$ is the same as the value of the expression $2 + 3x$ if x is replaced by 4. Indeed, the value of $3x + 2$ is the same as the value of $2 + 3x$ if x is replaced by any real number. Thus, we say that the expression $3x + 2$ is **equivalent** to the expression $2 + 3x$, and we write $3x + 2 = 2 + 3x$. In general, we have the following definition for equivalent expressions.

1.2.1 Definition: *Equivalent Expressions*

Two expressions are equivalent if the value of the first expression is the same as the value of the second expression when each variable in the expressions is replaced by any constant that is a member of the replacement set of both expressions.

Any fact that we accept without proof is called an **axiom**. For example, the fact that any expression is equivalent to itself is an axiom. Furthermore, if a first expression is equivalent to a second expression, then the second expression is also equivalent to the first expression. We state these axioms in symbols as follows.

1.2.2 Axioms of Equality

Reflexive $a = a$

Symmetric   If $a = b$, then $b = a$.

Suppose that it is known that

$$x \text{ is less than } 5 \tag{1}$$

Furthermore, suppose it is known that

$$x \text{ is equivalent to } y \tag{2}$$

Then because of Statement (2) we may replace x by y in Statement (1) and obtain

$$y \text{ is less than } 5$$

The above is an example of the substitution axiom, which follows.

1.2.3 Axiom of Substitution

If any expression in a true statement is replaced by an equivalent expression, the resulting statement is also a true statement.

Any fact that can be proved by using definitions and axioms is called a **theorem**. The following illustrates some simple theorems and their proofs.

1.2.4   Theorem: **Transitive**

If $a = b$, and $b = c$, then $a = c$.

PROOF: By hypothesis it is given that

$$a = b \tag{3}$$

and

$$b = c \tag{4}$$

Because of Statement (4) we may use the substitution axiom to replace b with c in Statement (3). This results in

$$a = c$$

which is the desired conclusion.

1.2.5   Theorem: **Multiplication**

If $a = b$, then $ac = bc$.

PROOF: By the reflexive axiom we have

$$ac = ac \tag{5}$$

By hypothesis we are given that

$$a = b$$

Thus, by the substitution axiom we may replace a by b in the expression that appears on the right side of Equation (5). This results in

$$ac = bc$$

which is the desired conclusion.

1.2.6   Theorem: **Addition**

If $a = b$, then $a + c = b + c$.

The proof of Theorem 1.2.6 is similar to that given for Theorem 1.2.5 and is omitted.

Example 1: If $x = ab$, use Theorem 1.2.6 to find an expression that is equivalent to $x + y$.

Solution: We are given that

$$x = ab \qquad (6)$$

By the Addition Theorem we may add y to both sides of Equation (6). This results in

$$x + y = ab + y$$

Thus, $ab + y$ is equivalent to $x + y$.

The following axioms are often used to replace a given expression by an expression that is equivalent to it. Hence, we call them the equivalence axioms.

1.2.7   **Axioms of Equivalence**

$$\text{Commutative} \begin{cases} a \cdot b = b \cdot a \\ a + b = b + a \end{cases}$$

$$\text{Associative} \begin{cases} (a \cdot b) \cdot c = a \cdot (b \cdot c) \\ (a + b) + c = a + (b + c) \end{cases}$$

$$\text{Distributive} \begin{cases} a \cdot (b + c) = a \cdot b + a \cdot c \\ (a + b) \cdot c = a \cdot c + b \cdot c \end{cases}$$

Example 2: Use the distributive axiom to replace $2x + 10$ by an equivalent expression.

Solution: Because $10 = 2 \cdot 5$, we have

$$2x + 10 = 2x + 2 \cdot 5$$

By the distributive axiom we have

$$2x + 2 \cdot 5 = 2(x + 5)$$

Thus, the desired expression is $2(x + 5)$.

Example 3: Which equivalence axiom is required to prove that $3(2x)$ is equivalent to $6x$?

Solution: By the associative axiom of multiplication we have

$$3(2x) = (3 \cdot 2)x \tag{7}$$

Because $3 \cdot 2 = 6$, we may substitute 6 for $3 \cdot 2$ in Equation (7). Thus,

$$3(2x) = 6x$$

Hence, the associative axiom is required.

The expression $a \cdot b$ is called the **product** of the **factors** a and b, while $a + b$ is the **sum** of the **terms** a and b. We assume that for each pair of real numbers there is one and only one product and one and only one sum, and that both the product and sum are also real numbers. The real numbers 1 and 0 are called the **identity elements** for multiplication and addition, respectively, because $a \cdot 1 = a$ and $a + 0 = a$ for each real number a. Corresponding to each real number a, if $a \neq 0$, there is a unique real number $1/a$, called the **reciprocal** of a, such that $a \cdot (1/a) = 1$. And for each real number a there is a unique real number $-a$, called the **opposite** of a, such that $a + (-a) = 0$. We have been discussing the existence axioms, which are now formally stated.

1.2.8   Axioms of Existence

Closure   If a and b are real numbers, then there exist unique real numbers $a \cdot b$ and $a + b$.

Identity   There exist unique real numbers 1 and 0, such that

$$a \cdot 1 = 1 \cdot a = a$$
$$a + 0 = 0 + a = a$$

Inverse   If a is a real number with $a \neq 0$, there exists a unique real number $1/a$, such that

$$a \cdot \left(\frac{1}{a}\right) = \left(\frac{1}{a}\right) \cdot a = 1$$

If a is a real number, there exists a unique real number $-a$, such that

$$a + (-a) = -a + a = 0$$

Example 4:   Use the identity axiom and the distributive axiom to simplify the expression $2x + x$.

Solution: By the identity axiom of multiplication we have

$$2x + x = 2x + 1 \cdot x \tag{8}$$

By the distributive axiom we have

$$2x + 1 \cdot x = (2 + 1)x$$
$$= 3x \tag{9}$$

From (8) and (9) we conclude that

$$2x + x = 3x$$

1.2.9   *Theorem:* **Zero-Factor**

$$a \cdot 0 = 0$$

PROOF:

Statement	Reason
$1 + 0 = 1$	Identity Axiom
$a \cdot (1 + 0) = a \cdot 1$	Multiplication Theorem
$a \cdot 1 + a \cdot 0 = a \cdot 1$	Distributive Axiom
$a + a \cdot 0 = a$	Identity Axiom
$-a + (a + a \cdot 0) = -a + a$	Addition Theorem
$(-a + a) + a \cdot 0 = -a + a$	Associative Axiom
$0 + a \cdot 0 = 0$	Inverse Axiom
$a \cdot 0 = 0$	Identity Axiom

1.2.10   *Theorem:*

$$-1 \cdot a = -a$$

The proof of Theorem 1.2.10 is similar to that given for Theorem 1.2.9 and is given in Exercise 51.

We assume that each real number is either **positive**, **negative**, or **zero**. If a is the coordinate of a point that is to the right of the origin (the point corresponding to 0 in Figure 1.1.1), then a is positive; if a is the coordinate of a point that is to the left of the origin, then a is negative. We accept the following two axioms.

1.2.11   Axioms of Order

Trichotomy   If a is a real number, then either a is positive, $a = 0$, or a
is negative.

Positive   If a is positive and b is positive, then $a \cdot b$ is positive
and $a + b$ is positive.

It can be shown that the opposite of each positive number is a negative
number and the opposite of each negative number is a positive number. The
opposite of zero is zero, which is neither positive nor negative.

1.2.12   Theorem: **Double Negative**
$$-(-a) = a$$

We now formally define the relations "less than" and "greater than"
for members of R.

1.2.13   Definition: **Less Than**
If a and b are real numbers, then $a < b$ if and only if there is a positive
number c such that $a + c = b$.

1.2.14   Definition: **Greater Than**
If a and b are real numbers, then $a > b$ if and only if $b < a$.

Thus, $2 < 5$ because there exists the positive number 3 such that
$2 + 3 = 5$. Furthermore, $5 > 2$ because $2 < 5$.

EXERCISES 1.2

1. If $r = s$, then what can we conclude by applying the symmetric axiom?
2. If $t < q$ and $p = t$, then what can we conclude by applying the substitution axiom?
3. What is the name of the axiom that allows us to conclude that $c = c$?
4. If $r = s$ and $s = t$, what can we conclude by applying the Transitive Theorem?

5. If $t = r$, use the Multiplication Theorem to find an expression that is equivalent to tq.

6. If $ps = q$, use the Addition Theorem to find an expression that is equivalent to $q + t$.

For Exercises 7–10 use the commutative axiom of addition to replace the given expression by an equivalent expression.

7. $xy + z$ **8.** $x + yz$ **9.** $x(y + z)$ **10.** $(x + y)z$

For Exercises 11–14 use the commutative axiom of multiplication to replace the given expression by an equivalent expression.

11. $xy + z$ **12.** $x + yz$ **13.** $x(y + z)$ **14.** $(x + y)z$

For Exercises 15–18 use the associative axiom to replace the given expression by an equivalent expression, and then simplify your result.

15. $4(5x)$ **16.** $(3x + 1) + 7$
17. $(2x + 5) + 4$ **18.** $6(5x)$

For Exercises 19–24 use the distributive axiom to replace the given expression by an equivalent expression, and then simplify your result, if possible.

19. $4(x + 3)$ **20.** $2(x + 6)$ **21.** $xy + xz$
22. $xy + zy$ **23.** $2x + 5x$ **24.** $3y + 7y$

For Exercises 25–44 name each <u>equivalence axiom</u> that is required to prove that the expressions are equivalent.

25. $(3x)y = 3(xy)$ **26.** $5x = x \cdot 5$
27. $x + 1 = 1 + x$ **28.** $(x + 3) + y = x + (3 + y)$
29. $3(x + y) = 3x + 3y$ **30.** $(x + 3)z = xz + 3z$
31. $x(yz) = x(zy)$ **32.** $x(y + z) = x(z + y)$
33. $5(3x) = 15x$ **34.** $(x + 2) + 3 = x + 5$
35. $3 + (4 + y) = 7 + y$ **36.** $2(5x) = 10x$
37. $2(x + 3) = 2x + 6$ **38.** $4x + 3x = 7x$
39. $3x + 2x = 5x$ **40.** $5(x + 3) = 5x + 15$
41. $(2 + x) + 3 = x + 5$ **42.** $(2x)3 = 6x$
43. $4(3x + 5) = 12x + 20$ **44.** $(x + 3)(7) = 7x + 21$

For Exercises 45–50 name each equivalence axiom and also name each existence axiom that is required to prove that the expressions are equivalent.

45. $x + 3x = 4x$ **46.** $5x + x = 6x$

47. $x + (-y + y) = x$ **48.** $\left(x \cdot \dfrac{1}{x}\right)y = y$ no closure

49. $xz + y = y + xz$ **50.** $(x + y)z = z(x + y)$

51. The following is a proof of Theorem 1.2.10. Give the name of the axiom or
theorem that is the reason for each step, as in the proof of Theorem 1.2.9.

(i)	$-1 + 1$	$= 0$	*inverse*
(ii)	$(-1 + 1) \cdot a$	$= 0 \cdot a$	*zero factor mult theor*
(iii)	$-1 \cdot a + 1 \cdot a$	$= 0 \cdot a$	*dist*
(iv)	$-1 \cdot a + a$	$= 0 \cdot a$	
(v)	$-1 \cdot a + a$	$= 0$	
(vi)	$(-1 \cdot a + a) + (-a)$	$= 0 + (-a)$	
(vii)	$-1 \cdot a + [a + (-a)]$	$= 0 + (-a)$	
(viii)	$-1 \cdot a + 0$	$= 0 + (-a)$	
(ix)	$-1 \cdot a$	$= -a$	

1.3   The Value of an Expression

Each real number has an **absolute value** that is nonnegative. The absolute
value of a positive number is the positive number itself. The absolute value of
a negative number is the positive number that is the opposite of the negative
number. The absolute value of zero is zero. The absolute value of the real
number a is represented by $|a|$. Thus, $|3| = 3$, $|-2| = 2$, and $|0| = 0$. We
formally state the definition for absolute value.

1.3.1   *Definition:* **Absolute Value**

$$\text{If } a \geq 0, |a| = a.$$
$$\text{If } a < 0, |a| = -a.$$

The expression $-a$ that appears in Definition 1.3.1 does not represent
a negative number. In fact, $-a$ represents the opposite of a, and because
$a < 0$, a is negative and $-a$ is positive. For example, if a is replaced by -3,
then $|a| = -a$ becomes $|-3| = -(-3) = 3$.

We use absolute value to state the rules for multiplying or adding with
negative numbers.

---

1. To find the product of two negative numbers, multiply their absolute
values.
2. To find the product of one negative number and one positive number,
multiply their absolute values and then take the opposite of this
product.
3. To find the sum of two negative numbers, add their absolute values
and then take the opposite of this sum.

4. To find the sum of one negative number and one positive number, subtract the smaller absolute value from the larger absolute value.

(**a**) If the positive number has the larger absolute value, then the sum is the above positive difference.

(**b**) If the negative number has the larger absolute value, then the sum is negative and is the opposite of the above positive difference.

The simplest expression that can be used to represent a number is called the **simplest form** of that number. For example, 8 is the simplest form of the number that can also be represented by $3 + 5, 2 \cdot 4$, etc. We usually represent a number in its simplest form.

Example 1: Calculate the simplest form.

(**a**) $(-2)(-5)$ (**b**) $4(-2)$

(**c**) $(-2) + (-4)$ (**d**) $5 + (-9)$

Solution: We apply the rules for multiplying and adding with negative numbers.

(**a**) $(-2)(-5) = 2 \cdot 5 = 10$

(**b**) $4(-2) = -(4 \cdot 2) = -8$

(**c**) $(-2) + (-4) = -(2 + 4) = -6$

(**d**) $5 + (-9) = -(9 - 5) = -4$

The operation of subtraction is the opposite of addition. Thus, $7 - 3 = 4$ because $4 + 3 = 7$. In general, we have

$$a - b = d \quad \text{if and only if} \quad d + b = a \tag{1}$$

1.3.2   Theorem: **Difference**

$$a - b = a + (-b)$$

PROOF: We apply the definition of subtraction.

$$[a + (-b)] + b = a + [-b + b]$$
$$= a + 0$$
$$= a \tag{2}$$

If we apply Statement (1) with d replaced by $a + (-b)$, then Equation (2) implies that

$$a - b = a + (-b)$$

Example 2:   Calculate the simplest form.
(a) $-3 - 4$ (b) $-2 - (-5)$

Solution: We apply the Difference Theorem.
(a) $-3 - 4 = (-3) + (-4) = -7$
(b) $-2 - (-5) = (-2) + (5) = 3$

The operation of division is the inverse of multiplication. Thus, $15 \div 3 = 5$ because $5 \cdot 3 = 15$. In general, if $b \neq 0$, then

$$a \div b = q \qquad \text{if and only if} \qquad qb = a$$

Note that division by zero is not possible. For example, $3 \div 0$ is not defined because there is no number q such that $q \cdot 0 = 3$. The quotient of two negative numbers is the positive number found by dividing the absolute values of the given numbers. The quotient of one negative number and one positive number is the negative number found by dividing the absolute values of the given numbers and taking the opposite of that quotient.

Example 3:   Calculate the simplest form.
(a) $(-12) \div (-2)$ (b) $20 \div (-4)$

Solution:
(a) $(-12) \div (-2) = 12 \div 2 = 6$
(b) $20 \div (-4) = -(20 \div 4) = -5$

When an expression contains more than one operation, we agree to first multiply and divide from left to right as indicated, and then add and subtract from left to right as indicated. If there are symbols of grouping, such as parentheses or brackets, we agree to perform those operations within the symbols of grouping first.

Example 4:   Calculate the simplest form.

$$(-2)[5 - 3(1 - 2 \cdot 2)]$$

Solution: We perform the operations within the innermost symbols of grouping first. Thus,

$$(-2)[5 - 3(1 - 2 \cdot 2)] = (-2)[5 - 3(1 - 4)]$$
$$= (-2)[5 - 3(-3)]$$
$$= (-2)[5 + 9]$$
$$= (-2)(14)$$
$$= -28$$

If we use the symbol $f(x)$, read "f of x," to represent an expression whose only variable is x, then the symbol $f(3)$ represents the value of the expression $f(x)$ when x is replaced by 3. In general, $f(a)$ represents the value of $f(x)$ when x is replaced by a.

Example 5:   Let $f(x) = 3x(5 - x) + x$, and calculate the simplest form of $f(-2)$.

Solution: We replace x by -2 in the expression $f(x)$.

$$f(x) = 3x(5 - x) + x$$
$$f(-2) = 3(-2)[5 - (-2)] + (-2)$$
$$= 3(-2)[5 + 2] + (-2)$$
$$= 3(-2)(7) + (-2)$$
$$= (-6)(7) + (-2)$$
$$= -42 + (-2)$$
$$= -44$$

The expression x^2 is called the **square** of x, and $x^2 = x \cdot x$. The expression x^3 is called the **cube** of x, and $x^3 = x \cdot x \cdot x$. The expression x^4 is called the **fourth power** of x, and $x^4 = x \cdot x \cdot x \cdot x$. In general, if n is a natural number, then x^n is called the **nth power** of x. The number n is called the **exponent**, and the number x is called the **base** of the power. We define x^n as follows.

1.3.3   *Definition: **Natural Number Power***

If n is a natural number, then

$$x^n = x \cdot x \cdot x \cdots x \qquad (n \text{ factors})$$

The expression $-x^n$ represents the opposite of x^n, and should not be confused with $(-x)^n$, which is the nth power of $-x$. The following example will illustrate the distinction.

Example 6:   Calculate the simplest form.

(a) -5^2 **(b)** $(-2)^4$

Solution:

(a) This is the opposite of the square of 5.

$$-5^2 = -(5^2) = -(5 \cdot 5) = -25$$

(b) This is the fourth power of -2.

$$(-2)^4 = (-2)(-2)(-2)(-2) = 16$$

If we use the symbol $f(x, y)$, read "f of x and y," to represent an expression whose only variables are x and y, then the symbol $f(a, b)$ represents the value of the expression $f(x, y)$ when x is replaced by a and y is replaced by b.

Example 7:   Let $f(x, y) = 2x^3 - y^2$, and calculate the simplest form of $f(-3, 4)$.

Solution: We replace x by -3 and y by 4.

$$f(x, y) = 2x^3 - y^2$$
$$f(-3, 4) = 2(-3)^3 - 4^2$$
$$= 2[(-3)(-3)(-3)] - (4 \cdot 4)$$
$$= 2(-27) - 16$$
$$= -54 - 16$$
$$= -70$$

Example 8:   If an object is thrown upward with an initial speed of k feet per second, after t seconds it will be h feet above its starting point, where $h = kt - 16t^2$. Find the height of a shell after 5 seconds if it is fired upward from the ground at a speed of 300 feet per second.

Solution: Because the initial speed is 300 feet per second, we replace k by 300. Because we want to find the height after 5 seconds, we replace t by 5. Thus,

$$h = kt - 16t^2$$
$$= 300 \cdot 5 - 16 \cdot 5^2$$
$$= 1500 - 16 \cdot 25$$
$$= 1500 - 400$$
$$= 1100$$

The height of the shell is 1100 feet.

EXERCISES 1.3

For Exercises 1–24 calculate the simplest form of the indicated expression.

1. $(3)(-2)$ 2. $(-4)(5)$

3. $(-7)(-3)$ 4. $(-2)(-9)$

5. $(-3) + (-8)$ 6. $(-5) + (-2)$

7. $4 + (-7)$ 8. $(-8) + 3$

9. $-2 + 5$ 10. $6 + (-5)$

11. $-5 - 2$ 12. $-3 - 8$

13. $-5 - (-2)$ 14. $-1 - (-2)$

15. $(-20) \div (-5)$ 16. $24 \div (-4)$

17. $2 - 3 \cdot 5$ 18. $-4 - 7 \cdot 3$

19. $(4 - 5)3 + 2$ 20. $6 - 2(5 - 8)$

21. $(4 + 8) \div 3 - 1$ 22. $3 \cdot 5 - 2(-3)$

23. $[2 - (3 - 7)](-3)$ 24. $(-30) \div [4 - (5 - 2 \cdot 3)]$

For Exercises 25–30 calculate the indicated value of the expression.

25. If $f(x) = -3x + 5$, find $f(4)$.

26. If $g(x) = x(2x - 9)$, find $g(3)$.

27. If $f(y) = (y + 2)(y - 5)$, find $f(-5)$.

28. If $g(y) = (2y - 1)y + 3$, find $g(-2)$.

29. If $h(z) = (2 - z)z - 3$, find $h(-3)$.

30. If $k(z) = -z[z - (2 - z)]$, find $k(-4)$.

For Exercises 31–34 calculate the simplest form of the indicated expression.

31. -4^2 32. -2^3 33. $(-3)^4$ 34. $(-2)^5$

For Exercises 35–40 calculate the indicated value of the expression.

35. If $f(x, y) = x^2 + y^3$, find $f(-3, 2)$.

36. If $g(x, y) = -x^4 + y^2$, find $g(2, 3)$.

37. If $h(x, y) = y^2 - x^3$, find $h(4, -5)$.

38. If $k(x, y) = x^3y - 3x$, find $k(-2, -3)$.

39. If $F(x, y) = y^2 - 2x^2y$, find $F(-2, -4)$.

40. If $G(x, y) = x^3y + y^4$, find $G(-2, -1)$.

For Exercises 41–46 make the indicated replacements, calculate the required value, and answer the stated question.

41. If a force of F pounds is applied to a certain spring whose natural length is k inches, the spring is stretched to a length of L inches, with $L = k + 3F$. What is the length of a spring whose natural length is 9 inches if a force of 5 pounds is applied?

42. If an object is thrown upward with an initial speed of k feet per second, after t seconds its velocity is v feet per second, with $v = k - 32t$. What is the velocity of a ball after 2 seconds if it is thrown upward with a speed of 50 feet per second?

43. If the price is P dollars per item, sales of a certain commodity yield a revenue of R dollars, with $R = 150P - 3P^2$. What is the revenue when the price is 25 dollars each?

44. If a ball is given an initial speed of k feet per second and allowed to roll down a certain inclined plane, it will roll a distance of s feet during the first t seconds, with $s = 3t^2 + kt$. How far will the ball roll in 4 seconds if it started with a speed of 3 feet per second?

45. If an object is thrown upward with an initial speed of k meters per second, after t seconds it will be h meters above its starting point, where $h = kt - 5t^2$. Find the height of a bullet after 8 seconds if it is fired upward from the ground with a muzzle speed of 150 meters per second.

46. If the electromotive force in a circuit is E volts, if the current is I amperes, and if the resistance is R ohms, then the power is P watts, with $P = EI - RI^2$. What is the power for a circuit with 20 volts electromotive force if the current is 3 amperes and the resistance is 2 ohms?

1.4 Natural Number Exponents and Products of Monomials

A **monomial** is any expression such as x^2 or $-2xy^4$ that is either a constant, a natural number power of some variable, or the product of a constant and natural number power or powers of one or more variables. Each factor in such a product is called a **coefficient** of the other factors, and the constant factor is called the **numerical coefficient** of the monomial. For example, -2 is the numerical coefficient of the expression $-2xy^4$, and because $x^2 = 1 \cdot x^2$, 1 is the numerical coefficient of x^2.

The **standard form** for a monomial with only one variable x is an expression of the form ax^n, provided the numerical coefficient a is the simplest form of a real number that is not a member of $\{1, -1, 0\}$ and provided the exponent n is the simplest form of a natural number with $n \neq 1$. The simplest form for x^1 is x, and the simplest forms for $1 \cdot x^n$, $-1 \cdot x^n$, and $0 \cdot x^n$ are x^n, $-x^n$, and 0, respectively.

The standard form for a monomial with two variables x and y is an expression of the form $ax^n y^m$, provided both ax^n and y^m are monomials in standard form. The standard form for a monomial with variables other than x and y is defined in a similar manner. We usually write the numerical coefficient first and arrange the other factors in alphabetical order.

Because $x^2 = x \cdot x$ and $x^3 = x \cdot x \cdot x$, it follows that

$$x^2 \cdot x^3 = (x \cdot x)(x \cdot x \cdot x) = x^5$$

Note that the exponent 5 is the sum of the exponents 2 and 3. The product of two powers that have the same base is always equivalent to a single power with that base and with exponent found by adding the given exponents. We state this in the following theorem, which is called the First Law of Exponents.

1.4.1   Theorem: First Law of Exponents

If m and n are natural numbers, then

$$a^m \cdot a^n = a^{m+n}$$

Division is the inverse of multiplication. Thus,

$$x^5 \div x^2 = x^3 \qquad \text{because} \qquad x^2 \cdot x^3 = x^5$$

Note that the exponent 3 is the difference of the exponents 5 and 2. We may always find a single power that is equivalent to the quotient of two powers with the same base if we subtract the exponents.

1.4.2   Theorem: Second Law of Exponents

If m and n are natural numbers with $m > n$, and if $a \neq 0$, then

$$a^m \div a^n = a^{m-n}$$

Example 1:   Find the standard form.

(a) $(2x^3y^2)(3x^4)$ (b) $(12x^7) \div (-3x^2)$

Solution:

(a) First we apply the associative and commutative axioms to group those factors together that have the same base. Then we may apply the First Law of Exponents.

$$(2x^3y^2)(3x^4) = (2 \cdot 3)(x^3 \cdot x^4)y^2$$
$$= 6(x^{3+4})y^2$$
$$= 6x^7y^2$$

(b) We divide the numerical coefficients and apply the Second Law of Exponents.

$$(12x^7) \div (-3x^2) = -4(x^7 \div x^2)$$
$$= -4x^{7-2}$$
$$= -4x^5$$

By applying the First Law of Exponents, we have

$$(x^2)^3 = x^2 \cdot x^2 \cdot x^2 = x^{2+2+2} = x^6$$

Note that the exponent 6 is the product of the exponents 2 and 3. When the base of a power is itself a power, we may always multiply the exponents.

1.4.3   Theorem: Third Law of Exponents

If m and n are natural numbers, then

$$(a^m)^n = a^{m \cdot n}$$

By applying the definition for natural number powers and the associative and commutative axioms, we have

$$(xy)^3 = (xy)(xy)(xy) = (x \cdot x \cdot x)(y \cdot y \cdot y) = x^3 y^3$$

The above is a special case of the following theorem.

1.4.4   Theorem: Fourth Law of Exponents

If n is a natural number, then

$$(ab)^n = a^n b^n$$

Example 2:   Find the standard form.

(a) $(2x^3)^3$ (b) $(-x^2 y^3)^4$

Solution:

(a) We first apply Theorem 1.4.4, and then we apply Theorem 1.4.3.

$$(2x^3)^3 = 2^3(x^3)^3$$
$$= 8x^{3 \cdot 3}$$
$$= 8x^9$$

(b) Because $-x^2 y^3 = -1 \cdot x^2 y^3$, we have

$$(-x^2 y^3)^4 = (-1 \cdot x^2 y^3)^4$$
$$= (-1)^4 (x^2)^4 (y^3)^4$$
$$= 1 \cdot x^{2 \cdot 4} \cdot y^{3 \cdot 4}$$
$$= x^8 y^{12}$$

If two monomials, such as $2xy^3$ and $3xy^3$, are identical except possibly for their numerical coefficients, they are called **similar** monomials. We may always replace the sum of two similar monomials by a single monomial. For example,

$$2xy^3 + 3xy^3 = (2 + 3)xy^3$$
$$= 5xy^3$$

The sum of two monomials is called a **binomial**. A binomial whose terms are not similar, such as $x^2 + xy$, cannot be replaced by a monomial. Sometimes there is more than one standard form for a binomial. If each term is the standard form of a monomial and if the terms are not similar, the binomial is in a standard form. If possible, we arrange the terms in descending powers of one of the variables. When the second term has a negative number coefficient, we express the sum as a difference. For example, the standard form for $-2x + x^3$ is $x^3 - 2x$.

Example 3:   Find a standard form for

$$(xy^2)^3(x - y^2)$$

Solution: First, we apply the laws of exponents to find the standard form for the factor $(xy^2)^3$. Then we apply the distributive axiom to "multiply out." Thus,

$$(xy^2)^3(x - y^2) = (x^3y^6)(x - y^2)$$
$$= (x^3y^6)x - (x^3y^6)y^2$$
$$= x^4y^6 - x^3y^8$$

The sum of three monomials is called a **trinomial**. A trinomial is in a standard form if it contains no two terms that are similar and if each term is the standard form of a monomial. If possible, we arrange the terms in descending powers of one of the variables. And if any term after the first has a negative number coefficient, we express the sum as a difference. For example, a standard form for $-xy + x^2 + y^2$ is $x^2 - xy + y^2$.

Monomials, binomials, and trinomials are all special cases of a **polynomial**. That is, a polynomial is any monomial or any sum of two or more monomials. A polynomial with more than three terms is in standard form if each of its terms is a monomial in standard form and if no two terms are similar.

Example 4:   Find a standard form.

(a) $x(x + 2y) + (x^2 - 5xy)$ (b) $(x^2 - x + 1) - (2x^2 + x - 2)$

Solution:
(a) First we use the distributive axiom to multiply out the product $x(x + 2y)$.
Then we combine similar terms.

$$x(x + 2y) + (x^2 - 5xy) = (x^2 + 2xy) + (x^2 - 5xy)$$
$$= (x^2 + x^2) + (2xy - 5xy)$$
$$= 2x^2 - 3xy$$

(b) Because $-a = -1 \cdot a$, we subtract the trinomials by first multiplying out
with -1.

$$(x^2 - x + 1) - (2x^2 + x - 2) = (x^2 - x + 1) + (-1)(2x^2 + x - 2)$$
$$= (x^2 - x + 1) + (-2x^2 - x + 2)$$
$$= (x^2 - 2x^2) + (-x - x) + (1 + 2)$$
$$= -x^2 - 2x + 3$$

When symbols of grouping are nested within other symbols of grouping,
we remove the innermost symbols of grouping first.

Example 5:   Find a standard form for
$$2x - [3x - (x - 1)]$$

Solution: First we remove the parentheses. Because $-(x - 1) = (-1)(x - 1) = -x + 1$, we have

$$2x - [3x - (x - 1)] = 2x - [3x - x + 1]$$
$$= 2x - [2x + 1]$$
$$= 2x - 2x - 1$$
$$= -1$$

Example 6:   If $f(x) = 3x - 1$, find a standard form for the expression
$f(2x + 3)$.

Solution: We replace x by $2x + 3$ in the expression $f(x)$. Thus,

$$f(x) = 3x - 1$$
$$f(2x + 3) = 3(2x + 3) - 1$$
$$= 6x + 9 - 1$$
$$= 6x + 8$$

EXERCISES 1.4

For Exercises 1–16 apply the laws of exponents to find an equivalent monomial in standard form.

1. $(3x^2)(2x^3)$ 2. $(-x^2y)(x^4y^3)$ 3. $(2xy^2)(-x^2y^2)$
4. $(-4xy^3)(-3x^2y)$ 5. $(6x^6) \div (-2x^2)$ 6. $(-8y^3) \div (2y^2)$
7. $(-x^4y^3) \div (-xy^2)$ 8. $(x^6y^4) \div (x^3y)$ 9. $(-2x)^4$
10. $(-3y)^3$ 11. $(-xy)^3$ 12. $(-xy)^4$
13. $(x^2y)^4$ 14. $(-x^2y)^3$ 15. $(-x^2y^3)^2$
16. $(-x^3y^2)^4$

For Exercises 17–24 use the laws of exponents and the distributive axiom to find an equivalent binomial in standard form.

CD
1/5

17. $3x^3(x^2 + 2x)$ 18. $x^2y(2x + y)$ 19. $2xy^3(x - y)$
20. $-x^2y^2(x^2 - 2y)$ 21. $(2x)^3(x + y)$ 22. $(-xy)^3(x + y)$
23. $(x^2y)^3(x - y^2)$ 24. $(-xy^3)^2(x^2 - y)$

For Exercises 25–44 find an equivalent polynomial in standard form by combining similar terms.

25. $(x^2 - 3x + 2) + (2x^2 + 3x - 1)$
26. $(2x - x^3 + 4) + (x^2 + 2x^3 - 3)$
27. $3x(x - 1) + 2(x^2 + x)$
28. $2(x^2 - 3x + 1) + x(x + 4)$
29. $(x^2 - 3x + 2) - (2x^2 + x - 1)$
30. $(1 + x - 2x^2) - (x + 1 + 2x^2)$
31. $2x(x - 3) - 3(x^2 - x)$
32. $-x(2x - 1) - 2x(x - 1)$
33. $x(y + 3) - x(y - 2)$
34. $x^2y - 3x(1 - xy)$
35. $-2xy^2 + 3x^2y + 2xy(x + y)$
36. $xy(2x - y) + 2xy^2 - x^2y$

CD
1/5

37. $xy(3x - y) - 3xy(x + y)$
38. $2xy(x - y) - xy(x + y)$
39. $3[x + 2(4 - x)]$
40. $x[x - (3x - 2)]$

CD
1/5

41. $2x - [x - (2x - 3)]$
42. $2x[y - 3(xy + 1)]$
43. $xy[x - (2x - 1)] + y(x^2 + x)$
44. $3x[x - (2x - y)] - [xy - (x^2 - xy)]$

For Exercises 45–50 find a standard form for the indicated expression.

45. If $f(x) = 2x + 1$, find $f(x + 3)$.
46. If $g(x) = 3x + 5$, find $g(x - 1)$.
47. If $h(x) = 5x - 1$, find $h(2x - 1)$.
48. If $k(x) = -x + 3$, find $k(3x + 1)$.
49. If $F(x) = x^2 + 5x + 1$, find $F(3x)$.
50. If $G(x) = 3x^2 + 4x + 2$, find $G(2x)$.

1.5   Products of Binomials and Trinomials

A standard form for the product of two binomials can be found by two applications of the distributive axiom.

Example 1:   Find a standard form.
(a) $(x + 3)(2x + y)$ **(b)** $(3x - y)(x + 2y)$

Solution:
(a) First, we multiply out by distributing the binomial factor $2x + y$.

$$(x + 3)(2x + y) = x(2x + y) + 3(2x + y)$$
$$= 2x^2 + xy + 6x + 3y$$

(b) We replace the difference $3x - y$ by an equivalent sum and then multiply out.

$$(3x - y)(x + 2y) = [3x + (-y)](x + 2y)$$
$$= 3x(x + 2y) + (-y)(x + 2y)$$
$$= 3x^2 + 6xy - xy - 2y^2$$
$$= 3x^2 + 5xy - 2y^2$$

A special case of the product of two binomials occurs when one binomial is the sum of two terms and the other binomial is the difference of the same two terms. We consider this special case in the following theorem.

1.5.1   *Theorem:* **Sum-Difference**
$$(a + b)(a - b) = a^2 - b^2$$

PROOF:
$$(a + b)(a - b) = a(a - b) + b(a - b)$$
$$= a^2 - ab + ab - b^2$$
$$= a^2 - b^2$$

Example 2: Find a standard form.

(a) $(x + 5y)(x - 5y)$ (b) $(x^2 - z)(x^2 + z)$

Solution:

(a) We apply the Sum-Difference Theorem.

$$(x + 5y)(x - 5y) = x^2 - (5y)^2$$
$$= x^2 - 25y^2$$

(b) Because $(x^2 - z)(x^2 + z) = (x^2 + z)(x^2 - z)$, we may apply the Sum-Difference Theorem.

$$(x^2 - z)(x^2 + z) = (x^2)^2 - z^2$$
$$= x^4 - z^2$$

Another special case of the product of two binomials occurs when we square a binomial.

1.5.2   Theorem: Binomial Square

$$(a + b)^2 = a^2 + 2ab + b^2$$

PROOF:

$$(a + b)^2 = (a + b)(a + b)$$
$$= a(a + b) + b(a + b)$$
$$= a^2 + ab + ab + b^2$$
$$= a^2 + 2ab + b^2$$

Example 3: Find a standard form.

(a) $(x + 3y)^2$ (b) $(x^3 - y)^2$

Solution:

(a) We apply the Binomial Square Theorem.

$$(x + 3y)^2 = x^2 + 2(x)(3y) + (3y)^2$$
$$= x^2 + 6xy + 9y^2$$

(b) We replace the difference by an equivalent sum and then apply the Binomial Square Theorem.

$$(x^3 - y)^2 = [x^3 + (-y)]^2$$
$$= (x^3)^2 + 2(x^3)(-y) + (-y)^2$$
$$= x^6 - 2x^3y + y^2$$

Next we consider a product of two polynomials in which one or more of the factors contains more than two terms.

Example 4:   Find a standard form.

$$(2x - 3y)(x^2 + 2xy - y^2)$$

Solution: We distribute the trinomial factor.

$$(2x - 3y)(x^2 + 2xy - y^2) = 2x(x^2 + 2xy - y^2) - 3y(x^2 + 2xy - y^2)$$
$$= 2x^3 + 4x^2y - 2xy^2 - 3x^2y - 6xy^2 + 3y^3$$
$$= 2x^3 + (4x^2y - 3x^2y) + (-2xy^2 - 6xy^2) + 3y^3$$
$$= 2x^3 + x^2y - 8xy^2 + 3y^3$$

Alternate Solution: We use the vertical arrangement shown below with terms in descending powers of x and with similar terms in the same column. The polynomial in line (1) is obtained by multiplying out $2x(x^2 + 2xy - y^2)$; the polynomial in line (2) is obtained by multiplying out $-3y(x^2 + 2xy - y^2)$; and the polynomial in line (3) is obtained by adding line (1) and line (2).

$$
\begin{array}{ll}
x^2 + 2xy - y^2 & \\
2x - 3y & \\
\hline
2x^3 + 4x^2y - 2xy^2 & (1) \\
- 3x^2y - 6xy^2 + 3y^3 & (2) \\
\hline
2x^3 + x^2y - 8xy^2 + 3y^3 & (3)
\end{array}
$$

We find a standard form for the expression $(a + b)^3$. Because

$$(a + b)^3 = (a + b)(a + b)^2$$
$$= (a + b)(a^2 + 2ab + b^2)$$

we find a standard form as follows.

$$
\begin{array}{l}
a^2 + 2ab + b^2 \\
a + b \\
\hline
a^3 + 2a^2b + ab^2 \\
a^2b + 2ab^2 + b^3 \\
\hline
a^3 + 3a^2b + 3ab^2 + b^3
\end{array}
$$

Thus, we have proved the following theorem.

> **1.5.3** **Theorem: Binomial Cube**
>
> $$(a + b)^3 = a^3 + 3a^2b + 3ab^2 + b^3$$

Example 5: Find a standard form for $(x - 2)^3$.

Solution: Because $x - 2 = x + (-2)$, we may apply the Binomial Cube Theorem with $a = x$ and $b = -2$.

$$
\begin{aligned}
(x - 2)^3 &= [x + (-2)]^3 \\
&= x^3 + 3(x^2)(-2) + 3(x)(-2)^2 + (-2)^3 \\
&= x^3 - 6x^2 + 12x - 8
\end{aligned}
$$

In the following example we consider a difference in which the second term is a product. We must be very careful about using parentheses in such a difference.

Example 6: Find a standard form.

$$(x + 3y)(x - 3y) - (x + y)(x - 2y)$$

Solution: We must multiply first and use parentheses to preserve the original grouping.

$$
\begin{aligned}
(x + 3y)(x - 3y) - (x + y)(x - 2y) &= (x^2 - 9y^2) - (x^2 - xy - 2y^2) \\
&= x^2 - 9y^2 - x^2 + xy + 2y^2 \\
&= -7y^2 + xy
\end{aligned}
$$

Example 7: If $f(x) = x^2 - 3x$, find the expression represented by $x \cdot f(x - 2)$.

Solution: First, we find $f(x - 2)$ by replacing x with $x - 2$ in the given expression. Thus,

$$
\begin{aligned}
f(x) &= x^2 - 3x \\
f(x - 2) &= (x - 2)^2 - 3(x - 2) \\
&= x^2 - 4x + 4 - 3x + 6 \\
&= x^2 - 7x + 10
\end{aligned}
$$

Multiplying on both sides by x, we obtain

$$x \cdot f(x-2) = x(x^2 - 7x + 10)$$
$$= x^3 - 7x^2 + 10x$$

EXERCISES 1.5

For Exercises 1–8 find a standard form by multiplying out.

1. $(2x - 3)(x + 4)$ **2.** $(x + 3)(2y + 1)$

3. $(x + 3y)(2x - y)$ **4.** $(5x - 2y)(x - 2y)$

5. $(2x^2 - y)(x - y)$ **6.** $(x^2 + y)(x + 2y)$

7. $(xy^2 + 3)(2xy^2 + 1)$ **8.** $(2x^2 - y)(x^2 + 3y)$

For Exercises 9–14 use the Sum-Difference Theorem to find a standard form.

9. $(5x + 3)(5x - 3)$ **10.** $(x - 4y)(x + 4y)$

11. $(2x + y^2)(2x - y^2)$ **12.** $(x^2y + 1)(x^2y - 1)$

13. $(x^3y + 4)(x^3y - 4)$ **14.** $(x^3 + y^2)(x^3 - y^2)$

For Exercises 15–20 use the Binomial Square Theorem to find a standard form.

15. $(3x + 5)^2$ **16.** $(2x - y)^2$ **17.** $(x^2 - y)^2$

18. $(4xy + 5)^2$ **19.** $(xy^2 + 2)^2$ **20.** $(x^2 - y^3)^2$

In Exercises 21–26 use the Binomial Cube Theorem to find a standard form.

21. $(x + 1)^3$ **22.** $(x - y)^3$ **23.** $(2x + y)^3$

24. $(x + 3y)^3$ **25.** $(4x - 3)^3$ **26.** $(2x - 5)^3$

For Exercises 27–40 use any method to find a standard form.

27. $(2x + 3)(x^2 - 4x + 1)$ **28.** $(x - 4)(x^2 + 4x - 1)$

29. $(x + 2y)(x^2 - 3xy + y^2)$ **30.** $(x - 3)(x + 3)(x^2 - x + 2)$

31. $(x + 3y)(x + y)(x - 2y)$ **32.** $(2x + 1)(x - 3)^2$

33. $(x^2 + x - 2)(x^2 + 3x + 1)$ **34.** $(2x - y + 3)^2$

35. $(x + y)^2(x - 2y)^2$ **36.** $[(x + 2)(x - 1)]^2$

37. $(2x + 3)(x - 1) - (x + 2)(x - 2)$ **38.** $(2x + 1)^2 - (4x + 1)(x - 1)$

39. $(x + 3y)(x - y) - (2x + y)^2$ **40.** $(x + 2y)(x - 2y) - (x - 3y)^2$

For Exercises 41–46 find a standard form for the given expression.

41. If $f(x) = x^2 - x$, find $f(x + 2)$.

42. If $g(x) = x^2 + 2x$, find $g(x - 1)$.

43. If $h(x) = 3x^2 + 1$, find $x \cdot h(x + 1)$.

44. If $k(x) = 5x^2 - 3x$, find $x + k(x + 1)$.

45. If $F(x) = x^2 + x$, find $F(x + 1) - F(x)$.

46. If $G(x) = x^2 - 2$, find $G(x + 2) - G(x)$.

1.6 Factoring Monomials and Binomials

An expression such as $3x(x + 2)$ or $(x - y)(x + 5y)$, the product of two or more factors, is said to be in **factored form**. On the other hand, the expressions $3x + 6$ and $x(x + y) - y$ are not in factored form, because multiplication is not the last operation performed when calculating their values. To write an expression in factored form is called factoring the expression.

Every monomial expression can be factored in more than one way. For example, the monomial $6xy^2$ may be written as $(6x)(y^2)$, $(6)(xy^2)$, $(6xy)(y)$, $(2)(3xy^2)$, $(3y)(2xy)$, and so forth. Even the simple monomial expression x can be factored as $(1)(x)$ or $(-1)(-x)$. An expression such as x or 5, whose only factored form is the product of 1 and itself or -1 and the opposite of itself, is said to be **prime**. (We disregard factored forms that contain fractions.)

If there is a factor that is common to both terms in a binomial, we may factor the binomial by applying the distributive axiom.

Example 1: Factor the binomial.

(a) $5x + 10y$ (b) $3x^2 - x$

Solution:

(a) Because both $5x$ and $10y$ are divisible by 5, each term in the binomial contains the factor 5. Thus we apply the distributive axiom to "remove" the repeated factor 5.

$$5x + 10y = (5)x + (5)2y$$
$$= 5(x + 2y)$$

(b) Because each term is divisible by x, we may remove the repeated factor x.

$$3x^2 - x = (3x)x + (-1) \cdot x$$
$$= [3x + (-1)]x$$
$$= x(3x - 1)$$

Note that the binomial factor $3x - 1$ may also be obtained by dividing each term of the given binomial $3x^2 - x$ by the repeated factor x.

The binomial $2x + 3$ is said to be prime because its only factored forms are $(1)(2x + 3)$ and $(-1)(-2x - 3)$. On the other hand, the binomial $4x^2 + 6x$ is not prime and has three different factored forms, as follows.

$$4x^2 + 6x = 2(2x^2 + 3x) \tag{1}$$

$$4x^2 + 6x = x(4x + 6) \tag{2}$$

$$4x^2 + 6x = 2x(2x + 3) \tag{3}$$

The factored forms given in (1) and (2) are not complete, because in each case the binomial factor is not prime. An expression is completely factored if each of its factors is prime. Thus, a complete factorization of the binomial $4x^2 + 6x$ is given in (3).

Example 2:   Factor completely.

(a) $3x^3 + 6x^2$ (b) $x^3y^3 - xy^4$

Solution:

(a) Because both 3 and 6 are divisible by 3, 3 is a common factor. Because both x^3 and x^2 are divisible by x^2, x^2 is a common factor. In general, the **greatest common factor** for two powers of a variable is that power of the variable whose exponent is the smaller of the two given exponents. Thus, $3x^2$ is the greatest common monomial factor, and we may obtain the binomial factor by dividing each term of the given binomial by $3x^2$. Because $3x^3 \div 3x^2 = x$ and $6x^2 \div 3x^2 = 2$, we have the following.

$$3x^3 + 6x^2 = (3x^2)x + (3x^2)2$$
$$= 3x^2(x + 2)$$

(b) The common monomial factor is xy^3, because x is the power of x with the smaller exponent and y^3 is the power of y with the smaller exponent. Thus, we divide each term by xy^3 to obtain the binomial factor.

$$x^3y^3 - xy^4 = (xy^3)x^2 - (xy^3)y$$
$$= xy^3(x^2 - y)$$

If a binomial is the difference of two squares, we may apply the Sum-Difference Theorem (1.5.1), which we restate now.

1.6.1   Theorem: *Difference of Squares*

$$a^2 - b^2 = (a + b)(a - b)$$

Example 3:   Factor the binomial.

(a) $4x^2 - 9y^2$ (b) $x^4y^2 - 1$

Solution:
(a) Because $4x^2 = (2x)^2$ and $9y^2 = (3y)^2$, we have a difference of two squares. Thus, we apply Theorem 1.6.1 with $a = 2x$ and $b = 3y$.

$$4x^2 - 9y^2 = (2x)^2 - (3y)^2$$
$$= (2x + 3y)(2x - 3y)$$

(b) Because $x^4y^2 = (x^2y)^2$ and $1 = 1^2$, we apply the Difference of Squares Theorem with $a = x^2y$ and $b = 1$. Thus,

$$x^4y^2 - 1 = (x^2y)^2 - 1^2$$
$$= (x^2y + 1)(x^2y - 1)$$

If a binomial is the sum of two cubes, we apply the following theorem to find a factored form.

$$a^3 - b^3 = (a-b)(a^2 + ab + b^2)$$

1.6.2   Theorem: Sum of Cubes
$$a^3 + b^3 = (a + b)(a^2 - ab + b^2)$$

PROOF: We find a standard form for the product $(a + b)(a^2 - ab + b^2)$.

$$
\begin{array}{r}
a^2 - ab + b^2 \\
a + b \\
\hline
a^3 - a^2b + ab^2 \\
a^2b - ab^2 + b^3 \\
\hline
a^3 \qquad\qquad\quad + b^3
\end{array}
$$

Example 4: Factor the binomial.
(a) $8x^3 + y^3$ (b) $x^3 - 1$

Solution:
(a) Because $8x^3 = (2x)^3$, the given binomial is the sum of two cubes. We apply Theorem 1.6.2 with $a = 2x$ and $b = y$.

$$8x^3 + y^3 = (2x)^3 + y^3$$
$$= [2x + y][(2x)^2 - (2x)(y) + y^2]$$
$$= (2x + y)(4x^2 - 2xy + y^2)$$

(b) Because $x^3 - 1 = x^3 + (-1)^3$, we apply the Sum of Cubes Theorem with $a = x$ and $b = -1$. Thus

$$x^3 - 1 = x^3 + (-1)^3$$
$$= [x + (-1)][x^2 - (x)(-1) + (-1)^2]$$
$$= (x - 1)(x^2 + x + 1)$$

By repeated applications of the preceding techniques we may sometimes find three or more factors for a binomial.

Example 5:   Factor completely.
(a) $2x^3 - 8x$ (b) $x^4 - y^4$

Solution:
(a) First, we remove the repeated factors and then apply the Difference of Squares Theorem.

$$2x^3 - 8x = 2x(x^2 - 4)$$
$$= 2x(x + 2)(x - 2)$$

(b) By repeated applications of the Difference of Squares Theorem we have the following.

$$x^4 - y^4 = (x^2 + y^2)(x^2 - y^2)$$
$$= (x^2 + y^2)(x + y)(x - y)$$

Note that $x^2 + y^2$, the sum of two squares, is prime. In particular, note that $x^2 + y^2 \neq (x + y)^2$. Indeed, by the Binomial Square Theorem, $(x + y)^2 = x^2 + 2xy + y^2$

The preceding techniques for factoring a binomial are the only ones that we consider in this book. To factor a binomial completely use the following steps in the order indicated.

To Factor a Binomial Completely

1. Use the distributive axiom to remove all repeated factors.
2. Use Theorem 1.6.1 to factor a difference of squares.
3. Use Theorem 1.6.2 to factor a sum or difference of cubes.

EXERCISES 1.6

For Exercises 1–12 factor completely by removing all repeated factors.

1. $6x - 9y$ 2. $x^2 + 4x$ 3. $xy + y$

4. $35x - 5$ 5. $2x^2 + 6x$ 6. $x^2y - 2xy$

7. $x^3 - x^2y$ **8.** $12x^3 + 8x^2$ **9.** $x^2y^2 - xy^4$

10. $x^3y^3 + x^2y^3$ **11.** $18x^2y + 12x^3y^4$ **12.** $9x^2y^2 - 12xy^4$

For Exercises 13–18 apply the Difference of Squares Theorem to factor.

13. $x^2 - 25y^2$ **14.** $9x^2 - 16y^2$ **15.** $36x^2 - y^4$

16. $4x^4 - y^2$ **17.** $x^2y^6 - 1$ **18.** $x^6 - 25y^4$

For Exercises 19–24 apply the Sum of Cubes Theorem to factor.

19. $x^3 + 8$ **20.** $x^3 + 27$ **21.** $64x^3 - y^3$

22. $8x^3 - y^3$ **23.** $8x^3 + 27y^3$ **24.** $125x^3 - 64y^3$

For Exercises 25–44 use any method to factor completely.

25. $x^3y + x^2y^3$ **26.** $6x^3y^2 - 8xy^3$ **27.** $12x^2y^3 - 4xy^3$

28. $x^4y^2 + 2x^8y^4$ **29.** $16x^2y^2 - 25$ **30.** $1 - 9x^6y^2$

31. $x^4 - 4y^6$ **32.** $36x^8 - 25y^2$ **33.** $x^3 + 1$

34. $x^3y^3 - 8$ **35.** $x^3 - 4x$ **36.** $2x^2y - 2y^3$

37. $9x^3y - xy^3$ **38.** $4x^2y^2 - y^4$ **39.** $x^4 - 1$

40. $x^4 - 16$ **41.** $x^4 - xy^3$ **42.** $y^4 + 64y$

43. $x^6 + y^6$ **44.** $x^6 - y^6$

1.7 Factoring Trinomials and Other Expressions

If there is a factor that is common to all three terms in a trinomial, we may factor by using the distributive axiom to remove the repeated factor.

Example 1: Factor the trinomial $x^3y + x^2y^2 - x^4$.

Solution: Each term contains a power of x. Because x^2 is the power of x with smallest exponent, x^2 is the highest power of x that is common to all three terms. Because the last term x^4 is not divisible by a power of y, there is no power of y that is common to all three terms. Thus, we remove the monomial factor x^2 by dividing each term by x^2.

$$x^3y + x^2y^2 - x^4 = (x^2)xy + (x^2)y^2 - (x^2)x^2$$
$$= x^2(xy + y^2 - x^2)$$

Because $(x + 3)(x + 2) = x^2 + 5x + 6$, $(x + 3)(x + 2)$ is a factored form of the trinomial $x^2 + 5x + 6$. Note that the constants 3 and 2 in the factored form are numbers whose product is 6, the constant term of the trinomial. Furthermore, the sum of 3 and 2 is 5, the coefficient of the term $5x$

in the trinomial. This suggests the following theorem, which we may sometimes use to factor a trinomial.

1.7.1   *Theorem*

$$x^2 + (a + b)x + a \cdot b = (x + a)(x + b)$$

PROOF: We multiply out the products that appear in the theorem. Thus,

$$x^2 + (a + b)x + ab = x^2 + ax + bx + ab \tag{1}$$

and

$$(x + a)(x + b) = x(x + b) + a(x + b)$$
$$= x^2 + bx + ax + ab \tag{2}$$

Because the expression on the right side of Equation (1) is equivalent
to the expression on the right side of Equation (2), we conclude that the
expressions on the left sides of (1) and (2) are also equivalent, which is what
we wish to prove.

Example 2:   Factor completely.
(a) $x^2 - 9x + 18$ 　　　　　　　　　**(b)** $x^3 + 2x^2 - 24x$

Solution:
(a) In order to apply Theorem 1.7.1, we find constants a and b such that
$ab = 18$ and $a + b = -9$. Because the product of a and b is positive,
either a and b are both positive or a and b are both negative. Because the
sum of a and b is negative, a and b cannot both be positive. Thus, a and
b are both negative. Because $(-6)(-3) = 18$, and $(-6) + (-3) = -9$,
we take $a = -6$ and $b = -3$ in Theorem 1.7.1. We have

$$x^2 - 9x + 18 = x^2 + [(-6) + (-3)]x + (-6)(-3)$$
$$= [x + (-6)][x + (-3)]$$
$$= (x - 6)(x - 3)$$

(b) First, we remove the repeated factor x. Thus,

$$x^3 + 2x^2 - 24x = x(x^2 + 2x - 24) \tag{3}$$

To factor the trinomial on the right side of Equation (3), we find constants
a and b such that $ab = -24$ and $a + b = 2$. Because ab is negative, a
and b have opposite signs. Suppose that a is positive and b is negative.
Because $a + b$ is positive, the absolute value of a is greater than the
absolute value of b. Because $6(-4) = -24$ and $6 + (-4) = 2$, we take
$a = 6$ and $b = -4$. Thus,

$$x^2 + 2x - 24 = x^2 + [6 + (-4)]x + (6)(-4)$$
$$= (x + 6)(x - 4) \qquad (4)$$

Substituting from Equation (4) into Equation (3), we have

$$x^3 + 2x^2 - 24x = x(x + 6)(x - 4)$$

The following equation is obtained by multiplying out the product that appears on the left side of the equation.

$$(2x + y)(3x + 4y) = 6x^2 + 11xy + 4y^2 \qquad (5)$$

Thus, Equation (5) gives a factored form for the trinomial that appears on the right side of the equation. Note that neither of the binomials contains a repeated factor and that there is no factor common to all three terms of the trinomial. Moreover, the binomial factor $2x + y$ is similar, term by term, to the binomial factor $3x + 4y$. That is, $2x$ is similar to $3x$ and y is similar to $4y$. Also note that $6x^2$, the first term of the trinomial, is the product of $2x$ and $3x$, the first terms of the binomial factors. Furthermore, $4y^2$, the last term of the trinomial, is the product of y and $4y$, the last terms of the binomial factors. Equation (5) illustrates some general facts about the factored form of a trinomial, which we state in the following theorem.

1.7.2   Theorem

If a trinomial contains no factor that is common to all three terms and if the trinomial is equivalent to the product of two binomials, then
  (i)   The binomial factors are similar, term by term.
  (ii) Neither binomial factor contains a repeated factor.
  (iii) The product of the first term from each binomial is a factored form of the first term of the trinomial.
  (iv) The product of the last term from each binomial is a factored form of the last term of the trinomial.

Although the conditions described in Theorem 1.7.2 are necessary conditions for factoring a trinomial, they are insufficient for finding a factored form. Indeed, we must often use trial and error to factor a trinomial.

Example 3:   Factor $4x^2 - 13xy - 12y^2$.

Solution: Because the trinomial contains no factor that is common to all three terms, we attempt to find binomial factors that satisfy the conditions of

Theorem 1.7.2. Because $4x^2 = (2x)(2x)$, we consider binomial factors whose first terms are $2x$ and $2x$. Because $-12y^2 = (-4y)(3y)$, we consider binomial factors whose last terms are $-4y$ and $3y$. We test one of these possibilities by multiplying out.

$$(2x - 4y)(2x + 3y) = 4x^2 - 2xy - 12y^2 \qquad (6)$$

Because the trinomial in Equation (6) is not equivalent to the given trinomial, we conclude that the binomials tested are not the factors we seek. Actually, we do not need to multiply out the product in Equation (6) to conclude that this product is not a factored form of the given trinomial. Because each term of the binomial $2x - 4y$ of Equation (6) is divisible by 2, the binomial contains a repeated factor, and thus condition (ii) of Theorem 1.7.2 is not satisfied. Indeed, if the first terms of the binomials are $2x$ and $2x$, we may disregard as last terms any monomials that are divisible by 2. Thus, we disregard $-12y^2 = (-6y)(2y)$, because $2y$ is divisible by 2, and hence the binomial $2x + 2y$ contains the repeated factor 2. Also, we disregard $-12y^2 = (-12y)(y)$, because $-12y$ is divisible by 2. Because we have now eliminated all the possible factored forms of $-12y^2$, we conclude that there do not exist binomial factors with first terms $2x$ and $2x$.

However, we must also consider $4x^2 = (4x)(x)$. That is, we must consider binomial factors with first terms $4x$ and x. Because $-12y^2 = (-3y)(4y)$, we test binomials with last terms $-3y$ and $4y$.

$$(4x - 3y)(x + 4y) = 4x^2 + 13xy - 12y^2 \qquad (7)$$

Note that the trinomial in Equation (7) would be equivalent to the given trinomial if we replace its middle term by the opposite of that term. We conclude that a factored form of the given trinomial may be obtained by interchanging the $+$ and $-$ signs in the factors that appear in the left side of Equation (7). Thus, a factored form is as follows.

$$(4x + 3y)(x - 4y) = 4x^2 - 13xy - 12y^2$$

To factor a trinomial completely, use the following steps in the order indicated.

To Factor a Trinomial Completely

1. Use the distributive axiom to remove any factors that are common to all three terms.
2. Use Theorem 1.7.2 with trial and error testing to find any binomial factors.
3. Factor each binomial completely, using the techniques of Section 1.6.

Recall that a binomial is an expression which is the sum of two *monomials*. In Section 1.6 we give techniques for factoring a binomial. We now consider techniques for factoring an expression with two terms that is not a binomial.

Example 4:   Find a factored form.

(a) $x(x - 6y) + 8y^2$ (b) $(x + 2)^2 - y^2$

Solution:

(a) Because the first term $x(x - 6y)$ is not a monomial, this expression is not a binomial. First, we multiply out to find a standard form, and then factor the resulting trinomial.

$$x(x - 6y) + 8y^2 = x^2 - 6xy + 8y^2$$
$$= (x - 4y)(x - 2y)$$

(b) Because this expression is the difference of squares, we do not multiply out. We apply Theorem 1.6.1, $a^2 - b^2 = (a + b)(a - b)$, with $a = x + 2$ and $b = y$. Thus,

$$(x + 2)^2 - y^2 = [(x + 2) + y][(x + 2) - y]$$
$$= (x + 2 + y)(x + 2 - y)$$

Next, we consider factoring a polynomial with four terms. If there is a factor common to all the terms, we apply the distributive axiom to remove the repeated factor. Otherwise, we attempt to factor by grouping the terms in any of several ways.

Example 5:   Find a factored form.

(a) $x^3 + 3x^2 + 2x + 6$ (b) $x^2 - y^2 + 2yz - z^2$

Solution:

(a) We group the first two terms and the last two terms and then remove the repeated factors from each group. We have

$$x^3 + 3x^2 + 2x + 6 = (x^3 + 3x^2) + (2x + 6)$$
$$= x^2(x + 3) + 2(x + 3) \qquad (8)$$

Equation (8) does not give a factored form of the polynomial because the expression on the right side of this equation contains two terms and thus is not a product. However, each term in the expression on the right side of Equation (8) contains the factor $x + 3$. Thus, we apply the distributive axiom to remove the repeated binomial factor $x + 3$. We have

$$x^2(x + 3) + 2(x + 3) = (x^2 + 2)(x + 3) \tag{9}$$

Substituting from Equation (9) into Equation (8), we obtain a factored form of the given polynomial.

$$x^3 + 3x^2 + 2x + 6 = (x^2 + 2)(x + 3)$$

(b) If we attempt to group the first two terms and the last two terms, we do not find a factored form. (Try it!) However, because the last three terms contain the variables y and z and the first term does not contain these variables, we group the last three terms. Note that we must change the signs of terms within the parentheses because the parentheses are preceded by a minus sign.

$$x^2 - y^2 + 2yz - z^2 = x^2 - (y^2 - 2yz + z^2)$$
$$= x^2 - (y - z)^2 \tag{10}$$

Because the right side of Equation (10) is the difference of squares, we apply $a^2 - b^2 = (a + b)(a - b)$ with $a = x$ and $b = y - z$.

$$x^2 - (y - z)^2 = [x + (y - z)][x - (y - z)]$$
$$= (x + y - z)(x - y + z) \tag{11}$$

Substituting from Equation (11) into Equation (10), we have the factored form of the given polynomial

$$x^2 - y^2 + 2yz - z^2 = (x + y - z)(x - y + z)$$

As the examples have illustrated, factoring polynomials with more than two terms is a process of trial and error. If none of the trials that we make leads to a factored form, then either the polynomial is prime, or we have not exhausted all the known techniques for factoring.

EXERCISES 1.7

For Exercises 1–6 factor by removing all repeated monomial factors.

1. $x^2 + xy - x$ **2.** $2x^2y - xy^2 + 3xy$

3. $x^4 + x^3 - x^2y$ **4.** $4x^2y^2 + 6xy^3 - 2xy^2$

5. $2xy + 6y^2 - 2yz + 4y$ **6.** $xyz - 2y^2z + yz^2$

For Exercises 7–14 apply Theorem 1.7.1 to find two binomial factors.

7. $x^2 + 8x + 12$ **8.** $x^2 + 2x - 24$

9. $x^2 - 16x + 64$ **10.** $x^2 - 13x + 40$

11. $y^2 - 2y - 48$ **12.** $y^2 - 15y + 36$

13. $x^4 - 5x^2 + 6$ **14.** $x^6 + 8x^3 + 16$

For Exercises 15–24 apply Theorem 1.7.2 to find two binomial factors.

15. $3x^2 + 4x + 1$ **16.** $4x^2 - 4x + 1$

17. $2x^2 + 3x - 2$ **18.** $3x^2 - 7x + 2$

19. $16x^2 + 24xy + 9y^2$ **20.** $3x^2 - 11xy + 6y^2$

21. $6x^2 - 11xy - 10y^2$ **22.** $4x^2 + 19xy - 30y^2$

23. $4x^2y^2 - 7xy - 2$ **24.** $3x^4 + 7x^2 - 6$

For Exercises 25–36 use any method to factor completely.

25. $x^3 + 3x^2 + 2x$ **26.** $x^2y + 2xy^2 + y^3$

27. $2x^3y + x^2y^2 - xy^3$ **28.** $x^3y^2 + 2x^2y^2 - 3xy^2$

CD
1/10   **29.** $x(x + 3) - 2(x + 6)$ **30.** $(x + 2)^2 - 8x$

31. $(3x - y)^2 + 12xy$ **32.** $x(x - 2y) - y(x + 4y)$

CD   **33.** $(x + y)^2 + 2(x + y)$ **34.** $(x - y)^2 - 3(x - y)$
1/10

35. $(x + y)^2 - 1$ **36.** $x^2 - (y + 1)^2$

For Exercises 37–46 group the terms and then factor completely.

37. $xy + 2y + 3x + 6$ **38.** $xy - 2x - y + 2$

39. $x^3 + 2x^2 - x - 2$ **40.** $x^3 - x^2 - 4x + 4$

41. $x^2 + 2xy + y^2 - z^2$ **42.** $x^2 + 4xy + 4y^2 - 1$

43. $x^2 - y^2 - 2yz - z^2$ **44.** $z^2 - x^2 + 2xy - y^2$

CD   **45.** $x^3 + 3x^2 + 3x + 1$ **46.** $x^3 - 6x^2 + 12x - 8$
1/10

REVIEW EXERCISES 1

For Exercises 1 and 2 answer true or false.

1. $\{1, 2, 3\} \subseteq \{2, 3, 4\}$ **2.** $\{3, 4\} \subseteq \{2, 3, 4\}$

For Exercises 3–6 let $A = \{2, 3, 4\}$, $B = \{3, 4, 5\}$, $C = \{1, 2, 4\}$ and represent the indicated set by listing its members within braces.

3. $A \cap B$ **4.** $A \cup C$

5. $\{x : x \in B \text{ or } x \in C\}$ **6.** $\{x : x \in B \text{ and } x \notin C\}$

For Exercises 7–8 let $D = \{0, 2, -1, \frac{4}{3}, -0.5, \sqrt{2}\}$ and represent the indicated set by listing its members within braces.

7. $D \cap I$ **8.** $\{x : x \in D \text{ and } x \in F\}$

For Exercises 9–10 sketch the graph of the indicated set.

9. $\{x : -2 < x \leq 2\}$ **10.** $\{x : 0 < x < 4\} \cap \{x : -2 < x < 3\}$

For Exercises 11–14 use the indicated axiom to find an expression that is equivalent to the given expression.

11. $xy + z$, commutative axiom of addition

12. $xy + z$, commutative axiom of multiplication

13. $x + y$, reflexive axiom

14. $x + y$, identity axiom for multiplication

For Exercises 15–18 name each equivalence axiom that is required to prove that the expressions are equivalent.

15. $(x + 3) + 4 = x + 7$ **16.** $5x + 2x = 7x$

17. $(2x)5 = 10x$ **18.** $3(2x + 1) = 6x + 3$

For Exercises 19–20 calculate the simplest form.

19. $(-2)(-5)(-3) - 18$ **20.** $(-5)[2 - (4 - 8)] \div (-2)$

For Exercises 21–24 calculate the indicated value of the expression.

21. If $f(x) = (2x - 1)(x - 8)$, find $f(4)$.

22. If $g(x) = x^4 + x^3$, find $g(-2)$.

23. If $h(x, y) = x^2y - y^2$, find $h(2, -3)$.

24. If $k(x, y) = -x^3 + 2xy^2$, find $k(-2, 3)$.

25. The total cost of producing x items is C dollars, with $C = 5000 + 30x + x^2$. What is the average cost per item if 40 items are produced?

26. If an object is thrown upward with an initial speed of a feet per second, after t seconds it is y feet above its starting point, where $y = at - 16t^2$. Find the height of a bullet after 20 seconds if it is fired upward from a height of 500 feet above the ground with a muzzle speed of 300 feet per second.

For Exercises 27–42 find a standard form.

27. $(-3x^2y)^4$ **28.** $(-x^3y^2)(x^2y^3)^2$

29. $(-xy^2)(x^3 - y^2)$ **30.** $(xy^2)^3(x^2 + y)$

31. $x(2x - 3) + 2x(1 - x)$ **32.** $xy(x - 2y) - x^2(y - x)$

33. $(2x - 3x^2) - (3x^2 + 2x)$ **34.** $3x[x - 2(x - 2)]$

35. $(x^2y - z^3)(x^2y + z^3)$ **36.** $(x^3 - y^2)^2$

37. $(x - 3)^3$ **38.** $(x + 4y)^3$

39. $(2x - 3y)(x^2 + xy - y^2)$ **40.** $(x + 2y)^2(x - 3y)$

41. $(2x + 3)(x - 4) - (x + 2)^2$ **42.** $(x + 2y)^4$

For Exercises 43–58 factor completely.

43. $3x^2y^4 - 6x^3y$ **44.** $4x^2y^2 - 9$

45. $8x^3 + y^3$ **46.** $x^3 - 27y^3$

47. $8x^4 - 2x^2$

48. $x^4 - x$

49. $x^4 - 64x$

50. $x^4 - 81$

51. $x^2 - 4xy - 5y^2$

52. $4x^2 + xy - 18y^2$

53. $12x^2 - 25xy + 12y^2$

54. $x^4 - 5x^2 + 4$

55. $2x^3 - 6x^2y - 8xy^2$

56. $(x - y)^2 - (x - y)^3$

57. $x^2 + 2xy + y^2 - 16$

58. $x^3 - 3x^2 + 3x - 1$

algebraic expressions that are not polynomials

2.1 Products of Rational Expressions

For each real number $b \neq 0$ there is a unique real number $1/b$, called the **reciprocal** of b, such that $b(1/b) = 1$. For example, the fraction $\frac{1}{3}$ represents the reciprocal of 3, and $3\left(\frac{1}{3}\right) = 1$. The fraction $\frac{2}{3}$ represents the product of 2 and $\frac{1}{3}$; that is, $\frac{2}{3} = 2 \cdot \frac{1}{3}$. In general, we have the following definition for a fraction.

2.1.1   Definition: *Fraction*

If $b \neq 0$, then

$$\frac{a}{b} = a \cdot \frac{1}{b}$$

From your study of arithmetic you know that

$$\frac{2}{3} = \frac{4}{6} \quad \text{and} \quad 2 \cdot 6 = 3 \cdot 4$$

We call $2 \cdot 6$ and $3 \cdot 4$ the **cross products** of the fractions $\frac{2}{3}$ and $\frac{4}{6}$. In the following theorem we show that two fractions are equivalent if and only if their cross products are equivalent.

2.1.2   *Theorem:* **Cross Product**

If $b \neq 0$ and $d \neq 0$, then

$$\frac{a}{b} = \frac{c}{d} \quad \text{if and only if} \quad ad = bc$$

PROOF: Suppose that

$$ad = bc \tag{1}$$

Because $b \neq 0$ and $d \neq 0$, $1/b$ and $1/d$ are real numbers, and we may multiply on both sides of Equation (1) by $1/b$ and also by $1/d$. Thus,

$$ad\left(\frac{1}{b}\right)\left(\frac{1}{d}\right) = bc\left(\frac{1}{b}\right)\left(\frac{1}{d}\right)$$

$$\left(a \cdot \frac{1}{b}\right)\left(d \cdot \frac{1}{d}\right) = \left(b \cdot \frac{1}{b}\right)\left(c \cdot \frac{1}{d}\right)$$

$$\left(a \cdot \frac{1}{b}\right)(1) = (1)\left(c \cdot \frac{1}{d}\right)$$

$$\frac{a}{b} = \frac{c}{d} \tag{2}$$

Because the above steps are reversible, we have shown that Equation (1) is true if and only if Equation (2) is true.

2.1.3   *Theorem*

If $b \neq 0$, then

$$\frac{-a}{-b} = \frac{a}{b}$$

PROOF: The cross products of the fractions are $(-a)(b)$ and $(-b)(a)$. Because the cross products are equivalent, by Theorem 2.1.2 we conclude that the fractions are equivalent.

2.1.4   Theorem

If $b \neq 0$, then

$$\frac{-a}{b} = \frac{a}{-b} = -\frac{a}{b}$$

PROOF: By the Cross Product Theorem we have

$$\frac{-a}{b} = \frac{a}{-b}$$

because $(-a)(-b) = ba$. Furthermore, by the definition of a fraction and and Theorem 1.2.10, we have

$$\frac{-a}{b} = -a \cdot \frac{1}{b}$$

$$= (-1)a \cdot \frac{1}{b}$$

$$= (-1)\frac{a}{b}$$

$$= -\frac{a}{b}$$

In arithmetic you learned to reduce a fraction. For example,

$$\frac{4}{6} = \frac{2 \cdot 2}{3 \cdot 2} = \frac{2}{3}$$

Whenever both the numerator and denominator of a fraction are in *factored form* and there is a factor that is common to both the numerator and denominator, we may cancel that common factor.

2.1.5   Theorem: Reduction

If $b \neq 0$ and $c \neq 0$, then

$$\frac{ac}{bc} = \frac{a}{b}$$

PROOF: The cross products of the two fractions are $(ac)b$ and $(bc)a$. Because the cross products are equivalent, the fractions are equivalent.

Any number that can be represented by the fraction a/b, where a and b are integers with $b \neq 0$, is called a **rational number**. The simplest form of a rational number that is not also an integer is a fraction whose numerator and denominator have no common factors. We use the Reduction Theorem to reduce a fraction to simplest form. For example,

$$\frac{30}{75} = \frac{10 \cdot 3}{25 \cdot 3} = \frac{10}{25} = \frac{2 \cdot 5}{5 \cdot 5} = \frac{2}{5}$$

A fraction, such as $x^2/(x + y)$, whose numerator and denominator are both polynomials with the denominator not zero is called a **rational expression**. A rational expression with denominator neither 1 nor -1 is in **reduced form** if there are no factors that are common to both its numerator and denominator and if its numerator and denominator are polynomials that are either in standard form or in factored form. If the denominator of a rational expression is either 1 or -1, then the rational expression is equivalent to a polynomial, and any standard form, or any factored form, of the polynomial is also a reduced form of the rational expression.

Example 1:   Find a reduced form.

(a) $\dfrac{-21xy^3}{6x^3y^2}$

(b) $\dfrac{x - 2}{x^2 - 2x}$

Solution:
(a) Because the numerator and denominator are both divisible by $3xy^2$, we may factor out $3xy^2$ and then cancel.

$$\frac{-21xy^3}{6x^3y^2} = \frac{(-7y)(3xy^2)}{(2x^2)(3xy^2)}$$

$$= \frac{-7y}{2x^2}$$

(b) We cannot cancel either x or 2 because neither of these expressions is a *factor* of both the numerator and denominator. However,

$$\frac{x - 2}{x^2 - 2x} = \frac{(1)(x - 2)}{x(x - 2)}$$

$$= \frac{1}{x}$$

Note that we must insert the factor 1 in the numerator before canceling the factor $x - 2$.

It is understood for rational expressions that we cannot make replacements for the variables that result in 0 for the denominator. Thus in Example 1(a) we understand that $x \neq 0$ and $y \neq 0$. And in Example 1(b) we understand that $x \neq 0$ and $x \neq 2$.

Example 2: Find a reduced form.

(a) $\dfrac{x(x+2)-3}{(x+3)(x+2)}$

(b) $\dfrac{y-x}{x-y}$

Solution:

(a) We cannot cancel $x+2$ because the numerator of the fraction is not in factored form. We must factor the numerator.

$$\frac{x(x+2)-3}{(x+3)(x+2)} = \frac{x^2+2x-3}{(x+3)(x+2)}$$

$$= \frac{(x+3)(x-1)}{(x+3)(x+2)}$$

$$= \frac{x-1}{x+2}$$

(b) Because $y-x = -x+y = (-1)(x-y)$, we may factor as follows and reduce the fraction.

$$\frac{y-x}{x-y} = \frac{(-1)(x-y)}{(1)(x-y)}$$

$$= \frac{-1}{1}$$

$$= -1$$

In arithmetic you learned that

$$\frac{1}{2} \cdot \frac{1}{3} = \frac{1}{2\cdot3} = \frac{1}{6}$$

In the following theorem we show that the product of the reciprocals of a and b is equivalent to the reciprocal of ab.

2.1.6 *Theorem*

If $a \neq 0$ and $b \neq 0$, then

$$\frac{1}{a} \cdot \frac{1}{b} = \frac{1}{ab}$$

PROOF: By the inverse axiom, we have

$$ab \cdot \frac{1}{ab} = 1$$

We multiply on both sides of the above equation by $1/a$ and also by $1/b$. This results in

$$\frac{1}{a} \cdot \frac{1}{b}\left(ab \cdot \frac{1}{ab}\right) = \frac{1}{a} \cdot \frac{1}{b}(1)$$

Next, we regroup the factors and apply the inverse and identity axioms.

$$\left(\frac{1}{a} \cdot a\right)\left(\frac{1}{b} \cdot b\right)\left(\frac{1}{ab}\right) = \frac{1}{a} \cdot \frac{1}{b}(1)$$

$$(1)(1)\left(\frac{1}{ab}\right) = \frac{1}{a} \cdot \frac{1}{b}(1)$$

$$\frac{1}{ab} = \frac{1}{a} \cdot \frac{1}{b}$$

In arithmetic you learned that

$$\frac{2}{5} \cdot \frac{3}{7} = \frac{2 \cdot 3}{5 \cdot 7} = \frac{6}{35}$$

We now use Theorem 2.1.6 to prove the following rule for multiplying with fractions.

2.1.7   Theorem: **Product of Fractions**

If $b \neq 0$ and $d \neq 0$, then

$$\frac{a}{b} \cdot \frac{c}{d} = \frac{ac}{bd}$$

PROOF: Because $a/b = a(1/b)$ and $c/d = c(1/d)$, then

$$\frac{a}{b} \cdot \frac{c}{d} = a\left(\frac{1}{b}\right) \cdot c\left(\frac{1}{d}\right)$$

$$= (a \cdot c)\left(\frac{1}{b} \cdot \frac{1}{d}\right)$$

$$= (a \cdot c)\left(\frac{1}{bd}\right)$$

$$= \frac{ac}{bd}$$

Example 3: Find a reduced form.

(a) $\dfrac{-2x^2}{y^3} \cdot \dfrac{y^2}{8x}$

(b) $\dfrac{x^2 - 9}{6x - 3} \cdot \dfrac{10x - 5}{x^2 + 3x}$

Solution:

(a) First, we apply Theorem 2.1.7, and then we reduce the fraction by canceling.

$$\frac{-2x^2}{y^3} \cdot \frac{y^2}{8x} = \frac{-2x^2y^2}{8xy^3}$$

$$= \frac{(-x)(2xy^2)}{(4y)(2xy^2)}$$

$$= \frac{-x}{4y}$$

(b) We apply Theorem 2.1.7, but we do *not* multiply out. Instead, we factor and then cancel.

$$\frac{x^2 - 9}{6x - 3} \cdot \frac{10x - 5}{x^2 + 3x} = \frac{(x^2 - 9)(10x - 5)}{(6x - 3)(x^2 + 3x)}$$

$$= \frac{(x + 3)(x - 3)(5)(2x - 1)}{3(2x - 1)(x)(x + 3)}$$

$$= \frac{5(x - 3)}{3x}$$

Example 4:   Find a reduced form.

$$\frac{x^2 + x - 6}{2x^2 - 3x - 2} \cdot \frac{2x^2 - x - 1}{x^2 + 2x - 3}$$

Solution: We factor, cancel, and then multiply the fractions.

$$\frac{x^2 + x - 6}{2x^2 - 3x - 2} \cdot \frac{2x^2 - x - 1}{x^2 + 2x - 3} = \frac{(x + 3)(x - 2)}{(2x + 1)(x - 2)} \cdot \frac{(2x + 1)(x - 1)}{(x + 3)(x - 1)}$$

$$= \frac{x + 3}{2x + 1} \cdot \frac{2x + 1}{x + 3}$$

$$= \frac{(x + 3)(2x + 1)}{(2x + 1)(x + 3)}$$

$$= \frac{(1)[(x + 3)(2x + 1)]}{(1)[(x + 3)(2x + 1)]}$$

$$= \frac{1}{1}$$

$$= 1$$

Note that when the numerator and denominator contain exactly the same factors, the fraction reduces to the constant 1.

Example 5:   Find a reduced form.

$$(x^2y - 2xy) \cdot \frac{2x + 6}{xy^2 - y^2} \cdot \frac{y - xy}{2x^2 + 6x}$$

Solution: We replace the polynomial $x^2y - 2xy$ by an equivalent rational expression and apply Theorem 2.1.7.

$$(x^2y - 2xy) \cdot \frac{2x + 6}{xy^2 - y^2} \cdot \frac{y - xy}{2x^2 + 6x} = \frac{x^2y - 2xy}{1} \cdot \frac{2x + 6}{xy^2 - y^2} \cdot \frac{y - xy}{2x^2 + 6x}$$

$$= \frac{(x^2y - 2xy)(2x + 6)(y - xy)}{(1)(xy^2 - y^2)(2x^2 + 6x)}$$

$$= \frac{(x)(y)(x - 2)(2)(x + 3)(y)(1 - x)}{(y)(y)(x - 1)(2)(x)(x + 3)}$$

$$= \frac{(x - 2)(1 - x)}{x - 1}$$

$$= \frac{(x - 2)(-1)(x - 1)}{(1)(x - 1)}$$

$$= (x - 2)(-1)$$

$$= -x + 2$$

By applying Theorem 2.1.7, we have

$$\left(\frac{a}{b}\right)^2 = \frac{a}{b} \cdot \frac{a}{b} = \frac{a \cdot a}{b \cdot b} = \frac{a^2}{b^2}$$

$$\left(\frac{a}{b}\right)^3 = \frac{a}{b} \cdot \frac{a}{b} \cdot \frac{a}{b} = \frac{a^3}{b^3}$$

and so on. In general, we have the following theorem, which is the last of the laws of exponents begun in Section 1.4.

2.1.8   Theorem: Fifth Law of Exponents

If n is a natural number and if $b \neq 0$, then

$$\left(\frac{a}{b}\right)^n = \frac{a^n}{b^n}$$

Example 6:   Find a reduced form.

$$\left(\frac{-2x}{y^2}\right)^3 \cdot \frac{y^4}{(2x^2)^2}$$

Solution: We apply Theorem 2.1.8 and the other laws of exponents.

$$\left(\frac{-2x}{y^2}\right)^3 \cdot \frac{y^4}{(2x^2)^2} = \frac{(-2x)^3}{(y^2)^3} \cdot \frac{y^4}{(2x^2)^2}$$

$$= \frac{-8x^3}{y^6} \cdot \frac{y^4}{4x^4}$$

$$= \frac{-8x^3y^4}{4x^4y^6}$$

$$= \frac{-2(4x^3y^4)}{xy^2(4x^3y^4)}$$

$$= \frac{-2}{xy^2}$$

EXERCISES 2.1

For Exercises 1–20 find an equivalent rational expression that is in a reduced form.

1. $\dfrac{2x^2y}{4xy^3}$

2. $\dfrac{-9xy^4}{12x^3y^3}$

3. $\dfrac{-15x^4y}{-5x^5}$

4. $-\dfrac{xy}{-x^2y}$

5. $\dfrac{(-2x^2y)^2}{-6xy^2}$

6. $\dfrac{-xy^3}{(-xy)^3}$

7. $\dfrac{x^2 + 5x + 6}{x^2 + 4x + 4}$

8. $\dfrac{2x^2 - 3x - 2}{2x^2 + 3x + 1}$

9. $\dfrac{x^2 - 9}{2x^2 - 5x - 3}$

10. $\dfrac{6x^2 + x - 1}{4x^2 + 4x + 1}$

11. $\dfrac{x(x - 2) - 3}{(x - 2)(x + 1)}$

12. $\dfrac{(x - 2)(x + 1) - 4}{(x + 2)(x - 2)}$

13. $\dfrac{2x - x^2}{x^2 - 4}$

14. $\dfrac{x^2 - xy}{y^2 - xy}$

15. $\dfrac{x + y}{x^3 + y^3}$

16. $\dfrac{x^3 - 1}{x^2 - 1}$

17. $\dfrac{x^3 + 8}{x^2 + 4x + 4}$

18. $\dfrac{x^2 + 2x + 4}{x^3 - 8}$

19. $\dfrac{xy + 3x + 2y + 6}{xy - x + 2y - 2}$

20. $\dfrac{x^2 - 2xy + y^2 - 4}{x^2 - xy - 2x}$

For Exercises 21–40 find a single fraction that is equivalent to the given product and then find a reduced form.

21. $\dfrac{-2x^2}{y} \cdot \dfrac{3xy}{4x}$

22. $\dfrac{-6x^2}{y^3} \cdot \dfrac{-y^2}{3x}$

23. $\dfrac{2x}{(-2y)^3} \cdot \dfrac{-2y^2}{x^2}$

24. $\dfrac{(2x)^3}{-4y} \cdot (-xy^2)^2$

25. $\left(\dfrac{3x}{y}\right)^2 \cdot \dfrac{y^3}{6x}$

26. $\dfrac{4x}{y^3} \cdot \left(\dfrac{-y}{2x}\right)^3$

27. $\left(\dfrac{y^2}{-x}\right)^3 \cdot \left(\dfrac{x^2}{y}\right)^2$

28. $\left(\dfrac{x}{-y^2}\right)^3 \cdot \left(\dfrac{-y}{x}\right)^2$

29. $\dfrac{x^2 + 3x - 10}{x^2 - 3x + 2} \cdot \dfrac{x^2 - 1}{x^2 + 7x + 10}$

30. $\dfrac{x^2 - x - 12}{x^2 - 5x + 4} \cdot \dfrac{x - 1}{x^2 + 5x + 6}$

31. $\dfrac{x^2 + xy - 2y^2}{x^2 + 4xy + 4y^2} \cdot \dfrac{2x^2 + 3xy + y^2}{x^2 - y^2}$

32. $\dfrac{6x^2 - xy - y^2}{3x^2 + 4xy + y^2} \cdot \dfrac{3x^2 + xy - 2y^2}{6x^2 - xy - 2y^2}$

33. $\dfrac{x^2 + 2x - 3}{x^3 - 9x} \cdot (x^2 - 5x + 6)$

34. $\dfrac{x^2y - xy^2}{3x^2 - 9xy + 6y^2} \cdot \dfrac{6x^3 - 6x^2y - 12xy^2}{x^3 + x^2y}$

35. $\dfrac{2x^4 - x^3 - 3x^2}{4x^2y - 9y} \cdot \dfrac{4x^2y + 12xy + 9y}{2x^3 + 5x^2 + 3x}$

36. $\dfrac{-x^3 + x}{x^2 - x - 2} \cdot \dfrac{x^2 - 5x + 6}{x^3 - x^2}$

37. $\dfrac{x^2 + 3x + 2}{x^2 + 2x - 3} \cdot \dfrac{x^2 + x - 2}{x^2 + 4x + 3} \cdot \dfrac{x^2 + 6x + 9}{x^2 - 4}$

38. $\dfrac{x^3 + 2x^2}{x^2 - 4} \cdot \dfrac{x + 3}{x^2 - 2x} \cdot \dfrac{x^2 - 4x + 4}{x^2 + 3x}$

39. $(x^2 + 3x) \cdot \dfrac{x^2 - x - 2}{x^2 + 4x + 3} \cdot \dfrac{x^2 + 3x - 4}{x^2 + 4x}$

40. $\dfrac{x^2 - xy}{x^2y + xy^2} \cdot (x^2 + 2xy + y^2) \cdot \dfrac{xy^2 + y^3}{x^3 - xy^2}$

2.2   Sums and Differences of Rational Expressions

In arithmetic you learned that the sum of two fractions which have a common denominator may be found by adding their numerators. For example,

$$\frac{2}{7} + \frac{3}{7} = \frac{2 + 3}{7} = \frac{5}{7}$$

We now prove the following general rule that may be used to find a single fraction which is equivalent to the sum of two rational expressions with a common denominator.

2.2.1   *Theorem:* **Common Denominator Rule for Adding**

If $b \neq 0$, then

$$\frac{a}{b} + \frac{c}{b} = \frac{a + c}{b}$$

PROOF: We apply the definition of a fraction and the distributive axiom.

$$\frac{a}{b} + \frac{c}{b} = a \cdot \frac{1}{b} + c \cdot \frac{1}{b}$$

$$= (a + c) \cdot \frac{1}{b}$$

$$= \frac{a + c}{b}$$

To find a single fraction that is equivalent to the difference of two rational expressions with a common denominator we use the following rule.

2.2.2 *Theorem:* **Common Denominator Rule for Subtracting**

If $b \neq 0$, then

$$\frac{a}{b} - \frac{c}{b} = \frac{a - c}{b}$$

PROOF: We apply the Subtraction Theorem, $a - b = a + (-b)$, and the Common Denominator Rule for Adding.

$$\frac{a}{b} - \frac{c}{b} = \frac{a}{b} + \left(-\frac{c}{b}\right)$$

$$= \frac{a}{b} + \frac{-c}{b}$$

$$= \frac{a + (-c)}{b}$$

$$= \frac{a - c}{b}$$

Example 1: Find a reduced form.

(a) $\dfrac{x + 2y}{xy} + \dfrac{3x - 2y}{xy}$

(b) $\dfrac{2x + 3}{x + 1} - \dfrac{4x + 5}{x + 1}$

Solution:

(a) We apply the Common Denominator Rule for Adding. Thus,

$$\frac{x + 2y}{xy} + \frac{3x - 2y}{xy} = \frac{(x + 2y) + (3x - 2y)}{xy}$$

$$= \frac{(x + 3x) + (2y - 2y)}{xy}$$

$$= \frac{4x}{xy}$$

$$= \frac{4}{y}$$

(b) We apply the Common Denominator Rule for Subtracting. Because the fraction bar is a symbol of grouping, we must insert parentheses to preserve the grouping indicated by the fractions.

$$\frac{2x+3}{x+1} - \frac{4x+5}{x+1} = \frac{(2x+3) - (4x+5)}{x+1}$$

$$= \frac{2x+3-4x-5}{x+1}$$

$$= \frac{-2x-2}{x+1}$$

$$= \frac{(-2)(x+1)}{(1)(x+1)}$$

$$= -2$$

Example 2: Find a reduced form.

(a) $\dfrac{2}{x} + \dfrac{x+1}{x^2}$ **(b)** $\dfrac{x^2+y}{xy} - \dfrac{x}{3y}$

Solution:

(a) Because the fractions do not have a common denominator, we cannot apply Theorem 2.2.1. However, by the Reduction Theorem (2.1.5) we may multiply the numerator and denominator of a fraction by any non-zero factor. If we multiply the numerator and denominator of the first fraction by x, then the two fractions will have a common denominator. Thus,

$$\frac{2}{x} + \frac{x+1}{x^2} = \frac{2 \cdot x}{x \cdot x} + \frac{x+1}{x^2}$$

$$= \frac{2x + (x+1)}{x^2}$$

$$= \frac{3x+1}{x^2}$$

(b) The least common denominator is the product of all those factors that are either in the first denominator, or the second denominator, or both. Thus, we take $3xy$ for a common denominator. We multiply both the numerator and denominator of the first fraction by 3 because this results in $3xy$ for the denominator. And we multiply both the numerator and denominator of the second fraction by x because this also results in the common denominator $3xy$. Thus,

$$\frac{x^2 + y}{xy} - \frac{x}{3y} = \frac{(x^2 + y)(3)}{xy(3)} - \frac{x(x)}{3y(x)}$$

$$= \frac{3x^2 + 3y}{3xy} - \frac{x^2}{3xy}$$

$$= \frac{(3x^2 + 3y) - x^2}{3xy}$$

$$= \frac{2x^2 + 3y}{3xy}$$

When two fractions have denominators that contain no common factors, we find a single fraction that is equivalent to their sum by applying the following rule for adding.

2.2.3   Theorem: **Cross Product Rule for Adding**

If $b \neq 0$ and $d \neq 0$, then

$$\frac{a}{b} + \frac{c}{d} = \frac{ad + bc}{bd}$$

PROOF: We multiply the numerator and denominator of the first fraction by d and of the second fraction by b. Thus,

$$\frac{a}{b} + \frac{c}{d} = \frac{ad}{bd} + \frac{bc}{bd}$$

$$= \frac{ad + bc}{bd}$$

2.2.4   Theorem: **Cross Product Rule for Subtracting**

If $b \neq 0$ and $d \neq 0$, then

$$\frac{a}{b} - \frac{c}{d} = \frac{ad - bc}{bd}$$

Example 3:   Find a reduced form.

(a) $\dfrac{x}{x + y} + \dfrac{x - y}{x}$

(b) $x - \dfrac{x + 1}{x - 2}$

Solution:

(a) Because the denominators $x + y$ and x have no common factors, we apply the Cross Product Rule for Adding.

$$\frac{x}{x+y} + \frac{x-y}{x} = \frac{x \cdot x + (x+y)(x-y)}{(x+y)x}$$

$$= \frac{x^2 + x^2 - y^2}{(x+y)x}$$

$$= \frac{2x^2 - y^2}{x(x+y)}$$

(b) We replace x by an equivalent fraction and apply the Cross Product Rule for Subtracting. Note the use of parentheses to preserve the grouping indicated by the fraction bar.

$$x - \frac{x+1}{x-2} = \frac{x}{1} - \frac{x+1}{x-2}$$

$$= \frac{x(x-2) - (1)(x+1)}{(1)(x-2)}$$

$$= \frac{x^2 - 2x - x - 1}{x-2}$$

$$= \frac{x^2 - 3x - 1}{x-2}$$

If the denominator of either fraction contains more than one term, we must factor completely before deciding whether to apply the Common Denominator Rule or the Cross Product Rule.

Example 4: Find a reduced form.

(a) $\dfrac{x-1}{x^2 + 2x + 1} + \dfrac{1}{x^2 + x}$
     (b) $\dfrac{x}{xy - y^2} + \dfrac{y}{xy - x^2}$

Solution:

(a) We factor each denominator completely.

$$x^2 + 2x + 1 = (x+1)^2$$

$$x^2 + x = x(x+1)$$

Because the denominators contain a common factor, namely $x + 1$, we apply the Common Denominator Rule. The least common denominator is the product of all factors that are either in the first denominator, or the second denominator, or both. We choose the power of $x + 1$ with larger exponent. Thus, the least common denominator is $x(x + 1)^2$.

$$\frac{x - 1}{x^2 + 2x + 1} + \frac{1}{x^2 + x} = \frac{x - 1}{(x + 1)^2} + \frac{1}{x(x + 1)}$$

$$= \frac{(x - 1)(x)}{(x + 1)^2(x)} + \frac{(1)(x + 1)}{x(x + 1)(x + 1)}$$

$$= \frac{x^2 - x}{x(x + 1)^2} + \frac{x + 1}{x(x + 1)^2}$$

$$= \frac{(x^2 - x) + (x + 1)}{x(x + 1)^2}$$

$$= \frac{x^2 + 1}{x(x + 1)^2}$$

(b) We factor each denominator.

$$xy - y^2 = y(x - y)$$

$$xy - x^2 = x(y - x)$$

Because the factor $y - x$ is the opposite of the factor $x - y$, we multiply both the numerator and denominator of the second fraction by -1.

$$\frac{x}{xy - y^2} + \frac{y}{xy - x^2} = \frac{x}{xy - y^2} + \frac{y(-1)}{(xy - x^2)(-1)}$$

$$= \frac{x}{xy - y^2} + \frac{-y}{x^2 - xy}$$

$$= \frac{x}{y(x - y)} + \frac{-y}{x(x - y)}$$

$$= \frac{x(x)}{y(x - y)(x)} + \frac{-y(y)}{x(x - y)(y)}$$

$$= \frac{x^2}{xy(x - y)} + \frac{-y^2}{xy(x - y)}$$

$$= \frac{x^2 - y^2}{xy(x - y)}$$

$$= \frac{(x + y)(x - y)}{xy(x - y)}$$

$$= \frac{x + y}{xy}$$

Use the following steps in the order indicated to find a single fraction that is equivalent to the sum or difference of two rational expressions by the Common Denominator Rule.

To Apply the Common Denominator Rule

1. Factor each denominator completely.
2. Choose the least common denominator by forming the product of all factors that are either in the first denominator, or the second denominator, or both. If any factor is raised to a power, choose the power with the larger exponent.
3. For each fraction multiply both its numerator and denominator by an expression chosen so that the resulting denominator will be equivalent to the least common denominator.
4. Use the Common Denominator Rule to find a single fraction that is equivalent to the sum or difference of the two fractions found in step 3.

Example 5: Find a reduced form.

$$\frac{1}{x^2 + x - 2} + \frac{1}{x^2 + 5x + 6} - \frac{4}{x^2 + 2x - 3}$$

Solution:

$$x^2 + x - 2 = (x + 2)(x - 1)$$
$$x^2 + 5x + 6 = (x + 2)(x + 3)$$
$$x^2 + 2x - 3 = (x + 3)(x - 1)$$

The least common denominator (L.C.D.) is given by

$$\text{L.C.D.} = (x + 2)(x - 1)(x + 3)$$

Thus, we have

$$\frac{1}{x^2 + x - 2} + \frac{1}{x^2 + 5x + 6} - \frac{4}{x^2 + 2x - 3}$$

$$= \frac{1}{(x + 2)(x - 1)} + \frac{1}{(x + 2)(x + 3)} - \frac{4}{(x + 3)(x - 1)}$$

$$= \frac{1 \cdot (x + 3)}{(x + 2)(x - 1)(x + 3)} + \frac{1 \cdot (x - 1)}{(x + 2)(x + 3)(x - 1)} - \frac{4 \cdot (x + 2)}{(x + 3)(x - 1)(x + 2)}$$

$$= \frac{(x + 3) + (x - 1) - 4(x + 2)}{(x + 2)(x - 1)(x + 3)}$$

$$= \frac{-2x - 6}{(x + 2)(x - 1)(x + 3)}$$

$$= \frac{-2(x + 3)}{(x + 2)(x - 1)(x + 3)}$$

$$= \frac{-2}{(x + 2)(x - 1)}$$

EXERCISES 2.2

For Exercises 1–12 use the Common Denominator Rule to find a single fraction that is equivalent to the given sum or difference, and then find a reduced form.

1. $\dfrac{2x - y}{3x^2} + \dfrac{4x + y}{3x^2}$

2. $\dfrac{2x + y}{xy} - \dfrac{2x - 3y}{xy}$

3. $\dfrac{5x + 3}{15} - \dfrac{2x + 9}{15}$

4. $\dfrac{x + 2y}{x^2} + \dfrac{x - 2y}{x^2}$

5. $\dfrac{x^2}{x - 1} - \dfrac{x}{x - 1}$

6. $\dfrac{x^2}{x - 2} + \dfrac{x - 6}{x - 2}$

7. $\dfrac{x + 3}{x} + \dfrac{x - 2}{x^2}$

8. $\dfrac{x - 3}{4x} - \dfrac{5}{2x^2}$

9. $\dfrac{1 - xy}{xy} + \dfrac{x + y}{2x}$

10. $\dfrac{x - y}{3x} + \dfrac{xy + 1}{xy}$

11. $\dfrac{x^3 + y^3}{x^3} - \dfrac{x - y}{x}$

12. $\dfrac{x^2 + y^2}{y^3} - \dfrac{x - 2y}{y^2}$

For Exercises 13–20 use the Cross Product Rule to find a single fraction that is equivalent to the given sum or difference, and then find a reduced form.

13. $\dfrac{x}{x + 2} + \dfrac{x - 1}{x}$

14. $\dfrac{x + 1}{x} + \dfrac{x + 2}{x - 3}$

15. $\dfrac{xy}{x - y} + x$

16. $x - y + \dfrac{2y^2}{x + y}$

17. $\dfrac{3}{x - 1} - \dfrac{2}{x + 1}$

18. $\dfrac{x}{x + 2} - \dfrac{x - 1}{x - 2}$

19. $\dfrac{x - 2}{x + 1} - \dfrac{x - 1}{x + 2}$

20. $\dfrac{x}{x - 2} - \dfrac{x + 2}{x + 1}$

For Exercises 21–40 use any method to find an equivalent expression in reduced form.

21. $\dfrac{x + 1}{x^2 + xy} + \dfrac{1 - y}{y^2 + xy}$

22. $\dfrac{x + 1}{2x + 1} + \dfrac{1}{4x^2 - 1}$

23. $\dfrac{x^2 - 2x + 1}{x^2 + x} - \dfrac{x - 3}{x + 1}$

24. $\dfrac{2x^2 + y^2}{x^2 - xy} - \dfrac{x + 2y}{x - y}$

25. $\dfrac{6xy}{x^2 - y^2} + \dfrac{x - 2y}{x + y}$

26. $\dfrac{x - 2y}{x + 2y} + \dfrac{8xy}{x^2 - 4y^2}$

27. $\dfrac{2x^2 - xy + 2y^2}{x^2 - 3xy} - \dfrac{5x + 2y}{3x - 9y}$

28. $\dfrac{x - 2y}{2xy - 6y^2} - \dfrac{y}{x^2 - 4xy + 3y^2}$

29. $\dfrac{1}{x^2 + 2x + 1} + \dfrac{1}{x^2 - 1}$

30. $\dfrac{x}{x^2 - 4xy + 4y^2} + \dfrac{2xy}{(x - 2y)^3}$

31. $\dfrac{x + 1}{x^3 + 4x^2 + 4x} - \dfrac{1}{x^3 + 2x^2}$

32. $\dfrac{x^2}{x^3 + y^3} - \dfrac{x - y}{x^2 - xy + y^2}$

33. $\dfrac{x^2 + 2x - 3}{x^2 + x - 2} + \dfrac{x^2 - x - 2}{x^2 - 4}$

34. $\dfrac{x^2 - y^2}{x^2 - 3xy + 2y^2} + \dfrac{x^2 - 4xy - 5y^2}{x^2 - xy - 2y^2}$

35. $\dfrac{x-1}{x^2} - \dfrac{x-1}{x+1} + \dfrac{x^3+2x+1}{x^3+x^2}$ **36.** $\dfrac{3}{x+1} - \dfrac{3}{x^2-x} + \dfrac{6}{x^2-1}$

37. $\dfrac{y}{x^2-xy} - \dfrac{1}{x+y} - \dfrac{2y}{x^2-y^2}$ **38.** $\dfrac{2}{x-2} - \dfrac{1}{x+3} - \dfrac{10}{x^2+x-6}$

39. $\dfrac{x^2}{x-2} + \dfrac{2}{2-x} - \dfrac{x}{x-2}$ **40.** $\dfrac{x^2+1}{1-x^2} + \dfrac{1}{x-1} + \dfrac{2}{x+1}$

2.3 Quotients of Rational Expressions; Complex Fractions

The operation of division is the inverse of multiplication. Thus, if $b \neq 0$, then

$$a \div b = q \qquad \text{if and only if} \qquad qb = a \qquad\qquad (1)$$

For example, $15 \div 3 = 5$ because $5 \cdot 3 = 15$.

> **2.3.1 Theorem: Quotient**
>
> If $b \neq 0$, then
>
> $$a \div b = a \cdot \frac{1}{b} = \frac{a}{b}$$

PROOF: We apply the definition of division. Because

$$\left(a \cdot \frac{1}{b}\right)b = a\left(\frac{1}{b} \cdot b\right)$$

$$= a(1)$$

$$= a$$

by Equation (1), with q replaced by $a \cdot \left(\dfrac{1}{b}\right)$, we conclude that

$$a \div b = a \cdot \frac{1}{b}$$

By the definition of a fraction, we have

$$a \cdot \frac{1}{b} = \frac{a}{b}$$

Thus,

$$a \div b = a \cdot \frac{1}{b} = \frac{a}{b}$$

Example 1: Find a reduced form.

$$(2x^2 - x - 1) \div (4x^2 + 4x + 1)$$

Solution: We apply the Quotient Theorem. Thus,

$$(2x^2 - x - 1) \div (4x^2 + 4x + 1) = \frac{2x^2 - x - 1}{4x^2 + 4x + 1}$$

$$= \frac{(x - 1)(2x + 1)}{(2x + 1)(2x + 1)}$$

$$= \frac{x - 1}{2x + 1}$$

We use the following rule for finding a single fraction that is equivalent to the quotient of two rational expressions.

2.3.2   Theorem: *Quotient of Fractions*

If $b \neq 0$, $c \neq 0$, and $d \neq 0$, then

$$\frac{a}{b} \div \frac{c}{d} = \frac{a}{b} \cdot \frac{d}{c}$$

PROOF: By the Quotient Theorem we have

$$\frac{a}{b} \div \frac{c}{d} = \frac{a}{b} \cdot \frac{1}{\dfrac{c}{d}} \tag{2}$$

Furthermore, by the Reduction Theorem, we have

$$\frac{1}{\dfrac{c}{d}} = \frac{1 \cdot d}{\dfrac{c}{d} \cdot d}$$

$$= \frac{d}{c} \tag{3}$$

Substituting from Equation (3) into Equation (2), we obtain

$$\frac{a}{b} \div \frac{c}{d} = \frac{a}{b} \cdot \frac{d}{c}$$

Example 2:   Find a reduced form.

$$\frac{x^2 + xy}{xy - y^2} \div \frac{x^2 - y^2}{x^2 y - 2xy^2 + y^3}$$

Solution: We apply the Quotient of Fractions Theorem and then the Product of Fractions Theorem (2.1.7).

$$\frac{x^2 + xy}{xy - y^2} \div \frac{x^2 - y^2}{x^2y - 2xy^2 + y^3} = \frac{x^2 + xy}{xy - y^2} \cdot \frac{x^2y - 2xy^2 + y^3}{x^2 - y^2}$$

$$= \frac{x(x + y)}{y(x - y)} \cdot \frac{y(x^2 - 2xy + y^2)}{(x + y)(x - y)}$$

$$= \frac{x(x + y)(y)(x - y)(x - y)}{y(x - y)(x + y)(x - y)}$$

$$= x$$

If a polynomial contains only one variable, then the exponent of the highest power of that variable which appears in the polynomial is called the **degree** of the polynomial. For example, $2x + 5$ is a first degree polynomial, and $x^3 - x^2$ is a third degree polynomial. A polynomial whose only term is a constant is said to have zero degree. If the degree of the polynomial in the numerator of a rational expression is less than the degree of the polynomial in the denominator, such as in $(x + 2)/x^2$, then the fraction is said to be **proper**. If the degree of the numerator is greater than or equal to the degree of the denominator, such as in $(x + 3)/x$ or $x^2/(x + 1)$, the fraction is **improper**. We may always use division to replace an improper fraction by the sum of a polynomial and a proper fraction.

Example 3: Express the following improper fraction as the sum of a polynomial and a proper fraction.

$$\frac{x^2 - 2x - 7}{x + 3}$$

Solution: First, we have

$$\frac{x^2 - 2x - 7}{x + 3} = (x^2 - 2x - 7) \div (x + 3)$$

We rewrite the quotient as in long division in arithmetic.

$$x + 3 \overline{)x^2 - 2x - 7}$$

To find the first term of the quotient, we divide the first term of the dividend by the first term of the divisor. Because $x^2 \div x = x$, x is the first term of the quotient.

$$
\begin{array}{r}
x \phantom{{}- 2x - 7} \\
x + 3 \overline{)x^2 - 2x - 7} \\
x^2 + 3x
\end{array}
$$

Note that we multiply $x(x + 3) = x^2 + 3x$ and write this product under the dividend, just as in arithmetic. Next, we subtract $x^2 + 3x$ from the dividend by adding the opposite of $x^2 + 3x$, namely $-x^2 - 3x$, to the dividend.

$$\begin{array}{r} x \\ x + 3 \overline{)\, x^2 - 2x - 7} \\ \underline{x^2 + 3x } \\ - 5x - 7 \end{array}$$

The next term of the quotient is found by dividing the first term of the remainder by the first term of the divisor. Because $-5x \div x = -5$, -5 is the next term of the quotient.

$$\begin{array}{r} x - 5 \\ x + 3 \overline{)\, x^2 - 2x - 7} \\ \underline{x^2 + 3x } \\ - 5x - 7 \\ \underline{- 5x - 15} \\ 8 \end{array}$$

As before, we multiply $-5(x + 3) = -5x - 15$ and then subtract this product from the previous remainder, $-5x - 7$. Because the degree of the new remainder 8 is less than the degree of the divisor $x + 3$, we terminate the division. The remainder 8 becomes the numerator of the proper fraction, and the divisor $x + 3$ becomes the denominator. Thus,

$$\frac{x^2 - 2x - 7}{x + 3} = x - 5 + \frac{8}{x + 3}$$

We show that the result given in Example 3 is correct. Applying the Cross Product Rule for the sum of the polynomial and the proper fraction, we obtain

$$\begin{aligned} x - 5 + \frac{8}{x + 3} &= \frac{x - 5}{1} + \frac{8}{x + 3} \\ &= \frac{(x - 5)(x + 3) + (1)(8)}{(1)(x + 3)} \\ &= \frac{x^2 - 2x - 15 + 8}{x + 3} \\ &= \frac{x^2 - 2x - 7}{x + 3} \end{aligned}$$

which agrees with the given improper fraction of Example 3.

If the final remainder is zero, then the improper fraction is equivalent to a polynomial, as we illustrate with the following example.

Example 4:   Find a polynomial in standard form that is equivalent to

$$(3x^2y - 8xy^2 + 2x^3 + 3y^3) \div (2x - y)$$

Solution: First, we arrange both the divisor and dividend in descending powers of x.

$$2x - y \overline{\smash{\big)}\, 2x^3 + 3x^2y - 8xy^2 + 3y^3}$$

Because $2x^3 \div 2x = x^2$, we take x^2 as ths first term in the quotient and multiply: $x^2(2x - y) = 2x^3 - x^2y$.

$$
\begin{array}{r}
x^2 \\
2x - y \overline{\smash{\big)}\, 2x^3 + 3x^2y - 8xy^2 + 3y^3} \\
\underline{2x^3 -\ x^2y} \\
4x^2y
\end{array}
$$

Note the term $4x^2y$ in the remainder is the result of subtracting. That is, $3x^2y - (-x^2y) = 4x^2y$. Next, we divide. Because $4x^2y \div 2x = 2xy$, we take $2xy$ as the next term in the quotient and multiply: $2xy(2x - y) = 4x^2y - 2xy^2$.

$$
\begin{array}{r}
x^2 + 2xy \\
2x - y \overline{\smash{\big)}\, 2x^3 + 3x^2y - 8xy^2 + 3y^3} \\
\underline{2x^3 -\ x^2y} \\
4x^2y \\
\underline{4x^2y - 2xy^2} \\
- 6xy^2
\end{array}
$$

As before, the remainder is found by subtracting. We have $(-8xy^2) - (-2xy^2) = -6xy^2$. Because $(-6xy^2) \div (2x) = -3y^2$, we take $-3y^2$ as the next term in the quotient and multiply: $-3y^2(2x - y) = -6xy^2 + 3y^3$.

$$
\begin{array}{r}
x^2 + 2xy\ - 3y^2 \\
2x - y \overline{\smash{\big)}\, 2x^3 + 3x^2y - 8xy^2 + 3y^3} \\
\underline{2x^3 -\ x^2y} \\
4x^2y \\
\underline{4x^2y - 2xy^2} \\
- 6xy^2 \\
\underline{- 6xy^2 + 3y^3}
\end{array}
$$

Because the remainder is zero, we terminate the division. We have

$$(3x^2y - 8xy^2 + 2x^3 + 3y^3) \div (2x - y) = x^2 + 2xy - 3y^2$$

Because $a \div b = q$ if and only if $qb = a$, if there is no remainder when we divide with polynomials, we conclude that the divisor and quotient are each factors of the dividend. Thus, from the result of Example 4 we have

$$2x^3 + 3x^2y - 8xy^2 + 3y^3 = (2x - y)(x^2 + 2xy - 3y^2)$$
$$= (2x - y)(x + 3y)(x - y)$$

Example 5:   One of the factors of $x^5 + 1$ is $x + 1$. Find a factored form of $x^5 + 1$.

Solution: We divide $(x^5 + 1) \div (x + 1)$, leaving a space in the dividend for each of the "missing" powers of x.

$$
\begin{array}{r}
x^4 - x^3 + x^2 - x + 1 \\
x + 1 \,\overline{\smash{\big)}\, x^5 + 1} \\
\underline{x^5 + x^4} \\
- x^4 \\
\underline{- x^4 - x^3} \\
x^3 \\
\underline{x^3 + x^2} \\
- x^2 \\
\underline{- x^2 - x} \\
x + 1 \\
\underline{x + 1}
\end{array}
$$

Thus,

$$x^5 + 1 = (x + 1)(x^4 - x^3 + x^2 - x + 1)$$

A **complex fraction** is any fraction whose numerator or denominator itself contains a fraction. There are two techniques, which we illustrate in the following example, that we use to reduce a complex fraction to a simple fraction.

Example 6:   Find a reduced form.

$$\dfrac{x + 2}{2 + \dfrac{1}{x - 1}}$$

Solution: We find a reduced form for the numerator and denominator separately and then apply Theorem 2.3.1. For the denominator we have

$$2 + \frac{1}{x - 1} = \frac{2(x - 1) + 1}{x - 1}$$

$$= \frac{2x - 1}{x - 1} \tag{4}$$

Substituting from Equation (4), we have

$$\frac{x+2}{2+\dfrac{1}{x-1}} = \frac{x+2}{\dfrac{2x-1}{x-1}}$$

$$= (x+2) \div \frac{2x-1}{x-1}$$

$$= (x+2) \cdot \frac{x-1}{2x-1}$$

$$= \frac{(x+2)(x-1)}{2x-1}$$

Alternate Solution: We multiply both the numerator and denominator of the complex fraction by $x-1$. Because

$$\frac{1}{x-1} \cdot (x-1) = \frac{x-1}{x-1} = 1$$

we have

$$\frac{x+2}{2+\dfrac{1}{x-1}} = \frac{(x+2)(x-1)}{\left(2+\dfrac{1}{x-1}\right)(x-1)}$$

$$= \frac{(x+2)(x-1)}{2(x-1)+\dfrac{1}{x-1}(x-1)}$$

$$= \frac{(x+2)(x-1)}{2(x-1)+1}$$

$$= \frac{(x+2)(x-1)}{2x-1}$$

Example 7:   Find a reduced form

$$\frac{\dfrac{y}{x} - \dfrac{x}{y}}{\dfrac{x+y}{x}}$$

Solution: We multiply both the numerator and denominator of the complex fraction by the least common denominator of the simple fractions, namely xy.

$$\frac{\dfrac{y}{x} - \dfrac{x}{y}}{\dfrac{x+y}{x}} = \frac{\left(\dfrac{y}{x} - \dfrac{x}{y}\right)(xy)}{\dfrac{x+y}{x}(xy)}$$

$$= \frac{\dfrac{y}{x}(xy) - \dfrac{x}{y}(xy)}{\dfrac{x+y}{x}(xy)}$$

$$= \frac{y^2 - x^2}{(x+y)y}$$

$$= \frac{(y+x)(y-x)}{(x+y)y}$$

$$= \frac{y-x}{y}$$

EXERCISES 2.3

For Exercises 1–10 apply Theorem 2.3.1 and Theorem 2.3.2 to find a reduced form.

1. $(x^2 - y^2) \div (x^2 + xy)$

2. $(x^2 - 4x - 21) \div (x^2 - 3x - 28)$

3. $\dfrac{-x^2 y}{z^3} \div \dfrac{xy^3}{z^2}$

4. $\dfrac{18x^3 y^2}{25z} \div \dfrac{81x^2 y^3}{125z^2}$

5. $\dfrac{x^2 - 4}{x^2 - 49} \div \dfrac{x+2}{x+7}$

6. $\dfrac{x^2 - y^2}{xy - 2y^2} \div \dfrac{x^2 - 2xy + y^2}{2x^2 - 4xy}$

7. $\dfrac{x^2 - 4xy}{x - y} \div \dfrac{16x^2 y^2 - x^4}{4y^2 - 3xy - x^2}$

8. $\dfrac{x^2 - 6x + 9}{x^4 - 81} \div \dfrac{x^2 - 7x + 12}{x^3 - 4x^2 + 9x - 36}$

9. $\dfrac{x^3 + 3x^2 - 4x - 12}{x^2 + 5x + 6} \div (x^3 - 8)$

10. $\dfrac{x^6 - 7x^3 - 8}{x^2 - x + 1} \div (x^2 + 2x + 4)$

For Exercises 11–16 use division to express the given improper fraction as the sum of a polynomial and a proper fraction.

11. $\dfrac{2x^3 - x^2 + x + 5}{x + 1}$

12. $\dfrac{x^3 + 2x^2 - 5x + 1}{x - 1}$

13. $\dfrac{x^3 - 8x - 6}{x - 3}$

14. $\dfrac{3x^4 - 2x^3 - 13x}{x - 2}$

15. $\dfrac{x^3 - 2x^2 + x - 3}{x^2 + 1}$

16. $\dfrac{x^4 + x^3 + 2x^2 + 3x - 1}{x^2 + x}$

For Exercises 17–24 use division to find a polynomial that is equivalent to the given improper fraction.

17. $\dfrac{2x^3 + 5x^2 - 2x - 2}{2x + 1}$

18. $\dfrac{3x^3 - 4x^2 + 7x - 2}{3x - 1}$

19. $\dfrac{3x^4 - 4x^3 + 6x^2 - 5x - 4}{3x - 4}$

20. $\dfrac{2x^4 - x^3 - x^2 + 6x + 3}{2x + 1}$

21. $\dfrac{x^3 - x^2y - 5xy^2 + 6y^3}{x - 2y}$

22. $\dfrac{x^3 - x^2y - 3xy^2 + 6y^3}{x + 2y}$

23. $\dfrac{6x^3 + x^2y + 3xy^2 + 2y^3}{2x + y}$

24. $\dfrac{4x^3 + 10y^3 - 11xy^2 + 4x^2y}{2x + 5y}$

For Exercises 25–30 a polynomial and one of its factors are given. Use division to factor the polynomial completely.

25. $x^3 - 5x^2 + 2x + 8;\ x - 2$

26. $x^3 + 4x^2 + x - 6;\ x + 2$

27. $2x^3 + 5x^2y - 4xy^2 - 3y^3;\ x + 3y$

28. $x^3 - 3xy^2 + 2y^3;\ x - y$

29. $x^5 - 1;\ x - 1$

30. $x^5 + y^5;\ x + y$

For Exercises 31–40 find a simple fraction in reduced form that is equivalent to the given complex fraction.

31. $\dfrac{1 + \dfrac{6}{x - 3}}{x + 3}$

32. $\dfrac{3x - 2y}{x - \dfrac{4xy}{3x + 2y}}$

33. $\dfrac{\dfrac{1}{x} - \dfrac{1}{y}}{x - y}$

34. $\dfrac{\dfrac{x}{6} - \dfrac{y}{4}}{\dfrac{x^2}{2} - \dfrac{3xy}{4}}$

35. $\dfrac{\dfrac{x - 2}{x}}{\dfrac{2x}{x + 2} - 1}$

36. $\dfrac{\dfrac{2x + 1}{x + 3} - 1}{x - 2}$

37. $\dfrac{1 + \dfrac{y}{x + y}}{1 + \dfrac{3y}{x - y}}$

38. $\dfrac{2 - \dfrac{3}{x + 2}}{\dfrac{y}{x - 1} + \dfrac{y}{x + 2}}$

39. $\dfrac{2 + \dfrac{3y}{x - y}}{2 - \dfrac{3y}{x + 2y}}$

40. $\dfrac{\dfrac{3}{x} - \dfrac{4}{x + 1}}{\dfrac{2}{x - 1} - \dfrac{3}{x}}$

2.4 Exponents That Are Integers

Definition 1.3.3 gives meaning to powers such as x^1, x^2, x^3, etc., whose exponents are positive integers. We now define powers in which the exponent is either zero or a negative integer. The definitions for such powers are chosen so that the laws of exponents for natural number powers also hold for all integer powers. First, we consider the expression x^0. By the First Law of

Exponents for natural number powers, we have

$$x^a \cdot x^b = x^{a+b} \qquad (1)$$

If this law holds when $b = 0$, then

$$x^a \cdot x^0 = x^{a+0} = x^a \qquad (2)$$

Because

$$x^a \cdot 1 = x^a \qquad (3)$$

we conclude from a comparison of Equation (2) and Equation (3) that $x^0 = 1$.

Next, we replace b by $-a$ in Equation (1). We have

$$x^a \cdot x^{-a} = x^{a+(-a)} = x^0 = 1 \qquad (4)$$

Because

$$x^a \cdot \frac{1}{x^a} = 1 \qquad (5)$$

we conclude from a comparison of Equation (4) and Equation (5) that $x^{-a} = 1/x^a$. Thus, we take the following definition for a power whose exponent is either zero or a negative integer.

2.4.1   Definition: Integer Power

If n is a positive integer and if $x \neq 0$, then

$$\text{(i)} \quad x^0 = 1$$

$$\text{(ii)} \quad x^{-n} = \frac{1}{x^n}$$

Example 1:   Calculate the simplest form.
(a) 5^0 (b) 3^{-1} (c) -4^{-2} (d) $(-2)^{-4}$

Solution:
(a) By Definition 2.4.1 the zero power of any nonzero number is one. Thus,

$$5^0 = 1$$

(b) We apply Definition 2.4.1 with $x = 3$ and $n = 1$. Thus,

$$3^{-1} = \frac{1}{3^1} = \frac{1}{3}$$

(c) This represents the opposite of 4^{-2} and should not be confused with $(-4)^{-2}$. Thus,

$$-4^{-2} = -(4^{-2}) = -\left(\frac{1}{4^2}\right) = -\frac{1}{16}$$

(d) Note the use of parentheses.

$$(-2)^{-4} = \frac{1}{(-2)^4} = \frac{1}{16}$$

Definition 2.4.1 implies that every negative integer power of a monomial is equivalent to a rational expression with all positive integer exponents. For such an expression we have defined a reduced form.

Example 2: Find a reduced form.

(a) xy^{-1} **(b)** $(xy)^{-2}$

Solution:

(a) The base of the exponent -1 is y, not xy. Thus,

$$xy^{-1} = x \cdot \frac{1}{y} = \frac{x}{y}$$

(b) The base of the exponent -2 is xy. Thus,

$$(xy)^{-2} = \frac{1}{(xy)^2} = \frac{1}{x^2y^2}$$

The definition for integer powers has been chosen so that the laws of exponents for natural number powers also hold when the powers have integer exponents. We now restate those laws.

2.4.2   *Theorem:* **Laws of Exponents**

If m and n are integers, then

1. $a^m \cdot a^n = a^{m+n}$
2. $a^m \div a^n = a^{m-n}$,   if $a \neq 0$
3. $(a^m)^n = a^{mn}$
4. $(ab)^n = a^n b^n$
5. $\left(\dfrac{a}{b}\right)^n = \dfrac{a^n}{b^n}$,   if $b \neq 0$

Example 3: Find a reduced form.

(a) $(x^5 y^{-1})(x^{-2} y^{-3})$ **(b)** $(x^2 y^{-3})^{-2}$

Solution:

(a) We regroup the factors and then apply the First Law of Exponents.

$$(x^5y^{-1})(x^{-2}y^{-3}) = (x^5x^{-2})(y^{-1}y^{-3})$$

$$= x^{5+(-2)}y^{-1+(-3)}$$

$$= x^3y^{-4}$$

$$= x^3 \cdot \frac{1}{y^4}$$

$$= \frac{x^3}{y^4}$$

(b) We apply the Fourth Law of Exponents and then the Third Law of Exponents.

$$(x^2y^{-3})^{-2} = (x^2)^{-2}(y^{-3})^{-2}$$

$$= x^{(2)(-2)}y^{(-3)(-2)}$$

$$= x^{-4}y^6$$

$$= \frac{y^6}{x^4}$$

A fraction that contains powers with negative exponents is a complex fraction. For such an expression we may always find an equivalent simple fraction with positive exponents and in a reduced form.

Example 4: Find a reduced form.

(a) $\dfrac{x^{-1}y}{x^2y^{-3}}$

(b) $\left(\dfrac{x}{y^{-2}}\right)^{-1}$

Solution:

(a) We regroup the factors and then apply the Second Law of Exponents.

$$\frac{x^{-1}y}{x^2y^{-3}} = \frac{x^{-1}}{x^2} \cdot \frac{y}{y^{-3}}$$

$$= (x^{-1} \div x^2)(y \div y^{-3})$$

$$= x^{-1-2} \cdot y^{1-(-3)}$$

$$= x^{-3}y^4$$

$$= \frac{y^4}{x^3}$$

(b) We apply the Fifth Law of Exponents and the Third Law of Exponents.

$$\left(\frac{x}{y^{-2}}\right)^{-1} = \frac{x^{-1}}{(y^{-2})^{-1}}$$

$$= \frac{x^{-1}}{y^{(-2)(-1)}}$$

$$= \frac{x^{-1}}{y^2}$$

$$= \frac{\frac{1}{x}}{y^2}$$

$$= \frac{1}{xy^2}$$

Example 5:   Find a reduced form.

$$\frac{x^{-1} + y^{-2}}{xy^{-1}}$$

Solution: Because the numerator and denominator are not both products, we cannot regroup and apply the laws of exponents, as in Example 4(a). However,

$$\frac{x^{-1} + y^{-2}}{xy^{-1}} = \frac{\frac{1}{x} + \frac{1}{y^2}}{\frac{x}{y}}$$

$$= \frac{\left(\frac{1}{x} + \frac{1}{y^2}\right)(xy^2)}{\left(\frac{x}{y}\right)(xy^2)}$$

$$= \frac{\frac{1}{x}(xy^2) + \frac{1}{y^2}(xy^2)}{\left(\frac{x}{y}\right)(xy^2)}$$

$$= \frac{y^2 + x}{x^2 y}$$

The numeral $(2.75) \cdot 10^{-4}$ is said to be in **scientific form**. In general, any numeral of the form $a \cdot 10^k$ is in scientific form if a is a decimal numeral with $1 \leq a < 10$ and k is an integer. The fixed point form of $(2.75) \cdot 10^{-4}$ is found by shifting the decimal point 4 places to the left. Thus,

$$(2.75) \cdot 10^{-4} = 0.000275$$

In general, the fixed point form of $a \cdot 10^k$ is found by shifting the decimal point in the numeral a by k places to the right if k is positive and by $|k|$ places to the left if k is negative.

Example 6:   Write the given numeral in scientific form.
(a) 345,000   (b) $(2 \cdot 10^{-3})(7 \cdot 10^{-4})$

Solution:
(a) If $a \cdot 10^k$ is in scientific form, then $1 \leq a < 10$. Thus, we shift the decimal point in the given numeral so that it is between the digit 3 and the digit 4. Because this requires a shift of 5 places, we take $k = 5$. Thus,

$$345,000 = (3.45) \cdot 10^5$$

(b) First, we regroup the factors and apply the First Law of Exponents. Thus,

$$(2 \cdot 10^{-3})(7 \cdot 10^{-4}) = (2 \cdot 7)(10^{-3} \cdot 10^{-4})$$
$$= 14 \cdot 10^{-7}$$

Because 14 is not between 1 and 10, we replace 14 by $(1.4) \cdot 10$. Thus,

$$(2 \cdot 10^{-3})(7 \cdot 10^{-4}) = 14 \cdot 10^{-7}$$
$$= (1.4) \cdot 10^1 \cdot 10^{-7}$$
$$= (1.4) \cdot 10^{-6}$$

EXERCISES 2.4

For Exercises 1–8 calculate the simplest form.

1. 2^0	**2.** 5^{-1}	**3.** 3^{-2}	**4.** 4^{-3}
5. -2^{-4}	**6.** -6^{-2}	**7.** $(-5)^{-2}$	**8.** $(-3)^{-4}$

For Exercises 9–14 make the indicated replacement and then calculate the simplest form.

9. If $f(x) = 3x^{-1}$, find $f(2)$.   **10.** If $g(x) = -5x^0$, find $g(3)$.
11. If $h(x) = -x^{-2}$, find $h(5)$.   **12.** If $k(x) = x^{-2}$, find $k(-5)$.
13. If $F(x) = x^{-4}$, find $F(-3)$.   **14.** If $G(x) = -x^{-4}$, find $G(-2)$.

For Exercises 15–22 use Definition 2.4.1 to replace the given expression by an equivalent expression with positive integer exponents and in a reduced form.

15. $2x^{-3}$	**16.** $(3x)^{-2}$	**17.** $(-xy)^{-1}$	**18.** $(-x)^{-3}$
19. $(-x)^{-4}$	**20.** $-xy^{-4}$	**21.** $-x^{-2}$	**22.** $(-xy)^{-2}$

For Exercises 23–36 use the laws of exponents and then Definition 2.4.1 to find an equivalent expression with all positive exponents and in a reduced form.

23. $x^{-5} \cdot x^3$ **24.** $x^2 \div x^5$ **25.** $x^{-1} \div x^{-3}$

26. $x^{-4} \cdot x^{-2}$ **27.** $(x^2 y^{-3})(x^{-1} y)$ **28.** $(2x^{-3})(-2x^2)$

29. $(-3x^{-2})(-x^{-1})$ **30.** $(x^{-1} y^3)(x^3 y^{-4})$ **31.** $x^3(x + x^{-1})$

32. $x^2(2x + x^{-2})$ **33.** $(x^{-2})^{-4}$ **34.** $(x^{-1})^3$

35. $(xy^{-2})^2$ **36.** $(x^{-2}y)^{-3}$

For Exercises 37–52 use any method to find an equivalent expression in a reduced form.

37. $\dfrac{2x^{-1}}{y}$ **38.** $\dfrac{x^{-2}y}{x^{-1}}$ **39.** $\dfrac{x^{-1}}{y^{-2}}$

40. $\dfrac{x^{-3}}{y^{-2}}$ **41.** $\dfrac{x^{-1}y^2}{xy^{-3}}$ **42.** $\dfrac{x^{-3}y^{-2}}{xy^{-4}}$

43. $\dfrac{x^{-1}y^{-2}}{xy^3}$ **44.** $\dfrac{x^{-3}y}{x^{-4}y^{-2}}$ **45.** $\left(\dfrac{x}{y^{-2}}\right)^3$

46. $\left(\dfrac{x}{y}\right)^{-2} \cdot \dfrac{x^3}{y}$ **47.** $\left(\dfrac{x}{y}\right)^3 \cdot \dfrac{x^{-2}}{(xy)^{-1}}$ **48.** $\dfrac{(xy^{-1})^{-2}}{x} \cdot \left(\dfrac{x}{y^{-1}}\right)^{-3}$

49. $\dfrac{x + x^{-1}}{x}$ **50.** $\dfrac{x^{-1} + x^{-2}}{x^{-2}}$ **51.** $\dfrac{1 + x^{-1}}{x + 1}$

52. $\dfrac{1 - x^{-2}}{x - 1}$

For Exercises 53–60 write the given numeral in scientific form.

53. 31,600   **54.** 0.000052   **55.** 0.0045

56. 3,000,000   **57.** $(2 \cdot 10^6)(4 \cdot 10^{-3})$ **58.** $(3 \cdot 10^{-2})(2 \cdot 10^{-5})$

59. $(5 \cdot 10^{-6})(3 \cdot 10^4)$ **60.** $(7 \cdot 10^6)(3 \cdot 10^{-3})$

2.5 Square Root Radicals

Because $3^2 = 9$, we say that 9 is the **square** of 3 and 3 is a **square root** of 9. In general, if $b^2 = a$, then a is the square of b and b is a square root of a. The opposite of 3 is also a square root of 9, because $(-3)^2 = 9$. Every positive number has two square roots; one square root is positive and the other square root is negative. The negative square root is the opposite of the positive square root. The only square root of zero is zero. A negative number does not have a real square root, because the square of any real number is greater than or equal to zero.

We use the **radical sign** $\sqrt{}$ to indicate the *positive* square root of a positive number. This square root is called the **principal square root**. For example, $\sqrt{16} = 4$ because $4^2 = 16$. The radical sign preceded by a minus sign, $-\sqrt{}$, is used to represent the negative square root of a positive number. Hence, $-\sqrt{16} = -4$. Because there is only one square root of 0, then $\sqrt{0} = -\sqrt{0} = 0$. In general, we have the following definition.

2.5.1 *Definition:* **Principal Square Root**

If $a \geq 0$, then $\sqrt{a} = b$ if and only if $b \geq 0$ and $b^2 = a$.

The expression $\sqrt{a}$ is called a **radical**, and the expression a that appears under the radical sign is called a **radicand**. The radical $\sqrt{a}$ represents a rational number if and only if the radicand a is the square of a rational number. For example, $\sqrt{25}$ is a rational number because $\sqrt{25} = \sqrt{5^2} = 5$. On the other hand $\sqrt{30}$ is irrational because 30 is not the square of a rational number. Irrational square roots cannot be represented *exactly* by either common fractions or decimals. Table 1 in the Appendix gives decimal approximations for the principal square roots of some positive integers. Decimal approximations for the principal square roots of other positive numbers are found by using an electronic calculator. We will not often use decimal approximations for square roots in this book. Instead, we will use radicals to represent irrational square roots. The following two theorems can sometimes be used to simplify radicals.

2.5.2 *Theorem*

If $a \geq 0$, then $\sqrt{a^2} = a$.

PROOF: We apply Definition 2.5.1. In the definition, replace a by a^2 and b by a. This results in $\sqrt{a^2} = a$ if and only if $a \geq 0$ and $a^2 = a^2$. Because $a \geq 0$ by hypothesis, we conclude that $\sqrt{a^2} = a$.

2.5.3 *Theorem*

If $a \geq 0$ and $b \geq 0$, then

$$\sqrt{a} \cdot \sqrt{b} = \sqrt{ab}$$

PROOF: Let $\sqrt{a} = p$ and $\sqrt{b} = q$. Then by Definition 2.5.1 we have $p \geq 0, q \geq 0, p^2 = a$, and $q^2 = b$. Thus,

$$(pq)^2 = p^2 q^2 = ab \tag{1}$$

Because $pq \geq 0$ and $ab \geq 0$, Equation (1) and Definition 2.5.1 imply that

$$pq = \sqrt{ab} \qquad\qquad (2)$$

Because $p = \sqrt{a}$ and $q = \sqrt{b}$, by substituting into Equation (2) we have

$$\sqrt{a} \cdot \sqrt{b} = \sqrt{ab}$$

A constant of the form $\sqrt{a}$ is in simplest form if a is the simplest form of a positive integer that is not divisible by the square of any integer greater than 1. For example, $\sqrt{30}$ is in simplest form because 30 is not divisible by any member of $\{4, 9, 16, 25, \ldots\}$. However, $\sqrt{50}$ is not in simplest form because 50 is divisible by $25 = 5^2$. A constant of the form $a\sqrt{b}$ is in simplest form if $\sqrt{b}$ is in simplest form and a is the simplest form of any integer that is not in $\{1, -1, 0\}$. The simplest forms for $1 \cdot \sqrt{b}$, $-1 \cdot \sqrt{b}$, and $0 \cdot \sqrt{b}$ are $\sqrt{b}$, $-\sqrt{b}$, and 0, respectively.

Example 1: Find the simplest form.

(a) $\sqrt{48}$ (b) $(2\sqrt{5})(3\sqrt{10})$

Solution:

(a) We apply Theorem 2.5.3 and Theorem 2.5.2.

$$\sqrt{48} = \sqrt{16 \cdot 3} = \sqrt{16} \cdot \sqrt{3} = \sqrt{4^2} \cdot \sqrt{3} = 4\sqrt{3}$$

(b) We regroup the factors and then apply the theorems.

$$(2\sqrt{5})(3\sqrt{10}) = (2 \cdot 3)(\sqrt{5}\sqrt{10})$$
$$= 6\sqrt{5 \cdot 10}$$
$$= 6\sqrt{5^2 \cdot 2}$$
$$= 6\sqrt{5^2} \cdot \sqrt{2}$$
$$= 6 \cdot 5\sqrt{2}$$
$$= 30\sqrt{2}$$

A constant of the form $a + b\sqrt{c}$ is in simplest form if a is the simplest form of an integer and $b\sqrt{c}$ is in simplest form. A constant of the form $a\sqrt{b} + c\sqrt{d}$ is in simplest form if both $a\sqrt{b}$ and $c\sqrt{d}$ are in simplest form and $b \neq d$.

Example 2: Find the simplest form.

(a) $\sqrt{8} + \sqrt{18}$ (b) $\sqrt{3} - \sqrt{12}$

Solution:

(a) Note that $\sqrt{8} + \sqrt{18} \neq \sqrt{26}$. In general, $\sqrt{a} + \sqrt{b} \neq \sqrt{a + b}$.

However,

$$\sqrt{8} + \sqrt{18} = \sqrt{4} \cdot \sqrt{2} + \sqrt{9} \cdot \sqrt{2}$$
$$= 2\sqrt{2} + 3\sqrt{2}$$
$$= (2 + 3)\sqrt{2}$$
$$= 5\sqrt{2}$$

(b) $\sqrt{3} - \sqrt{12} = \sqrt{3} - \sqrt{4} \cdot \sqrt{3}$
$$= 1 \cdot \sqrt{3} - 2 \cdot \sqrt{3}$$
$$= (1 - 2)\sqrt{3}$$
$$= -\sqrt{3}$$

By applying the theorems of this section, we have

$$(\sqrt{5})^2 = \sqrt{5} \cdot \sqrt{5} = \sqrt{5 \cdot 5} = \sqrt{5^2} = 5$$

In general, we have the following result.

2.5.4   *Theorem*

If $a \geq 0$, then

$$(\sqrt{a})^2 = \sqrt{a} \cdot \sqrt{a} = a$$

PROOF: We apply Theorems 2.5.3 and 2.5.2. Thus, because $a \geq 0$, we have

$$(\sqrt{a})^2 = \sqrt{a} \cdot \sqrt{a} = \sqrt{a \cdot a} = \sqrt{a^2} = a$$

Example 3:   Find the simplest form.

(a) $\sqrt{3}(\sqrt{3} + 5\sqrt{2})$ (b) $(2 + \sqrt{5})(4 - \sqrt{5})$

Solution: First, we apply the distributive axiom to multiply out, and then we apply the theorems of this section.

(a) $\sqrt{3}(\sqrt{3} + 5\sqrt{2}) = \sqrt{3} \cdot \sqrt{3} + \sqrt{3} \cdot 5\sqrt{2}$
$$= 3 + 5\sqrt{6}$$

Note that $3 + 5\sqrt{6} \neq 8\sqrt{6}$, because multiplication is performed before addition.

(b) $(2 + \sqrt{5})(4 - \sqrt{5}) = 2(4 - \sqrt{5}) + \sqrt{5}(4 - \sqrt{5})$
$$= 8 - 2\sqrt{5} + 4\sqrt{5} - 5$$
$$= (8 - 5) + (-2 + 4)\sqrt{5}$$
$$= 3 + 2\sqrt{5}$$

Example 4: Find the simplest form.

(a) $(-3\sqrt{17})^2$ **(b)** $(3 + \sqrt{5})^2$

Solution:

(a) First, we apply the Fourth Law of Exponents, $(ab)^2 = a^2b^2$.

$$(-3\sqrt{17})^2 = (-3)^2(\sqrt{17})^2$$
$$= 9 \cdot 17$$
$$\boxed{= 153}$$

(b) First, we apply the Binomial Square Theorem, $(a + b)^2 = a^2 + 2ab + b^2$.

$$(3 + \sqrt{5})^2 = 3^2 + 2(3)(\sqrt{5}) + (\sqrt{5})^2$$
$$= 9 + 6\sqrt{5} + 5$$
$$\boxed{= 14 + 6\sqrt{5}}$$

Next, we define a standard form for some variable expressions that contain radicals. An expression of the form $\sqrt{b}$ is in standard form if b is the standard form of a monomial with integer coefficient and b is not divisible by the square of any monomial. For example, $\sqrt{3xy}$ is in standard form, but $\sqrt{x^3y}$ is not in standard form because x^3y is divisible by x^2. An expression of the form $a\sqrt{b}$ is in standard form if a is the standard form of a monomial with integer coefficient and $\sqrt{b}$ is in standard form. The standard form $a\sqrt{b}$ is similar to the standard form $c\sqrt{d}$ if a and c are integer constants and b is equivalent to d. For example, $3\sqrt{xy}$ is similar to $-2\sqrt{xy}$. However, $x\sqrt{y}$ is not similar to $\sqrt{y}$ because x is not a constant, and $\sqrt{3x}$ is not similar to $\sqrt{x}$ because $3x$ is not equivalent to x. An expression with two or more terms is in standard form if each term is in standard form and no two terms are similar. Because a negative number does not have a real square root, it is understood that we cannot make replacements for the variables that result in a negative number for any radicand.

Example 5: Find a standard form if $x \geq 0$, $y \geq 0$.

(a) $\sqrt{xy} \cdot \sqrt{x^2y}$ **(b)** $(x\sqrt{y} + y)(x\sqrt{y} - y)$

Solution:

(a) We apply Theorems 2.5.3 and 2.5.2. Thus,

$$\sqrt{xy} \cdot \sqrt{x^2y} = \sqrt{x^3y^2}$$
$$= \sqrt{(x^2y^2)x}$$
$$= \sqrt{(xy)^2} \cdot \sqrt{x}$$
$$\boxed{= xy\sqrt{x}}$$

(b) We apply the Sum-Difference Theorem, $(a + b)(a - b) = a^2 - b^2$.

$$(x\sqrt{y} + y)(x\sqrt{y} - y) = (x\sqrt{y})^2 - y^2$$

$$\boxed{= x^2 y - y^2}$$

Theorem 2.5.2 does not apply when a is negative. For example, if a is replaced by -3, the equation $\sqrt{a^2} = a$ becomes $\sqrt{9} = -3$, which is false because $\sqrt{9}$ represents the positive square root of 9. However, the equation $\sqrt{a^2} = |a|$ is satisfied by every real number, whether that number is positive or negative. For example, if a is replaced by -3 in this equation, the result is $\sqrt{9} = |-3|$, which is true because $\sqrt{9}$ and $|-3|$ both represent 3.

2.5.5   *Theorem*   See p. 15

$$\sqrt{a^2} = |a|$$

Example 6:   Simplify the expression $\sqrt{x^6}$ if x is any real number.

Solution: We apply Theorem 2.5.5.

$$\sqrt{x^6} = \sqrt{(x^3)^2}$$

$$= |x^3|$$

EXERCISES 2.5

For Exercises 1–34 find the simplest form.

1. $\sqrt{72}$
2. $-\sqrt{75}$
3. $-\sqrt{7} \cdot \sqrt{28}$
4. $\sqrt{5} \cdot \sqrt{45}$
5. $\sqrt{6} \cdot \sqrt{10} \cdot \sqrt{15}$
6. $\sqrt{21} \cdot \sqrt{24} \cdot \sqrt{32}$
7. $(3\sqrt{6})(\sqrt{2})$
8. $(\sqrt{6})(2\sqrt{3})$
9. $(-2\sqrt{5})(3\sqrt{15})$
10. $(3\sqrt{10})(5\sqrt{12})$
11. $\sqrt{8} + \sqrt{50}$
12. $2\sqrt{8} - \sqrt{18}$
13. $\sqrt{20} - 3\sqrt{45}$
14. $3\sqrt{27} + 2\sqrt{48}$
15. $\sqrt{24} - \sqrt{54} + \sqrt{6}$
16. $\sqrt{20} + \sqrt{125} - 2\sqrt{45}$
17. $\sqrt{3}(\sqrt{3} + 2)$
18. $\sqrt{2}(\sqrt{3} - \sqrt{2})$
19. $2\sqrt{5}(\sqrt{5} - \sqrt{2})$
20. $3\sqrt{2}(2\sqrt{2} + 3)$
21. $(\sqrt{3} + 2)(\sqrt{3} + 3)$
22. $(\sqrt{5} - 1)(\sqrt{5} + 4)$
23. $(2\sqrt{3} + 1)(\sqrt{3} - 1)$
24. $(3\sqrt{2} - 1)(\sqrt{2} - 1)$

25. $(2\sqrt{5})^2$

26. $(-4\sqrt{3})^2$

27. $(2 + \sqrt{5})^2$

28. $(\sqrt{3} - 1)^2$

29. $(\sqrt{2} - 2\sqrt{3})^2$

30. $(2\sqrt{3} + 3\sqrt{2})^2$

31. $(\sqrt{5} + 2)(\sqrt{5} - 2)$

32. $(3 + 2\sqrt{7})(3 - 2\sqrt{7})$

33. $(\sqrt{7} - 4\sqrt{3})(\sqrt{7} + 4\sqrt{3})$

34. $(5\sqrt{2} - \sqrt{11})(5\sqrt{2} + \sqrt{11})$

For Exercises 35–48 find a standard form if $x \geq 0$ and $y \geq 0$.

35. $\sqrt{x^4 y}$

36. $\sqrt{xy^3}$

37. $\sqrt{2x} \cdot \sqrt{8x}$

38. $\sqrt{3x^3} \cdot \sqrt{12x}$

39. $\sqrt{xy} \cdot \sqrt{xy^3}$

40. $\sqrt{x^5 y} \cdot \sqrt{xy^2}$

41. $\sqrt{4x} + \sqrt{9x}$

42. $\sqrt{8x} - \sqrt{2x}$

43. $\sqrt{y}(x\sqrt{y} - \sqrt{x})$

44. $\sqrt{xy}(x\sqrt{y} + \sqrt{x})$

45. $(\sqrt{x} + y)(\sqrt{x} - y)$

46. $(x\sqrt{y} + \sqrt{x})(x\sqrt{y} - \sqrt{x})$

47. $(x + \sqrt{y})^2$

48. $(x\sqrt{y} - y)^2$

For Exercises 49–54 apply Theorem 2.5.5 to simplify the expression if x and y are any real numbers.

49. $\sqrt{4x^2}$

50. $\sqrt{x^2 y^2}$

51. $\sqrt{x^4}$

52. $\sqrt{x^6 y^4}$

53. $\sqrt{x^2 + 2xy + y^2}$

54. $\sqrt{x^6 - 4x^3 + 4}$

2.6   Cube Root Radicals; Fractions with Radicals

Because $2^3 = 8$, we say that 8 is the **cube** of 2 and 2 is a **cube root** of 8. In general, if $b^3 = a$, then a is the cube of b and b is a cube root of a. The opposite of 2 is not a cube root of 8. Because $(-2)^3 = -8$, -2 is a cube root of -8. Each positive number has one real cube root, and the root is positive. Each negative number has one real cube root, and the root is negative. The only cube root of zero is zero. We use the symbol $\sqrt[3]{a}$ to represent the real cube root of the real number a.

2.6.1   Definition: *Principal Cube Root*

If a is a real number, then $\sqrt[3]{a} = b$ if and only if b is a real number and $b^3 = a$.

The radical $\sqrt[3]{a}$ represents a rational number if and only if the radicand a is the cube of a rational number. For example, $\sqrt[3]{27}$ is a rational number because $\sqrt[3]{27} = \sqrt[3]{3^3} = 3$. On the other hand, $\sqrt[3]{25}$ is irrational because 25 is not the cube of a rational number. Decimal approximations for the principal cube roots of real numbers are found by using an electronic calculator. However, we will use radicals to represent irrational cube roots in this book. A constant expression of the form $a\sqrt[3]{b}$ is in simplest form if a is the simplest form of any integer (except 1, -1 or 0) and b is the simplest form of any positive integer that is not divisible by the cube of an integer greater than 1. For example, $\sqrt[3]{30}$ is in simplest form because 30 is not divisible by any member of $\{8, 27, 64, 125, \ldots\}$. However, $\sqrt[3]{40}$ is not in simplest form because 40 is divisible by $8 = 2^3$. We use the following two theorems to find the simplest form of a cube root radical. The proofs of the theorems are similar to those given for the corresponding theorems about square roots in Section 2.5 and are omitted.

2.6.2   *Theorem*

$$\sqrt[3]{a^3} = a$$

2.6.3   *Theorem*

$$\sqrt[3]{a} \cdot \sqrt[3]{b} = \sqrt[3]{ab}$$

Example 1:   Find the simplest form.
(a) $\sqrt[3]{-54}$ (b) $\sqrt[3]{2} \cdot \sqrt[3]{20}$

Solution: We apply Theorem 2.6.3 and Theorem 2.6.2.

(a) $\sqrt[3]{-54} = \sqrt[3]{-27 \cdot 2}$
$\phantom{\sqrt[3]{-54}} = \sqrt[3]{(-3)^3} \cdot \sqrt[3]{2}$
$\phantom{\sqrt[3]{-54}} = -3\sqrt[3]{2}$

(b) $\sqrt[3]{2} \cdot \sqrt[3]{20} = \sqrt[3]{2}(\sqrt[3]{4} \cdot \sqrt[3]{5})$
$\phantom{\sqrt[3]{2} \cdot \sqrt[3]{20}} = \sqrt[3]{8} \cdot \sqrt[3]{5}$
$\phantom{\sqrt[3]{2} \cdot \sqrt[3]{20}} = 2\sqrt[3]{5}$

A variable expression of the form $a\sqrt[3]{b}$ is in a standard form if a is the standard form of a monomial with integer coefficient, b is the standard form of a monomial that has a positive integer coefficient, and b is not divisible by the cube of any monomial. For example, $x\sqrt[3]{y^2}$ is in standard form, but $\sqrt[3]{x^4}$ is not in standard form because x^4 is divisible by x^3.

Example 2: Find a standard form.

(a) $\sqrt[3]{x^4}$ (b) $\sqrt[3]{-xy^2} \cdot \sqrt[3]{xy^4}$

Solution: We apply the theorems of this section.

(a) $\sqrt[3]{x^4} = \sqrt[3]{x^3} \cdot \sqrt[3]{x}$

$\phantom{\sqrt[3]{x^4}} = x\sqrt[3]{x}$

(b) $\sqrt[3]{-xy^2} \cdot \sqrt[3]{xy^4} = \sqrt[3]{-x^2y^6}$

$\phantom{\sqrt[3]{-xy^2} \cdot \sqrt[3]{xy^4}} = \sqrt[3]{(-1)^3 x^2 (y^2)^3}$

$\phantom{\sqrt[3]{-xy^2} \cdot \sqrt[3]{xy^4}} = \sqrt[3]{(-y^2)^3} \cdot \sqrt[3]{x^2}$

$\phantom{\sqrt[3]{-xy^2} \cdot \sqrt[3]{xy^4}} = -y^2 \sqrt[3]{x^2}$

A fraction that contains either the square root radical or the cube root radical is in a reduced form if both the numerator and denominator of the fraction are either constants in simplest form or variables in standard form and if the numerator and denominator contain no common factor. The following two theorems are used when reducing fractions that contain radicals.

2.6.4   *Theorem*

If $a \geq 0$ and $b > 0$, then

$$\sqrt{\frac{a}{b}} = \frac{\sqrt{a}}{\sqrt{b}}$$

PROOF: Because $b(a/b) = a$ if $b \neq 0$, from Theorem 2.5.3 we conclude that

$$\sqrt{b} \cdot \sqrt{\frac{a}{b}} = \sqrt{a}$$

We multiply on both sides by the reciprocal of $\sqrt{b}$ and simplify.

$$\frac{1}{\sqrt{b}}\left(\sqrt{b} \cdot \sqrt{\frac{a}{b}}\right) = \frac{1}{\sqrt{b}} \cdot \sqrt{a}$$

$$\sqrt{\frac{a}{b}} = \frac{\sqrt{a}}{\sqrt{b}}$$

2.6.5   *Theorem*

If $b \neq 0$, then

$$\sqrt[3]{\frac{a}{b}} = \frac{\sqrt[3]{a}}{\sqrt[3]{b}}$$

The proof of Theorem 2.6.5 is similar to that given for Theorem 2.6.4 and is omitted.

Example 3:   Find a reduced form if $x > 0$ and $y > 0$.

(a) $\sqrt{\dfrac{27x}{16y^2}}$ (b) $\dfrac{\sqrt[3]{4x}}{\sqrt[3]{2x^4}}$

Solution:

(a) We apply Theorem 2.6.4.

$$\sqrt{\frac{27x}{16y^2}} = \frac{\sqrt{27x}}{\sqrt{16y^2}}$$

$$= \frac{\sqrt{3^2}\sqrt{3x}}{\sqrt{(4y)^2}}$$

$$= \frac{3\sqrt{3x}}{4y}$$

(b) We apply Theorem 2.6.5.

$$\frac{\sqrt[3]{4x}}{\sqrt[3]{2x^4}} = \sqrt[3]{\frac{4x}{2x^4}}$$

$$= \sqrt[3]{\frac{2}{x^3}}$$

$$= \frac{\sqrt[3]{2}}{\sqrt[3]{x^3}}$$

$$= \frac{\sqrt[3]{2}}{x}$$

To **rationalize the denominator** of a fraction whose denominator contains a radical means to replace the fraction by an equivalent fraction whose denominator does not contain a radical. If the denominator is of the form $a\sqrt{b}$, we may rationalize the denominator by multiplying both the numerator and denominator by $\sqrt{b}$, because $(a\sqrt{b})\sqrt{b} = ab$. If the denominator is of the form $\sqrt[3]{b}$, we may rationalize the denominator by multiplying both the numerator and denominator by $\sqrt[3]{b^2}$, because $\sqrt[3]{b} \cdot \sqrt[3]{b^2} = \sqrt[3]{b^3} = b$.

Example 4: Rationalize the denominator and find a reduced form if $x > 0$ and $y > 0$.

(a) $\dfrac{6x}{\sqrt{2x^3}}$ (b) $\sqrt[3]{\dfrac{2}{xy^2}}$

Solution:

(a) First, we reduce the fraction.

$$\frac{6x}{\sqrt{2x^3}} = \frac{6x}{x\sqrt{2x}}$$

$$= \frac{6}{\sqrt{2x}} \tag{1}$$

Next, we multiply both the numerator and denominator by $\sqrt{2x}$, because $\sqrt{2x} \cdot \sqrt{2x} = 2x$.

$$\frac{6}{\sqrt{2x}} = \frac{6\sqrt{2x}}{\sqrt{2x} \cdot \sqrt{2x}}$$

$$= \frac{6\sqrt{2x}}{2x}$$

$$= \frac{3\sqrt{2x}}{x} \tag{2}$$

Substituting from Equation (2) into Equation (1), we have

$$\frac{6x}{\sqrt{2x^3}} = \frac{3\sqrt{2x}}{x}$$

(b) We want to make the denominator of the fraction under the radical sign the cube of a monomial. Thus, we multiply both the numerator and denominator by x^2y.

$$\sqrt[3]{\frac{2}{xy^2}} = \sqrt[3]{\frac{2(x^2y)}{xy^2(x^2y)}}$$

$$= \sqrt[3]{\frac{2x^2y}{x^3y^3}}$$

$$= \frac{\sqrt[3]{2x^2y}}{\sqrt[3]{x^3y^3}}$$

$$= \frac{\sqrt[3]{2x^2y}}{xy}$$

By the Sum-Difference Theorem

$$(\sqrt{a} + \sqrt{b})(\sqrt{a} - \sqrt{b}) = a - b$$

If the denominator of a fraction is of the form $\sqrt{a} + \sqrt{b}$, we may rationalize the denominator by multiplying both the numerator and denominator of the fraction by $\sqrt{a} - \sqrt{b}$.

Example 5:   Rationalize the denominator and find a reduced form if $x > 0$.

(a) $\dfrac{\sqrt{3}}{\sqrt{2} + \sqrt{3}}$ (b) $\dfrac{x - 4}{\sqrt{x} - 2}$

Solution:

(a) We multiply both the numerator and denominator by $\sqrt{2} - \sqrt{3}$ and distribute the multiplier.

$$\frac{\sqrt{3}}{\sqrt{2} + \sqrt{3}} = \frac{\sqrt{3}(\sqrt{2} - \sqrt{3})}{(\sqrt{2} + \sqrt{3})(\sqrt{2} - \sqrt{3})}$$

$$= \frac{\sqrt{3} \cdot \sqrt{2} - \sqrt{3} \cdot \sqrt{3}}{(\sqrt{2})^2 - (\sqrt{3})^2}$$

$$= \frac{\sqrt{6} - 3}{2 - 3}$$

$$= \frac{\sqrt{6} - 3}{-1}$$

$$= 3 - \sqrt{6}$$

(b) We multiply both the numerator and denominator by $\sqrt{x} + 2$, but we do not distribute the multiplier in the numerator.

$$\frac{x - 4}{\sqrt{x} - 2} = \frac{(x - 4)(\sqrt{x} + 2)}{(\sqrt{x} - 2)(\sqrt{x} + 2)}$$

$$= \frac{(x - 4)(\sqrt{x} + 2)}{(\sqrt{x})^2 - 2^2}$$

$$= \frac{(x - 4)(\sqrt{x} + 2)}{x - 4}$$

$$= \sqrt{x} + 2$$

EXERCISES 2.6

For Exercises 1–8 find the simplest form.

1. $\sqrt[3]{27}$ **2.** $\sqrt[3]{-64}$ **3.** $\sqrt[3]{-24}$ **4.** $\sqrt[3]{54}$

5. $\sqrt[3]{-5} \cdot \sqrt[3]{25}$ **6.** $\sqrt[3]{4} \cdot \sqrt[3]{12}$ **7.** $\sqrt[3]{12} \cdot \sqrt[3]{16}$ **8.** $\sqrt[3]{15} \cdot \sqrt[3]{-18}$

For Exercises 9–16 find a standard form.

9. $\sqrt[3]{x^6}$ **10.** $\sqrt[3]{-x^5}$ **11.** $\sqrt[3]{-x^3y}$

12. $\sqrt[3]{x^4y^3}$ **13.** $\sqrt[3]{xy^2}\cdot\sqrt[3]{x^2y}$ **14.** $\sqrt[3]{x^2y^2}\cdot\sqrt[3]{xy^4}$

15. $\sqrt[3]{-x^2y}\cdot\sqrt[3]{x^5y^2}$ **16.** $\sqrt[3]{-x^4y^2}\cdot\sqrt[3]{-xy^5}$

For Exercises 17–24 find a reduced form if $x > 0$ and $y > 0$.

17. $\sqrt{\dfrac{x^3}{25y^2}}$ **18.** $\sqrt{\dfrac{x^3y}{xy^5}}$ **19.** $\dfrac{\sqrt{18xy}}{\sqrt{2x^3y}}$

20. $\dfrac{\sqrt{3x^3y^2}}{\sqrt{12xy}}$ **21.** $\sqrt[3]{\dfrac{16x}{2x^4}}$ **22.** $\sqrt[3]{\dfrac{-x^5y}{xy^4}}$

23. $\dfrac{\sqrt[3]{-x^2y^2}}{\sqrt[3]{-xy^5}}$ **24.** $\dfrac{\sqrt[3]{3x^4y^5}}{\sqrt[3]{24x^2y^2}}$

For Exercises 25–44 rationalize the denominator and find a reduced form if $x > 0$ and $y > 0$.

25. $\dfrac{10}{\sqrt{5}}$ **26.** $\dfrac{6}{\sqrt{12}}$ **27.** $\dfrac{2x}{\sqrt{6x}}$

28. $\dfrac{xy}{\sqrt{xy^3}}$ **29.** $\sqrt{\dfrac{2}{xy^2}}$ **30.** $\sqrt{\dfrac{2}{3x^2y}}$

31. $\dfrac{4}{\sqrt[3]{2}}$ **32.** $\sqrt[3]{\dfrac{2}{9}}$ **33.** $\sqrt[3]{\dfrac{3x}{2y^2}}$

34. $\dfrac{xy}{\sqrt[3]{x^2y}}$ **35.** $\dfrac{1}{\sqrt{2}+1}$ **36.** $\dfrac{2}{1+\sqrt{3}}$

37. $\dfrac{3\sqrt{2}}{\sqrt{2}-\sqrt{5}}$ **38.** $\dfrac{3-\sqrt{7}}{3+\sqrt{7}}$ **39.** $\dfrac{\sqrt{3}}{3\sqrt{2}-2\sqrt{3}}$

40. $\dfrac{5\sqrt{2}}{4\sqrt{2}-3\sqrt{3}}$ **41.** $\dfrac{x-9}{\sqrt{x}+3}$ **42.** $\dfrac{x-1}{\sqrt{x}-1}$

43. $\dfrac{x^2-xy}{\sqrt{x}+\sqrt{y}}$ **44.** $\dfrac{x^2-y^2}{\sqrt{x}-\sqrt{y}}$

2.7 Rational Number Exponents

We may generalize the concepts of square root and cube root. If n is a positive integer with $n \geq 2$ and if $b^n = a$, then a is the **nth power** of b and b is an **nth root** of a. For example, 2 is a fourth root of 16, because $2^4 = 16$. The opposite of 2 is also a fourth root of 16, because $(-2)^4 = 16$. A fifth root of 32 is 2, because $2^5 = 32$. The opposite of 2 is not a fifth root of 32. Because $(-2)^5 = -32$, -2 is a fifth root of -32. In general, we have the following facts.

---

1. If n is an even integer with $n \geq 2$, then:

    (a) Each positive number has two real nth roots, and each root is the opposite of the other.

(b) No negative number has a real nth root.

(c) The only nth root of zero is zero.

2. If n is an odd integer with $n \geq 3$, then:

    (a) Each positive number has one real nth root and the root is positive.

    (b) Each negative number has one real nth root and the root is negative.

    (c) The only nth root of zero is zero.

The **principal nth root** of a positive number is the nth root that is positive. If n is odd, the principal nth root of a negative number is the nth root that is negative. We use the radical sign with index n, $\sqrt[n]{}$, to represent the principal nth root of a number.

2.7.1 Definition: Principal nth Root

If n is an integer with $n \geq 2$ and

  (i) If $a \geq 0$, then $\sqrt[n]{a} = b$ if and only if $b \geq 0$ and $b^n = a$.

  (ii) If $a < 0$ and n is odd, then $\sqrt[n]{a} = b$ if and only if $b < 0$ and $b^n = a$.

When $n = 2$, we usually omit the index in the radical $\sqrt[n]{a}$. Thus, $\sqrt[2]{16} = \sqrt{16} = 4$. The radical $\sqrt[n]{a}$ represents a rational number if and only if a is the nth power of a rational number. A decimal approximation for the principal nth root of a number may be found by using an electronic calculator. However, we will represent irrational nth roots either by using radicals or by using powers with rational number exponents, which we now define.

Definitions 1.3.3 and 2.4.1 give meaning to powers, such as x^2 and x^{-3}, whose exponents are integers. We now define powers, such as $x^{1/2}$, whose exponents are rational numbers, and we do so in such a way that the laws of exponents for integer powers also hold (with minor exceptions) for rational number powers. By the Third Law of Exponents for integer powers we have

$$(x^m)^n = x^{mn} \tag{1}$$

If this law holds when $m = \frac{1}{2}$ and $n = 2$, then

$$(x^{1/2})^2 = x^{(1/2)2} = x \tag{2}$$

Because

$$(\sqrt{x})^2 = x \tag{3}$$

we conclude from a comparison of Equation (2) and Equation (3) that $x^{1/2} = \sqrt{x}$. Similarly, if we let $m = \frac{1}{3}$ and $n = 3$ in Equation (1), the result is

$$(x^{1/3})^3 = x^{(1/3)3} = x \tag{4}$$

Because

$$(\sqrt[3]{x})^3 = x \tag{5}$$

by comparing Equation (4) and Equation (5), we conclude that $x^{1/3} = \sqrt[3]{x}$. In general, we make the following definition.

2.7.2   Definition

If n is a positive integer with $n \geq 2$ and if $\sqrt[n]{a}$ is a real number, then

$$a^{1/n} = \sqrt[n]{a}$$

Example 1: Find the simplest form.
(a) $25^{1/2}$ (b) $64^{1/3}$ (c) $16^{1/4}$ (d) $-16^{1/2}$

Solution: We apply Definition 2.7.2.
(a) $25^{1/2} = \sqrt[2]{25} = \sqrt{25} = 5$
(b) $64^{1/3} = \sqrt[3]{64} = 4$
(c) $16^{1/4} = \sqrt[4]{16} = 2$
(d) This is the opposite of $16^{1/2}$ and is not equivalent to $(-16)^{1/2}$. Thus,

$$-16^{1/2} = -\sqrt{16} = -4$$

Definition 2.7.2 does not give meaning to the power $x^{2/3}$ because the numerator of the fractional exponent is not 1. However, if we let $m = \frac{1}{3}$ and $n = 2$ in Equation (1), the result is

$$(x^{1/3})^2 = x^{(1/3)2} = x^{2/3} \tag{6}$$

Because $x^{1/3} = \sqrt[3]{x}$, by substituting into Equation (6), we have $x^{2/3} = (\sqrt[3]{x})^2$. In general, we make the following definition.

2.7.3   Definition

If m/n is the simplest form of a positive rational number and if $\sqrt[n]{a}$ is a real number, then

$$a^{m/n} = (\sqrt[n]{a})^m$$

Example 2: Find the simplest form.
(a) $4^{3/2}$ (b) $(-8)^{4/3}$

Solution:

(a) We apply Definition 2.7.3 with $m = 3$ and $n = 2$.

$$4^{3/2} = (\sqrt[2]{4})^3 = 2^3 = 8$$

(b) Because the base is -8, we let $a = -8$ in Definition 2.7.3.

$$(-8)^{4/3} = (\sqrt[3]{-8})^4 = (-2)^4 = 16$$

Definition 2.7.3 does not give meaning to the power $x^{-2/3}$ because $-\frac{2}{3}$ is not a positive rational number. For powers with exponents that are negative rational numbers, we generalize the definition for negative integer powers.

2.7.4   Definition

If m/n is the simplest form of a positive rational number, if $\sqrt[n]{a}$ is a real number, and if $a \neq 0$, then

$$a^{-m/n} = \frac{1}{a^{m/n}}$$

The definitions in this section have been chosen so that the laws of exponents for integer powers, Theorem 2.4.2, hold when m and n are replaced by any rational numbers, provided the base of each power is a positive number.

Example 3:   Find the simplest form.

(a) $8^{-2/3}$ **(b)** $4^{-3/4} \cdot 4^{1/4}$

Solution:

(a) We apply Definition 2.7.4. Thus,

$$8^{-2/3} = \frac{1}{8^{2/3}} = \frac{1}{(\sqrt[3]{8})^2} = \frac{1}{2^2} = \frac{1}{4}$$

(b) We apply the laws of exponents. Thus,

$$4^{-3/4} \cdot 4^{1/4} = 4^{-3/4+1/4}$$
$$= 4^{-1/2}$$
$$= \frac{1}{4^{1/2}}$$
$$= \frac{1}{2}$$

Because there are some exceptions to the laws of exponents when the base is a negative number and the exponent is a rational number that is not an integer, when we use the laws of exponents to simplify variable expressions with rational number exponents, we must restrict the replacements for the variables so that each base is a positive number.

2.7.5   Theorem

If m/n is the simplest form of a positive rational number and if $a > 0$, then

$$a^{m/n} = \sqrt[n]{a^m}$$

PROOF: We apply the Third Law of Exponents and Definition 2.7.2. Thus,

$$a^{m/n} = (a^m)^{1/n} = \sqrt[n]{a^m}$$

Example 4:   Find an equivalent expression without radicals and simplify the result if $x > 0$.

(a) $\sqrt{x} \cdot \sqrt[3]{x}$ (b) $(\sqrt[4]{x^3})^2$

Solution:

(a) We replace each radical with an expression with rational exponents and then apply the laws of exponents. Thus,

$$\sqrt{x} \cdot \sqrt[3]{x} = x^{1/2} \cdot x^{1/3}$$
$$= x^{1/2+1/3}$$
$$= x^{5/6}$$

(b) We apply Theorem 2.7.5 and then the laws of exponents.

$$(\sqrt[4]{x^3})^2 = (x^{3/4})^2$$
$$= x^{(3/4)(2)}$$
$$= x^{3/2}$$

We do not define a standard form for variables that contain rational number exponents. Such an expression is in a reduced form if all its exponents are positive rational numbers in simplest form, none of the laws of exponents can be used to simplify the expression, no factor contains more than one term, and no two terms are similar.

Example 5: Find a reduced form if $x > 0$ and $y > 0$.

(a) $(x^{1/4} + 3)(x^{1/4} - 1)$ (b) $(x^2y)^{-1/2}(x^{3/2}y^{-1})$

Solution:

(a) We multiply out, apply the First Law of Exponents, and combine similar terms.

$$(x^{1/4} + 3)(x^{1/4} - 1) = x^{1/4}(x^{1/4} - 1) + 3(x^{1/4} - 1)$$
$$= x^{1/4} \cdot x^{1/4} - x^{1/4} + 3x^{1/4} - 3$$
$$= x^{1/4+1/4} + (-1 + 3)x^{1/4} - 3$$
$$= x^{1/2} + 2x^{1/4} - 3$$

(b) We apply the laws of exponents.

$$(x^2y)^{-1/2}(x^{3/2}y^{-1}) = (x^{(2)(-1/2)}y^{-1/2})(x^{3/2}y^{-1})$$
$$= (x^{-1}y^{-1/2})(x^{3/2}y^{-1})$$
$$= (x^{-1}x^{3/2})(y^{-1/2}y^{-1})$$
$$= x^{-1+3/2}y^{-1/2-1}$$
$$= x^{1/2}y^{-3/2}$$
$$= \frac{x^{1/2}}{y^{3/2}}$$

EXERCISES 2.7

For Exercises 1–20 find the simplest form for each rational number, find a radical form for each irrational number, and identify any numbers that are not real.

1. $36^{1/2}$
2. $-9^{1/2}$
3. $-6^{1/2}$
4. $(-16)^{1/2}$
5. $27^{1/3}$
6. $-8^{1/3}$
7. $(-64)^{1/3}$
8. $-(-27)^{1/3}$
9. $12^{1/3}$
10. $-20^{1/4}$
11. $9^{3/2}$
12. $16^{3/4}$
13. $-4^{5/2}$
14. $(-27)^{2/3}$
15. $9^{-1/2}$
16. $64^{-1/3}$
17. $-8^{-1/3}$
18. $4^{-3/2}$
19. $16^{-3/4}$
20. $-81^{-3/4}$

For Exercises 21–30 make the indicated replacement for the variable, and then proceed as in Exercises 1–20.

21. If $f(x) = 5x^{1/2}$, find $f(9)$.
22. If $g(x) = -x^{1/2}$, find $g(4)$.
23. If $h(x) = x^{1/4}$, find $h(-4)$.
24. If $k(x) = 3x^{2/3}$, find $k(8)$.
25. If $F(x) = -x^{3/2}$, find $F(16)$.
26. If $G(x) = 2x^{-1/4}$, find $G(16)$.
27. If $H(x) = x^{3/4}$, find $H(0)$.
28. If $K(x) = x^{2/5}$, find $K(1)$.
29. If $P(x) = x^{4/3}$, find $P(-1)$.
30. If $Q(x) = x^{5/7}$, find $Q(-1)$.

For Exercises 31–40 apply the laws of exponents to simplify the expression, and then proceed as in Exercises 1–20.

31. $4^{3/4} \cdot 4^{-5/4}$ **32.** $16^{1/3} \cdot 16^{1/6}$ **33.** $8^{1/2} \div 8^{1/6}$

34. $9^{-3/4} \div 9^{-1/4}$ **35.** $(2^{-1/2})^4$ **36.** $(5^{-1/3})^{-6}$

37. $2^{2/3} \cdot 4^{2/3}$ **38.** $3^{-1/2} \cdot 12^{-1/2}$ **39.** $\left(\dfrac{4}{9}\right)^{3/2}$

40. $\left(\dfrac{-8}{27}\right)^{2/3}$

For Exercises 41–48 find an equivalent expression that does not contain radicals, and then simplify the result, if possible. Assume $x > 0$.

41. $\sqrt{x^3}$ **42.** $\sqrt[3]{x^2}$ **43.** $\sqrt{x} \cdot \sqrt[4]{x}$ **44.** $\sqrt[3]{x} \cdot \sqrt[6]{x}$

45. $\dfrac{x}{\sqrt[3]{x}}$ **46.** $\dfrac{\sqrt{x}}{\sqrt[4]{x}}$ **47.** $(x\sqrt{x})^4$ **48.** $(\sqrt[3]{x^4})^{3/2}$

For Exercises 49–60 find a reduced form if $x > 0$ and $y > 0$.

49. $x^{1/2}(x^{3/2} + x^{1/2})$ **50.** $(x^{3/2} + y^{1/2})(x^{3/2} - y^{1\,2})$

51. $(x^{1/3} - y^{2/3})^2$ **52.** $(x^{1/4} + 2)(x^{1/4} + 3)$

53. $(x^{2/3} y^{1/3})^3$ **54.** $(x^4 y)^{1/2} y^{1/2}$

55. $(x^{-1/2}y)(x^{3/2} y^{1/2})$ **56.** $(x^{2/3} y^{1/2})(x^{-1} y^{3/2})$

57. $(xy^2)^{1/3} \cdot x^{-2/3}$ **58.** $\left(\dfrac{x}{y}\right)^{-1/2} \cdot \dfrac{x^{1/2}}{y}$

59. $\dfrac{xy^{2/3}}{x^{1/2} y^{-1/3}}$ **60.** $\dfrac{x^{-1/2} y^{1/2}}{xy^{-1/2}}$

REVIEW EXERCISES 2

For Exercises 1–28 find an equivalent rational expression that is in a reduced form.

1. $\dfrac{x^3 + 8}{x^4 - 16}$ **2.** $\dfrac{3x^2 - 6xy}{4xy^2 - 2x^2 y}$

3. $\dfrac{3x^4 + 9x^3 y + 6x^2 y^2}{x^4 + x^3 y - 2x^2 y^2}$ **4.** $\dfrac{6x^3 + 3x^2 y + 2xy^2 + y^3}{3x^3 + xy^2 - 3x^2 y - y^3}$

5. $\dfrac{-2x^2 y}{3xy^3} \cdot \dfrac{9xy^2}{8y}$ **6.** $\left(\dfrac{-x^2 y}{z^3}\right)^3 \cdot \dfrac{z^4}{(-xy^3)^2}$

7. $\dfrac{x^2 y^3 - xy^4}{x^4 y^3 + x^3 y^4} \cdot \dfrac{x^3 y^3 + x^2 y^4}{x^3 y - x^2 y^2}$ **8.** $\dfrac{x^2 + y^2}{x^2 y - xy^2} \cdot \dfrac{x^2 + xy}{x^4 - y^4} \cdot (x - y)^2$

9. $\dfrac{x^2 - 1}{x^2 - 9} - \dfrac{5x - 7}{x^2 - 9}$ **10.** $\dfrac{3x - y}{x} + \dfrac{2x - y}{x + 2y}$

11. $\dfrac{2xy}{x - y} + x - y$ **12.** $\dfrac{2x + y}{4x^2 y} - \dfrac{x + 3y^2}{6xy^3}$

13. $\dfrac{4}{x^2 - 4} + \dfrac{x - 2}{x^2 + 3x + 2}$ **14.** $\dfrac{2x}{x^3 - 1} + \dfrac{x - 1}{x^2 + x + 1}$

15. $\dfrac{y}{x^2 - xy} - \dfrac{x}{y^2 - xy}$

16. $\dfrac{2x}{x^2 - 1} - \dfrac{1}{x + 1} - \dfrac{x + 2}{x^2 - x}$

17. $\dfrac{x^2 - 2xy + 4y^2}{x + 2y} \div (x^3 + 8y^3)$

18. $\dfrac{x^2 + 6x + 9}{x^2 - 2x - 15} \div \dfrac{x^2 + 2x - 3}{x^2 - 4x - 5}$

19. $\dfrac{x^5 + x^4 + 5x^2 - 9x + 6}{x^2 + 3}$

20. $\dfrac{2x^3 + x^2 y - 8xy^2 + 3y^3}{2x - 3y}$

21. $\dfrac{\dfrac{1}{y} + \dfrac{1}{x} - \dfrac{2y}{x^2}}{\dfrac{1}{y} - \dfrac{1}{x}}$

22. $\dfrac{\dfrac{x}{x + 1} - \dfrac{1 - x}{x}}{\dfrac{x}{x + 1} + \dfrac{1 - x}{x}}$

23. $x^3 y(x^{-2} y - xy^{-1})$

24. $x^{-2} y^{-1} + xy^{-2}$

25. $(xy^{-2})^{-3}(x^2 y^{-3})$

26. $\left(\dfrac{xy^{-1}}{z^{-2}}\right)^{-2}$

27. $\dfrac{x^{-2} y}{z^{-3}} \cdot \dfrac{x^{-1} y^2}{z^{-1}}$

28. $\dfrac{x - 4x^{-1}}{4x^{-1} + x - 4}$

29. Express the improper fraction $\dfrac{2x^3 + x - 9}{x - 2}$ as the sum of a polynomial and a proper fraction.

30. One of the factors of $x^5 + 32$ is $x + 2$. Find a factored form of $x^5 + 32$.

For Exercises 31–36 find the simplest form.

31. $(-2\sqrt{14})(\sqrt{35})$

32. $\sqrt[3]{16} \cdot \sqrt[3]{20}$

33. $\sqrt{45} + \sqrt{20} - \sqrt{5}$

34. $2\sqrt{75} - 3\sqrt{27} + \sqrt{2}$

35. $(2\sqrt{5} + 3\sqrt{2})(3\sqrt{5} - \sqrt{2})$

36. $(3\sqrt{7} - 4)^2$

For Exercises 37–40 find a standard form if $x > 0$ and $y > 0$.

37. $\sqrt{x^3 y} \cdot \sqrt{xy^2}$

38. $\sqrt{xy}(y\sqrt{x} - \sqrt{y})$

39. $\sqrt[3]{-16x^5 y^6}$

40. $\sqrt[3]{x^4 y^5} \cdot \sqrt[3]{-xy^2}$

For Exercises 41–44 rationalize the denominator and find a reduced form if $x > 0$ and $y > 0$.

41. $\dfrac{12x}{\sqrt{6xy}}$

42. $\sqrt[3]{\dfrac{3}{4xy^2}}$

43. $\dfrac{\sqrt{3}}{3 + 2\sqrt{3}}$

44. $\dfrac{x^2 - xy}{\sqrt{x} - \sqrt{y}}$

For Exercises 45–46 simplify the expression if x and y are any real numbers.

45. $\sqrt{x^4 y^6}$

46. $\sqrt[3]{x^3 + 3x^2 y + 3xy^2 + y^3}$

For Exercises 47–52 find the simplest form for each rational number, find a radical form for each irrational number, and identify any numbers that are not real.

47. 6^{-2}

48. $-16^{1/2}$

49. $\left(\dfrac{-1}{64}\right)^{2/3}$

50. $9^{-3/2}$

51. $25^{1/6} \cdot 25^{1/3}$

52. $(8^{3/2})^{4/9}$

For Exercises 53–56 make the indicated replacement and then follow the instructions for Exercises 47–52.

53. If $f(x) = -x^{3/4}$, find $f(16)$.

54. If $g(x) = x^{-2}$, find $g(-3)$.

55. If $h(x) = x^{-4/3}$, find $h(-8)$.

56. If $k(x) = -x^{2/3}$, find $k(64)$.

For Exercises 57–60 find a reduced form that does not contain radicals if $x > 0$ and $y > 0$.

57. $\sqrt[4]{x^3} \div \sqrt[3]{x^2}$

58. $(x\sqrt{xy})^{2/3}$

59. $(x^{1/2}y)^3(x^{-1/2} + x^{1/2}y^{-2})$

60. $\left(\dfrac{x^{1/2}}{y^{1/3}}\right)^3 \cdot \dfrac{x^{3/2}}{y}$

equations and inequalities with one variable

3.1 First Degree Equations with Integer Coefficients

We have used the "equals" sign to indicate that two expressions are equivalent. For example, we write

$$2x + 6 = 2(x + 3) \tag{1}$$

because the expression $2x + 6$ has the same value as the expression $2(x + 3)$ for each real replacement of x. An equation such as (1), which states that two expressions are equivalent, is called an **identity**.

We now consider equations that are not identities. An equation, such as

$$2x + 1 = x + 5 \tag{2}$$

in which the left expression is not equivalent to the right expression is called a **conditional equation**. If x is replaced by 4 in Equation (2), the result is $2 \cdot 4 + 1 = 4 + 5$, which is a true statement because each side of the equation has the value 9. On the other hand, if x is replaced by 3 in Equation (2), a false statement results, because it is false that $7 = 8$.

The number 4 is said to **satisfy** Equation (2), and 4 is called a **solution** of the equation. In general, any replacement for the variable in an equation with

one variable that results in a true statement is said to **satisfy** the equation, and
the replacement is called a **solution** of the equation. The set that contains
exactly those numbers that satisfy an equation is called the **solution set** of the
equation. Because every real number satisfies an identity, the solution set for
an identity is R, the set of all real numbers. If there are no real numbers that
satisfy an equation, its solution set is $\varnothing$, the empty set.

Two equations that have the same solution set are said to be **equivalent
equations**. The substitution axiom, the Addition Theorem (1.2.6), and the
Multiplication Theorem (1.2.5) can be used to prove the following facts about
equivalent equations.

3.1.1   Theorem: Equivalent Equations

(i)   If we replace any expression in an equation by an equivalent
expression, the resulting equation is equivalent to the original
equation.
(ii) If we add or subtract the same expression on both sides of an
equation, the resulting equation is equivalent to the original
equation.
(iii) If we multiply or divide on both sides of an equation by the same
expression, provided that expression does not have the value zero,
the resulting equation is equivalent to the original equation.

The equation $3x - 2 = 0$ is called a first degree equation because
$3x - 2$ is a first degree polynomial. If the expression on one side of the
equals sign of an equation is a first degree polynomial and the expression on
the other side of the equals sign is either a constant or a first degree polynomial,
then the equation is said to be a first degree equation. Theorem 3.1.1 is used
to find the solution set for a first degree equation.

Example 1:   Find the solution set.
(a) $7x - 2 = 4x + 13$ **(b)** $x + 3(2 - x) = 2(x + 2)$

Solution: We apply Theorem 3.1.1 to simplify the equation.
(a) First, we eliminate the term that contains x from one side of the equation.
To eliminate the term $4x$, we add $-4x$ to both sides.

$$7x - 2 = 4x + 13$$
$$(7x - 2) + (-4x) = (4x + 13) + (-4x)$$
$$3x - 2 = 13$$

Next, we eliminate the constant term from the side of the equation that contains x. To eliminate the constant -2, we add 2 to both sides. Thus, we have

$$(3x - 2) + 2 = 13 + 2$$
$$3x = 15$$

Finally, we want the coefficient of x to be 1. Thus, we multiply on both sides by $\frac{1}{3}$ (or divide on both sides by 3).

$$(\tfrac{1}{3})3x = (\tfrac{1}{3})15$$
$$x = 5$$

The solution set is $\{5\}$.

Check: We replace x by 5 in the original equation.

$$7x - 2 = 4x + 13$$
$$7 \cdot 5 - 2 = 4 \cdot 5 + 13 \qquad (x \longleftarrow 5)$$
$$35 - 2 = 20 + 13$$
$$33 = 33$$

(b) First, we reduce each side to a standard form.

$$x + 3(2 - x) = 2(x + 2)$$
$$x + 6 - 3x = 2x + 4$$
$$-2x + 6 = 2x + 4$$

We may eliminate the term containing x from either side of the equation. To eliminate the term $-2x$, we add $2x$ to both sides.

$$2x + (-2x + 6) = 2x + (2x + 4)$$
$$6 = 4x + 4$$

To eliminate the constant term from the side that contains x, we add -4 to both sides.

$$6 + (-4) = (4x + 4) + (-4)$$
$$2 = 4x$$

To make the coefficient of x equal to 1, we divide both sides by 4.

$$\frac{2}{4} = \frac{4x}{4}$$
$$\tfrac{1}{2} = x$$

The solution set is $\{\tfrac{1}{2}\}$.

We cannot find the solution set for an equation such as

$$x + a = b \qquad\qquad (3)$$

because the constants a and b are not known. However, if we add $-a$ to both sides of Equation (3) and simplify, the result is

$$x = b - a \qquad (4)$$

Equation (4) is called an x-form of Equation (3), and we say that Equation (4) is solved for x. In general, if the left expression of an equation is x and the right expression does not contain x, then the equation is in an **x-form** and we say that the equation is **solved** for x.

Example 2: Solve for t: $v = k + gt$.

Solution: We find a t-form of the equation.

$$v = k + gt$$
$$v - k = gt$$
$$\frac{v - k}{g} = t$$
$$t = \frac{v - k}{g}$$

Example 3: If an object is thrown upward with a speed of k feet per second, after t seconds it will have a velocity of v feet per second, with $v = k - 32t$. If a bullet is fired upward with a muzzle speed of 500 feet per second, how long will it take for the bullet to reach a velocity of only 100 feet per second?

Solution: Because the muzzle speed of the bullet is 500 feet per second, we replace k by 500 in the formula $v = k - 32t$. Because we want to find the time it takes for the bullet to reach a velocity of 100 feet per second, we also replace v by 100 and find the solution of the resulting equation.

$$v = k - 32t$$
$$100 = 500 - 32t$$
$$-500 + 100 = -500 + (500 - 32t)$$
$$-400 = -32t$$
$$(-1)(-400) = (-1)(-32t)$$
$$400 = 32t$$
$$\frac{400}{32} = t$$
$$12.5 = t$$

It will take 12.5 seconds.

Alternate Solution: We first solve the equation for t, and then make the indicated replacements for k and v.

$$v = k - 32t$$
$$v + 32t = k$$
$$32t = k - v$$
$$t = \frac{1}{32}(k - v)$$
$$t = \frac{1}{32}(500 - 100) \qquad (k \longleftarrow 500, v \longleftarrow 100)$$
$$t = 12.5$$

Sometimes the formula necessary to solve a problem is not given. In that case we must recall some formula from our previous study that can be used.

Example 4: We have a roll of wire fencing 120 feet long that we will use to enclose a rectangular garden, and we want the garden to be three times as long as it is wide. What are the dimensions of the garden if all the fencing is used?

Solution: We want to find the length and the width of a rectangle. Because the length of the wire used is the distance around the rectangle, the formula we need is

$$P = 2l + 2w$$

where P units is the perimeter of a rectangle whose length is l units and whose width is w units. Because the length of the rectangle is three times the width, we let x feet be the width and $3x$ feet be the length of the rectangle. That is, we replace w by x and l by $3x$ in the formula. Because the wire is 120 feet long, we replace P by 120. Thus, we have

$$120 = 2(3x) + 2x$$
$$120 = 8x$$
$$15 = x$$

Therefore, the width of the garden is 15 feet, and because $3x = 3 \cdot 15 = 45$, the length is 45 feet.

If an object moves at a constant rate of r miles per hour for t hours, the distance it travels is d miles, where

$$r \cdot t = d \tag{5}$$

When Formula (5) is applied, the units of measurements of the rate, time, and distance must be consistent. For example, if the rate is measured in feet per second, then time must be measured in seconds and distance must be measured in feet.

‖‖‖

Example 5: A ship leaves a harbor and travels at a constant speed of 15 miles per hour. Three hours later a second ship leaves the same harbor and travels the same course at a speed of 25 miles per hour. How long will it take for the second ship to overtake the first?

Solution: Because there are two different rates of travel, we must apply Formula (5) two times. Let t hours be the time required for the second ship to overtake the first. Because the second ship is traveling at a rate of 25 miles per hour for t hours, the distance it travels is $25t$ miles. Because the first ship left the harbor 3 hours before the second ship, the first ship travels for $t + 3$ hours. Because the speed of the first ship is 15 miles per hour, $15(t + 3)$ miles is the distance traveled by the first ship. This discussion is summarized in the table below.

	Rate $\times$	Time $=$	Distance
Second Ship	25	t	$25t$
First Ship	15	$t + 3$	$15(t + 3)$

Because the two ships travel the same distance, the expressions in the table that represent distance are equal. Thus,

$$25t = 15(t + 3)$$
$$25t = 15t + 45$$
$$10t = 45$$
$$t = \tfrac{45}{10}$$
$$t = 4\tfrac{1}{2}$$

It takes $4\tfrac{1}{2}$ hours for the second ship to overtake the first ship.

Example 6: A motorist maintains a steady speed for 3 hours, and then he decreases that speed by 10 miles per hour for the next 2 hours. If he travels a distance of 245 miles altogether, what is his speed at first?

Solution: Because the motorist travels at two different constant speeds, we apply Formula (5) two times. If r miles per hour is the speed during the first 3 hours, then $3r$ miles is the distance traveled during the first 3 hours. Because the speed is decreased by 10 miles per hour for the next 2 hours, $r - 10$ miles per hour is the speed during that time, and $2(r - 10)$ miles is the distance traveled at that speed. The following table summarizes this discussion.

	Rate	×	Time	=	Distance
Beginning	r		3		$3r$
Ending	$r - 10$		2		$2(r - 10)$

Because 245 miles is the total distance traveled and this total is the sum of the distances traveled at the two different speeds, we add the expressions for distance in the table. Thus,

$$3r + 2(r - 10) = 245$$
$$3r + 2r - 20 = 245$$
$$5r - 20 = 245$$
$$5r = 265$$
$$r = 53$$

The motorist travels at a speed of 53 miles per hour at first.

EXERCISES 3.1

For Exercises 1–12 find the solution set.

1. $2x + 3 = 11$
2. $1 - 3x = 7$
3. $5x + 4 = 3x - 2$
4. $2x - 4 = 3x + 1$
5. $4(x + 3) = x + 10$
6. $3(x + 1) = 5(x - 1)$
7. $x + 3(x - 1) = 7x - 8$
8. $x - 2(x - 3) = x + 6$
9. $3(x - 2) + x = 4(x - 1)$
10. $x + 3(2x - 1) = 7(x + 1) - 10$
11. $x - [2x - (x - 3)] = 2x + 1$
12. $3x + 4 = 4x - [x - (3 - 2x)]$

For Exercises 13–16 solve for x.

13. $ax + b = c$
14. $a - bx = c$
15. $a(b - x) = c$
16. $a(x + b) = c$

For Exercises 17–20 solve for the indicated variable.

17. $h = vt - at^2$; for v **18.** $S = 2\pi rh + \pi r^2$; for h

19. $L = a + (n - 1)d$; for n **20.** $A = P(1 + rt)$; for r

For Exercises 21–26 use the given formula to find the answer to the stated question.

21. If a force of F pounds is applied to a certain spring whose length is k inches, the spring is stretched to a length of L inches, with $L = k + 2F$. What force is required to stretch a 10-inch spring to a length of 17 inches?

22. The total cost of manufacturing n items is c dollars, with $c = a + bn$, where a dollars is the overhead cost and b dollars is the unit cost. How many items can be produced for $1000 if the unit cost is $5 and the overhead cost is $150?

23. If a certain rolling ball is given an initial speed of k centimeters per second, after t seconds its speed is v centimeters per second, with $v = -15t + k$. How long will it take for the ball to come to rest if it is given an initial speed of 50 centimeters per second?

24. If a projectile is fired upward from the ground with a speed of v feet per second, after t seconds it is at a height of s feet, with $s = vt - 16t^2$. With what speed must an object be launched to obtain a height of 300 feet in 5 seconds?

25. If the pressure and volume of an ideal gas are P_1 units and V_1 units at one particular moment and P_2 units and V_2 units at another moment, then $P_1V_1 = P_2V_2$, provided the temperature of the gas is held constant. If 35 cubic inches of oxygen has a pressure of 20 pounds per square inch, what is the volume of the gas if the pressure is increased to 25 pounds per square inch and the temperature is held constant?

26. If a force of F_1 units is applied to one side of a lever at a distance of d_1 units from the fulcrum and a force of F_2 units is applied on the other side of the lever at a distance of d_2 units from the fulcrum, then the lever is in equilibrium if and only if $F_1d_1 = F_2d_2$. What force must be applied to the end of a 7-inch rod to balance a weight of 12 pounds hung on the other end if the rod rests on a fulcrum located 2 inches from the weight?

For Exercises 27–32 use the solution to an equation to find the answer to the stated question.

27. The sum of a certain number and 3 more than twice that number is 20. What is the number?

28. The length of a rectangle is 2 inches greater than its width, and its perimeter is 14 inches. What is the width?

29. Bill caught twice as many fish as Sam, but after he traded 9 perch for 5 bass, Bill had the same number of fish as Sam. How many fish did Sam catch?

30. One year the Giants lost 36 more baseball games than they won. If 160 games were played in all, how many games did the Giants win?

31. A photograph is twice as long as it is wide, and it has a frame whose width is 2 centimeters. If the area of the frame without the picture is 184 square centimeters, what are the dimensions of the photograph?

32. Mrs. Gabor will not tell her age because she is 3 years older than her husband. Next year she will be twice as old as he was on their wedding day. If the Gabors have been married for 18 years, how old is Mrs. Gabor?

For Exercises 33–38 use Formula (5) to find the answer to the stated question.

33. One runner leaves the starting gate and runs at a speed of 20 feet per second. Three seconds later another runner leaves the starting gate and runs at a speed of 24 feet per second. How long will it take the second runner to overtake the first runner?

34. The speed of a passenger train is 15 miles per hour faster than the speed of a freight train. One hour after the freight train departs the station, the passenger train leaves on the same track and reaches the freight train after 3 hours. What is the speed of the freight train?

35. Two planes leave from the same airport and fly in opposite directions. The ground speed of one plane is 40 miles per hour greater than the ground speed of the other plane. After 2 hours the planes are 560 miles apart. What is the speed of the slower plane?

36. At noon a motorist leaves city A and heads toward city B. One hour later a second motorist leaves city B and heads toward city A. The two motorists meet at 4:00 P.M. If the speed of the first motorist is 5 miles per hour less than the speed of the second and if the two cities are 330 miles apart, what is the speed of each motorist?

37. A cyclist can travel twice as fast when going downhill as when going uphill. He travels for 3 hours downhill and for 4 hours uphill. If the distance traveled downhill is 12 miles more than the distance traveled uphill, how fast does he travel when going uphill?

38. A train is 500 meters long and is moving at the rate of 22 meters per second. The train overtakes a hiker who is walking beside the track at the rate of 2 meters per second. How long does it take for the train to pass the hiker?

3.2 First Degree Equations with Fractional Coefficients

To find the solution set for an equation that contains a fraction, we eliminate the fraction by multiplying on both sides of the equation by the denominator of the fraction. If the equation contains more than one fraction, we multiply on both sides by the least common denominator of the fractions.

Example 1: Find the solution set.

(a) $\dfrac{x-1}{3} = x + 2$
          (b) $x - \dfrac{1}{6} = \dfrac{1}{4}x + 1$

Solution:

(a) To eliminate the fraction we multiply on both sides by 3.

$$\frac{x-1}{3} = x + 2$$

$$(3)\frac{x-1}{3} = 3(x+2)$$

$$x - 1 = 3x + 6$$

$$-1 = 2x + 6$$

$$-7 = 2x$$

$$\frac{-7}{2} = x$$

The solution set is $\{-\frac{7}{2}\}$.

(b) We multiply on both sides by the least common denominator of the fractions, namely 12.

$$x - \tfrac{1}{6} = \tfrac{1}{4}x + 1$$

$$12(x - \tfrac{1}{6}) = 12(\tfrac{1}{4}x + 1)$$

$$12x - 2 = 3x + 12$$

$$9x - 2 = 12$$

$$9x = 14$$

$$x = \tfrac{14}{9}$$

The solution set is $\{\tfrac{14}{9}\}$.

Example 2: Solve for r.

$$s = \frac{t(r+s)}{s}$$

Solution: We multiply on both sides by s to eliminate the fraction.

$$s = \frac{t(r+s)}{s}$$

$$s^2 = t(r+s)$$

$$s^2 = tr + ts$$

$$s^2 - ts = tr$$

$$\frac{s^2 - ts}{t} = r$$

$$r = \frac{s^2 - ts}{t}$$

If a principal of P dollars is invested at a rate of R percent per year, then the simple interest paid is I dollars per year, where

$$R\%\cdot P = I \qquad (1)$$

We use Formula (1) to solve problems concerning simple interest.

Example 3: If $2000 more is invested at 7% than is invested at 9% and if the simple interest paid each investment is the same, how much is invested at 9%?

Solution: Let x dollars be the amount invested at 9%. Then $x + 2000$ dollars is the amount invested at 7%. To find an expression that represents the annual interest on each investment we apply Formula (1). Because $9\% = 9 \div 100 = 0.09$, then $(0.09)x$ dollars is the annual interest paid on the 9% investment. Because $x + 2000$ dollars is invested at 7%, then $(0.07)(x + 2000)$ dollars is the annual interest paid on this investment. The following table summarizes this discussion.

Rate	×	Principal	=	Interest
9%		x		$(0.09)x$
7%		$x + 2000$		$(0.07)(x + 2000)$

Because the interest earned on each investment is the same, the expressions in the table that represent interest are equal. Thus,

$$0.09x = 0.07(x + 2000)$$
$$9x = 7(x + 2000)$$
$$9x = 7x + 14{,}000$$
$$2x = 14{,}000$$
$$x = 7000$$

Hence, $7000 is invested at 9%.

Example 4: A total of $60,000 is invested, partly in bonds that pay 6% per year and the rest in stocks that pay 10% per year. If the annual interest from the two investments totals $5000, how much is invested at each rate?

Solution: Let x dollars be the amount invested in bonds. Because a total of $60,000 is invested, $60,000 - x$ dollars is the amount invested in stocks. We apply Formula (1) to construct the following table.

Rate	×	Principal	=	Interest
6%		x		$(0.06)x$
10%		$60,000 - x$		$(0.10)(60,000 - x)$

Because $5000 is the total annual interest from the two investments and because the whole equals the sum of its parts, we add the expressions in the table that represent interest.

$$(0.06)x + (0.10)(60,000 - x) = 5000$$
$$(0.06)x + 6000 - (0.10)x = 5000$$
$$(-0.04)x = -1000$$
$$4x = 100,000$$
$$x = 25,000$$

We conclude that $25,000 is invested in bonds, and because $60,000 - 25,000 = 35,000$, $35,000 is invested in stocks.

If a mixture has a total volume of V units and if R percent of the mixture consists of a certain substance, then V_1 units is the volume of that substance, where

$$(R\%)V = V_1 \tag{2}$$

Formula (2) may also be applied to a mixture whose total weight is V units and that contains $R\%$ of a certain substance. In that case the weight of the substance is V_1 units.

Example 5: How much water must be added to 200 milliliters of a 12% alcohol solution to dilute the solution to only 10%?

Solution: Let x milliliters be the volume of water added. Then the volume of the final solution is $200 + x$ milliliters. Because the original solution is 12% alcohol, the original solution contains $(0.12)(200)$ milliliters of pure alcohol. Because the final solution is 10% alcohol, the final solution contains

$(0.10)(200 + x)$ milliliters of pure alcohol. We summarize this discussion in the following table.

Percent Alcohol $\times$	Milliliters of Mixture	= Milliliters of Pure Alcohol
12%	200	$(0.12)(200)$
10%	$200 + x$	$(0.10)(200 + x)$

Because pure water is added to the original solution, the original solution and the final solution contain the same volume of pure alcohol. Thus, the expressions in the table that represent the number of milliliters of pure alcohol are equal. We have

$$(0.10)(200 + x) = (0.12)(200)$$
$$20 + (0.10)x = 24$$
$$(0.10)x = 4$$
$$x = 40$$

We conclude that 40 milliliters of water must be added.

Example 6:   How many grams of an alloy containing 40% silver must be melted with 80 grams of an alloy containing 15% silver to obtain an alloy that contains 25% silver?

Solution: Let x grams be the weight of the 40% alloy. Because we begin with 80 grams of alloy and add x grams of alloy to it, the final alloy weighs $x + 80$ grams. We construct the following table.

Percent Silver $\times$	Grams of Mixture	= Grams of Pure Silver
40%	x	$(0.40)x$
15%	80	$(0.15)(80)$
25%	$x + 80$	$(0.25)(x + 80)$

Because the whole equals the sum of its parts, the sum of the first two expressions in the table that represent the weight of pure silver equals the third expression that represents the weight of pure silver. Thus,

$$0.40x + (0.15)80 = 0.25(x + 80)$$
$$40x + 1200 = 25x + 2000$$
$$15x = 800$$
$$x = 53\tfrac{1}{3}$$

Thus, $53\tfrac{1}{3}$ grams of alloy containing 40% silver must be added.

EXERCISES 3.2

For Exercises 1–12 find the solution set.

1. $\dfrac{x + 1}{2} = x - 3$

2. $\dfrac{2x - 1}{5} = x + 1$

3. $2(x + 1) = \dfrac{3(x - 2)}{4}$

4. $2(x - 1) = \dfrac{x + 3}{3}$

5. $\dfrac{2x + 1}{4} = \dfrac{x - 1}{8} + 1$

6. $\dfrac{2x - 3}{6} = \dfrac{x + 1}{3} + x$

7. $\tfrac{2}{3}x + 1 = x - \tfrac{1}{2}$

8. $\tfrac{2}{3}x - 2 = \tfrac{1}{4}x + 3$

9. $x + \tfrac{5}{6}(x + 1) = 2x - \tfrac{1}{4}$

10. $x + \tfrac{1}{2}(x + 3) = x + \tfrac{1}{5}$

11. $\dfrac{x}{2} - \dfrac{2x + 1}{6} = \dfrac{x + 1}{3} + 1$

12. $\dfrac{3x - 6}{4} - \dfrac{x + 6}{6} = 1 - \dfrac{2x}{3}$

For Exercises 13–16 solve for x.

13. $\dfrac{ax}{b} = c$

14. $\dfrac{x + a}{b} = c$

15. $\dfrac{ax - b}{c} = c$

16. $\dfrac{a(x - b)}{c} = c$

For Exercises 17–20 solve for the indicated variable.

17. $V = \tfrac{1}{3}\pi r^2 h$; for h

18. $s = vt + \tfrac{1}{2}gt^2$; for v

19. $A = \dfrac{h}{2}(b + B)$; for b

20. $E = I\left(R + \dfrac{r}{n}\right)$; for r

For Exercises 21–24 use the given formula to find the answer to the stated question.

21. A temperature of F degrees Fahrenheit is equivalent to a temperature of C degrees Celsius, with $F = \tfrac{9}{5}C + 32$. What is the Celsius temperature if the Fahrenheit temperature is 86°?

22. If a principal of P dollars is invested at the rate of r percent per year, the simple interest earned in n years is I dollars, with $I = \tfrac{1}{100}Prn$. How much is invested at 8% if the simple interest after 5 years is $1600?

23. If a ball is given an initial speed of v meters per second and allowed to roll down a certain slope, the ball will roll s meters during the first t seconds, with $s = vt + \frac{1}{2}t^2$. What is the initial speed of the ball if it rolls 20 meters in 3 seconds?

24. If the altitude of a trapezoid is h units and if the parallel sides are a units long and b units long, then the area of the trapezoid is A square units, with $A = \frac{1}{2}h(a + b)$. If one of the parallel sides is 20 centimeters, the altitude is 13 centimeters, and the area is 221 square centimeters, what is the length of the other parallel side?

For Exercises 25–32 use either Formula (1) or Formula (2) to find the answer to the stated question.

25. If $1000 more is invested at 6% than is invested at 8% and if the simple interest paid on the 8% investment is $200 more per year than the simple interest paid on the 6% investment, how much is invested at 8%?

26. A total of $32,000 is invested, partly at 6% per year and the remainder at 10% per year. If the simple interest paid on each investment is the same, how much is invested at each rate?

27. A total of $40,000 is invested, partly at 7% per year and the rest at 9% per year. If the annual interest from the two investments totals $3300, how much is invested at each rate?

28. If $24,000 is invested at 5% per year, what additional amount should be invested at 8% per year in order for the total investment to yield an annual income of 6%?

29. How much water must be added to 600 milliliters of a 12% acid solution to dilute the solution to only 8%?

30. How much pure alcohol must be added to 120 milliliters of a 40% alcohol solution to result in a solution that is 50% alcohol?

31. How many grams of an alloy containing 30% copper must be melted with 200 grams of an alloy containing 12% copper to obtain an alloy that contains 25% copper?

32. An automobile radiator holds 12 quarts of coolant, which is 5% alcohol. How much should be drained off and replaced by antifreeze, which is 80% alcohol, to raise the alcohol content to $17\frac{1}{2}$%?

For Exercises 33–36 use formulas similar to Formulas (1) and (2) to find the answer to the stated question.

33. Orchestra seats are $4.00 and balcony seats are $3.50 for a cinema. If there are twice as many sitting in the orchestra as in the balcony, and if the box office receipts total $1380, how many patrons are in attendance?

34. Mary has 6 more dimes than quarters. If she has $5.15 altogether, how many dimes and how many quarters does she have?

35. A coffee vendor has 60 pounds of South American coffee beans on hand that sell for $4.00 per pound. How many pounds of Jamaica Blue Mountain beans, retailing at \$9.60 per pound, should he mix with the South American beans to make a blend that retails for \$5.60 per pound?

36. There are 40 students in an algebra class, but $\frac{2}{3}$ of the boys and $\frac{3}{4}$ of the girls cannot solve word problems. If 12 of the students are able to solve word problems, how many boys and how many girls are in the class?

3.3 Equations with Rational Expressions

The solution set for an equation that contains rational expressions is found by eliminating the fractions and then solving the resulting equation. Because the denominator of a fraction cannot have value zero, we must check each solution to see whether it is a replacement for the variable that is allowed. We disregard any solutions that result in a value of zero for the denominator of a fraction.

Example 1: Find the solution set.

(a) $\dfrac{x}{x-2} = \dfrac{x+3}{x}$

(b) $\dfrac{2x+3}{x-1} - 2 = \dfrac{x+4}{x-1}$

Solution:
(a) We use the Cross Product Theorem (2.1.2) to eliminate the fractions. Thus,

$$\frac{x}{x-2} = \frac{x+3}{x}$$
$$x \cdot x = (x-2)(x+3)$$
$$x^2 = x^2 + x - 6$$
$$0 = x - 6$$
$$x = 6$$

Because neither the denominator $x-2$ nor the denominator x has value 0 when $x=6$, 6 satisfies the original equation and the solution set is $\{6\}$.

(b) The Cross Product Theorem does not apply. We multiply on both sides by $x-1$ and distribute the multiplier to eliminate the fractions.

$$\frac{2x+3}{x-1} - 2 = \frac{x+4}{x-1}$$
$$(x-1)\left(\frac{2x+3}{x-1} - 2\right) = (x-1)\frac{x+4}{x-1}$$
$$(x-1)\frac{2x+3}{x-1} - 2(x-1) = (x-1)\frac{x+4}{x-1}$$

$$2x + 3 - 2(x - 1) = x + 4$$
$$2x + 3 - 2x + 2 = x + 4$$
$$5 = x + 4$$
$$1 = x$$

Because the denominator $x - 1$ has value 0 when $x = 1$, then 1 does not satisfy the original equation. We conclude that the solution set is $\varnothing$, the empty set. Note that in the first step in solving the equation, we multiply on both sides by zero, because $x - 1 = 0$ when $x = 1$. This contradicts condition (iii) in Theorem 3.1.1, and thus the resulting equation is not equivalent to the original equation.

Example 2:   Find the solution set.

$$\frac{2}{1 + x} - \frac{5}{x} = \frac{3}{1 - x}$$

Solution: Because the denominators have no factors in common, we first apply the Cross Product Rule for Subtracting to simplify the equation.

$$\frac{2}{1 + x} - \frac{5}{x} = \frac{3}{1 - x}$$
$$\frac{2x - 5(1 + x)}{(1 + x)x} = \frac{3}{1 - x}$$
$$\frac{-5 - 3x}{(1 + x)x} = \frac{3}{1 - x}$$

Now we apply the Cross Product Theorem to eliminate the fractions.

$$(-5 - 3x)(1 - x) = (1 + x)(3x)$$
$$3x^2 + 2x - 5 = 3x^2 + 3x$$
$$2x - 5 = 3x$$
$$-5 = x$$

We must test the replacement -5 in the original equation. Because this replacement does not result in 0 for the denominator of a fraction, we conclude that -5 satisfies the equation. The solution set is $\{-5\}$.

Example 3:   Find the solution set.

$$\frac{x + 17}{x^2 - 6x + 8} + \frac{x - 2}{x - 4} = \frac{x - 4}{x - 2}$$

Solution: First, we factor each denominator.

$$\frac{x + 17}{(x - 4)(x - 2)} + \frac{x - 2}{x - 4} = \frac{x - 4}{x - 2}$$

To eliminate the fractions, we multiply on both sides by the least common denominator, which is $(x - 4)(x - 2)$, and distribute the multiplier.

$$(x - 4)(x - 2)\frac{x + 17}{(x - 4)(x - 2)} + (x - 4)(x - 2)\frac{x - 2}{x - 4}$$

$$= (x - 4)(x - 2)\frac{x - 4}{x - 2}$$

$$x + 17 + (x - 2)(x - 2) = (x - 4)(x - 4)$$

$$x + 17 + x^2 - 4x + 4 = x^2 - 8x + 16$$

$$x^2 - 3x + 21 = x^2 - 8x + 16$$

$$-3x + 21 = -8x + 16$$

$$5x + 21 = 16$$

$$5x = -5$$

$$x = -1$$

Because neither of the factors $x - 4$ and $x - 2$ that appear in the denominator has value 0 when $x = -1$, then -1 satisfies the original equation and its solution set is $\{-1\}$.

If an equation contains two or more fractions whose denominators have no factors in common, then we eliminate the fractions by using cross products, as in Example 2. When the denominators contain one or more common factors, we use the Common Denominator Method to eliminate the fractions, as in Example 3.

Example 4: Solve for s.

$$r = \frac{s + t}{s - t}$$

Solution: First, we eliminate the fraction.

$$r = \frac{s + t}{s - t}$$

$$r(s - t) = s + t$$

$$rs - rt = s + t$$

Next, we separate the terms that contain s from the terms that do not contain s.

$$rs - s = rt + t$$

Finally, we factor out s and divide both sides by the coefficient of s.

$$s(r - 1) = rt + t$$

$$s = \frac{rt + t}{r - 1}, \qquad \text{if } r \neq 1$$

Example 5: A motorboat can travel at the rate of 8 miles per hour in still water. If a trip that is 20 miles upstream in a river takes the boat the same time as a trip that is 30 miles downstream, what is the speed of the river current?

Solution: Because this is a problem that involves motion at a constant speed, we apply the formula $d = rt$. Let x miles per hour be the speed of the river current. When the boat travels upstream, the river current reduces the speed of the boat by x miles per hour; when the boat travels downstream, the river current increases the speed of the boat by x miles per hour. Because the boat travels at the rate of 8 miles per hour in still water, the rate of the boat when it travels upstream is $8 - x$ miles per hour and the rate of the boat when it travels downstream is $8 + x$ miles per hour. To find an expression that represents the number of hours spent traveling in each direction, we solve the formula $d = rt$ for t. Thus, $t = d/r$.

We construct the following table of expressions.

	Miles $\div$	Miles per hour =	Hours
Upstream	20	$8 - x$	$\dfrac{20}{8 - x}$
Downstream	30	$8 + x$	$\dfrac{30}{8 + x}$

Because the time is the same in either direction, the expressions in the table that represent hours are equal. Thus,

$$\frac{20}{8 - x} = \frac{30}{8 + x}$$

We divide on both sides by 10 and then eliminate the fractions.

$$\frac{2}{8 - x} = \frac{3}{8 + x}$$

$$2(8 + x) = 3(8 - x)$$

$$16 + 2x = 24 - 3x$$

$$5x = 8$$

$$x = 1.6$$

The speed of the river current is 1.6 miles per hour.

If it takes 8 hours to complete a job and if we assume that there is a uniform rate of work, then in 1 hour exactly $\frac{1}{8}$ of the job is completed. We call

$\frac{1}{8}$ the rate of work. In general, if it takes t units of time to complete a job and we assume a uniform rate of work, then $1/t$ is the rate of work. Suppose the rate of work is $\frac{1}{8}$ and this rate is maintained for 3 units of time. Then exactly $3 \cdot \frac{1}{8} = \frac{3}{8}$ of the job is completed. In general, if the rate of work is $1/t$ and if this rate is maintained for s units of time, then the fractional part of the job completed is f, where

$$\left(\frac{1}{t}\right)s = f \tag{1}$$

We use Formula (1) to solve problems concerning work at a uniform rate.

Example 6:   If it takes 20 minutes to empty a tank with one pump and 30 minutes to empty the tank with another pump, how long will it take to empty the tank if both pumps are used?

Solution: Let x minutes be the time required to empty the tank if both pumps are used, and suppose that each pump is operated for x minutes. The rate of work for the first pump is $\frac{1}{20}$, and the rate of work for the second pump is $\frac{1}{30}$. Because there are two different rates of work, we apply Formula (1) twice. We construct the following table.

	Rate of Work	$\times$ Minutes Worked $=$	Fractional Part of Job Done
First Pump	$\frac{1}{20}$	x	$\frac{x}{20}$
Second Pump	$\frac{1}{30}$	x	$\frac{x}{30}$

Because the complete job is done by the two pumps, the fractional part done by the first pump plus the fractional part done by the second pump equals 1. Thus, we set the sum of the entries in the last column of the table equal to 1. We have

$$\frac{x}{20} + \frac{x}{30} = 1$$

$$60\left(\frac{x}{20} + \frac{x}{30}\right) = 60(1)$$

$$3x + 2x = 60$$

$$5x = 60$$

$$x = 12$$

It takes 12 minutes to empty the tank if both pumps are used.

Example 7: One pipe takes 2 hours to fill a pool. After it has been running for 45 minutes, it is shut off. A second pipe is then opened, and it finishes filling the pool in $1\frac{1}{2}$ hours. How long would it have taken the second pipe alone to fill the pool?

Solution: Let x hours be the time that it takes the second pipe alone to fill the pool. Then $1/x$ is the rate of work for the second pipe, and this rate is maintained for $\frac{3}{2}$ hour. The rate of work for the first pipe is $\frac{1}{2}$, and this rate is maintained for $\frac{3}{4}$ hour. We construct the following table.

	Rate of Work	× Hours Worked =	Fractional Part of Job Done
First Pipe	$\dfrac{1}{2}$	$\dfrac{3}{4}$	$\dfrac{3}{8}$
Second Pipe	$\dfrac{1}{x}$	$\dfrac{3}{2}$	$\dfrac{3}{2x}$

Because the job is completed by the two pipes, the sum of the fractions in the last column of the table equals 1.

$$\frac{3}{8} + \frac{3}{2x} = 1$$

$$8x\left(\frac{3}{8} + \frac{3}{2x}\right) = 8x\cdot 1$$

$$3x + 12 = 8x$$

$$2\tfrac{2}{5} = x$$

Thus, it would take the second pipe $2\frac{2}{5}$ hours to fill the pool alone.

EXERCISES 3.3

For Exercises 1–20 find the solution set.

1. $\dfrac{3x + 4}{x} = 5$ **2.** $\dfrac{x}{x + 2} = 3$

3. $\dfrac{x - 3}{x - 1} = 2$ **4.** $\dfrac{2x - 1}{x - 2} = -1$

5. $\dfrac{3}{x + 2} = \dfrac{1}{x - 2}$ **6.** $\dfrac{1}{x - 3} = \dfrac{2}{x + 1}$

7. $\dfrac{x + 1}{x - 1} = \dfrac{x}{x + 1}$ **8.** $\dfrac{x}{x + 3} = \dfrac{x + 1}{x + 2}$

9. $\dfrac{2x-1}{3x} - 1 = \dfrac{x+5}{x}$

10. $\dfrac{x-1}{2x} + 2 = \dfrac{9x+1}{4x}$

11. $\dfrac{2x+1}{x-2} + 2 = \dfrac{x+3}{x-2}$

12. $\dfrac{x-5}{2x+1} - 3 = \dfrac{x-2}{2x+1}$

13. $\dfrac{2x+1}{x-1} - 1 = \dfrac{x+4}{x+2}$

14. $\dfrac{3x+4}{x+1} - 2 = \dfrac{x-3}{x-2}$

15. $\dfrac{1}{x} + \dfrac{2}{x+1} = \dfrac{3}{x-2}$

16. $\dfrac{4}{x-2} - \dfrac{3}{x} = \dfrac{1}{x-4}$

17. $\dfrac{x+3}{x^2-4} = \dfrac{2}{x+2}$

18. $\dfrac{3}{x+4} = \dfrac{2x-3}{x^2+5x+4}$

19. $\dfrac{2x+5}{x^2+x} - \dfrac{3}{x} = \dfrac{2}{x+1}$

20. $\dfrac{3x-1}{1-x^2} + \dfrac{x+3}{x+1} = \dfrac{x-2}{x-1}$

For Exercises 21–24 solve for x.

21. $ax = \dfrac{x}{a} + b$

22. $\dfrac{ax+b}{x} = b$

23. $\dfrac{ax-b}{c} + x = b$

24. $\dfrac{x-a}{x+a} = b$

For Exercises 25–28 solve for the indicated variable.

25. $r = \dfrac{s+r}{s}$; for s

26. $r = \dfrac{st}{s+t}$; for t

27. $s = \dfrac{r-t}{r+t}$; for r

28. $t = \dfrac{r+s}{r-s}$; for s

For Exercises 29–36 use the solution of an equation to answer the stated question.

29. If two resistors have resistance R_1 ohms and R_2 ohms and the resistors are wired in parallel, then the net resistance is R ohms, with

$$R = \dfrac{R_1 R_2}{R_1 + R_2}$$

If one of the individual resistances is 6 ohms, what must the other be if the net resistance is 4 ohms?

30. If a and b are the first and last terms, respectively, in a geometric progression and r is the ratio of successive terms in the progression, then the sum of all the terms is given by the formula

$$S = \dfrac{a - br}{1 - r}$$

What is the ratio of successive terms in a geometric progression whose first term is 3 and whose last term is 48 if the sum of the terms is 93?

31. A motorboat can make 10 miles per hour in still water, but a trip 15 miles upstream in a river takes the same time as a trip 21 miles downstream in the river. What is the speed of the river current?

32. A boat maintained a speed of 12 kilometers per hour during a trip from point A to point B. For the return trip from B to A she was able to increase her speed to 18 kilometers per hour. If the round trip took a total of 2 hours to complete, how far is it between points A and B?

33. The regular painter takes 10 hours to do a job that his helper can do in 15 hours. How long will it take them to finish the job if they work together?

34. With the old sorter, a deck of punched cards can be processed in 14 minutes. When both the old and the new sorter are used together, the job takes only 6 minutes. How long would the new sorter take if used alone?

35. After 2 hours of operation with one pump, a pool is half emptied. A second pump is brought in, and together the two pumps complete the job of emptying the pool in an additional 45 minutes. How long would the second pump have taken to empty the pool if it had been used alone from the beginning?

36. The main press takes 2 hours to print the daily newspaper. After it has been running for 20 minutes, it breaks down, and a second press finishes the run in an additional $2\frac{1}{2}$ hours. How long would the second press have taken if used alone from the beginning?

3.4   Second Degree Equations with Rational Solutions

An equation such as $2x^2 - 3x + 1 = 0$ is called a second degree equation. In general, if $a \neq 0$, an equation of the form $ax^2 + bx + c = 0$ is called a second degree, or **quadratic**, equation. To find the solution set for a second degree equation, we must use methods that we have not yet considered and techniques that are not required when solving a first degree equation. Sometimes the following theorem can be used to find the solution set for a second degree equation.

> **3.4.1   Theorem:**
>
> $a \cdot b = 0$ if and only if $a = 0$ or $b = 0$

PROOF: By the Zero-Factor Theorem (1.2.9) if $a = 0$ or $b = 0$, then $a \cdot b = 0$. Next, we must show that if $a \cdot b = 0$, then either $a = 0$ or $b = 0$. Suppose that

$$a \cdot b = 0 \tag{1}$$

Then either $a = 0$ or $a \neq 0$. If $a = 0$, the proof is complete. If $a \neq 0$, then $1/a$ is a real number and we multiply on both sides of Equation (1) by $1/a$. Thus,

$$\frac{1}{a}(ab) = \frac{1}{a} \cdot 0$$

$$b = 0$$

Thus, if $ab = 0$, then either $a = 0$ or $b = 0$, and the proof is complete.

Example 1:   Find the solution set.

(a) $x^2 + 4x = 0$ (b) $6x^2 + x = 12$

Solution:

(a) In order to apply Theorem 3.4.1, we factor. Thus,

$$x^2 + 4x = 0$$

$$x(x + 4) = 0$$

By Theorem 3.4.1 we conclude that either

$$x = 0 \quad \text{or} \quad x + 4 = 0$$

$$x = -4$$

We conclude that the solution set is $\{0, -4\}$.

(b) In order to apply Theorem 3.4.1, we must have zero on one side of the equation.

$$6x^2 + x = 12$$

$$6x^2 + x - 12 = 0$$

$$(3x - 4)(2x + 3) = 0$$

Thus, by Theorem 3.4.1 either

$$3x - 4 = 0 \quad \text{or} \quad 2x + 3 = 0$$

$$3x = 4 \qquad\qquad 2x = -3$$

$$x = \tfrac{4}{3} \qquad\qquad x = -\tfrac{3}{2}$$

The solution set is $\{\tfrac{4}{3}, -\tfrac{3}{2}\}$.

Example 2:   Find the solution set.

(a) $x + \dfrac{9}{x} = 6$ (b) $\dfrac{x}{x^2 - 4} = \dfrac{2}{x^2 - 4} + \dfrac{x}{x + 2}$

Solution:

(a) To eliminate the fraction, we multiply on both sides by x. Thus,

$$x + \frac{9}{x} = 6$$

$$x\left(x + \frac{9}{x}\right) = 6x$$

$$x^2 + 9 = 6x$$

$$x^2 - 6x + 9 = 0$$

$$(x - 3)(x - 3) = 0$$

Either

$$x - 3 = 0 \quad \text{or} \quad x - 3 = 0$$

$$x = 3 \qquad\qquad x = 3$$

Because the denominator of the fraction is not 0 when $x = 3$, the solution set is $\{3\}$.

(b) We factor and then eliminate the fractions.

$$\frac{x}{x^2 - 4} = \frac{2}{x^2 - 4} + \frac{x}{x + 2}$$

$$\frac{x}{(x + 2)(x - 2)} = \frac{2}{(x + 2)(x - 2)} + \frac{x}{x + 2}$$

We multiply on both sides by $(x + 2)(x - 2)$ and distribute the multiplier.

$$(x + 2)(x - 2)\frac{x}{(x + 2)(x - 2)}$$

$$= (x + 2)(x - 2)\frac{2}{(x + 2)(x - 2)} + (x + 2)(x - 2)\frac{x}{x + 2}$$

$$x = 2 + (x - 2)x$$

$$x = 2 + x^2 - 2x$$

$$0 = x^2 - 3x + 2$$

$$0 = (x - 1)(x - 2)$$

$$x - 1 = 0 \quad \text{or} \quad x - 2 = 0$$

$$x = 1 \qquad\qquad x = 2$$

Because the denominator $x^2 - 4$ has value 0 when $x = 2$, we disregard this solution. Hence, the solution set is $\{1\}$.

There are often two x-forms for a second degree equation with unknown variable x. To solve such an equation for x means to find each of its x-forms.

Example 3: Solve for x: $\quad 4x^2 - 3ax = a^2$.

Solution: We use Theorem 3.4.1 to find each x-form.

$$4x^2 - 3ax = a^2$$

$$4x^2 - 3ax - a^2 = 0$$

$$(x - a)(4x + a) = 0$$

$$x - a = 0 \quad \text{or} \quad 4x + a = 0$$

$$x = a \qquad\qquad 4x = -a$$

$$x = -\frac{a}{4}$$

Example 4: If an object is thrown upward with initial speed k meters per second, after t seconds it will be h meters above its starting point, with

$h = kt - 5t^2$. If a bullet is fired upward from the ground with a muzzle speed of 60 meters per second, how long will it take for the bullet to reach a height of 135 meters?

Solution: Because the muzzle speed is 60 meters per second, we let $k = 60$ in the formula. Because we want to find the time it takes for the bullet to rise to a height of 135 meters, we also let $h = 135$ and then solve for t.

$$h = kt - 5t^2$$
$$135 = 60t - 5t^2$$
$$5t^2 - 60t + 135 = 0$$
$$\tfrac{1}{5}(5t^2 - 60t + 135) = \tfrac{1}{5} \cdot 0$$
$$t^2 - 12t + 27 = 0$$
$$(t - 3)(t - 9) = 0$$
$$t - 3 = 0 \qquad \text{or} \qquad t - 9 = 0$$
$$t = 3 \qquad\qquad\qquad t = 9$$

The bullet is 135 meters above the ground after 3 seconds and again after 9 seconds. We conclude that after 3 seconds the bullet is rising and is at a height of 135 meters and after 9 seconds the bullet is falling and is at a height of 135 meters. Thus, it takes 3 seconds to rise to a height of 135 meters.

If the legs of a right triangle are a units long and b units long, then the hypotenuse of the triangle is c units long, with

$$a^2 + b^2 = c^2 \tag{2}$$

We use Equation (2), which is the formula of the Pythagorean Theorem, to solve problems that concern the dimensions of a right triangle.

Example 5:   Find the dimensions of a rectangle if its length is 3 inches more than its width and if the length of its diagonal is 3 inches less than twice the width.

Solution: Let x inches be the width. Then $x + 3$ inches is the length and $2x - 3$ inches is the length of the diagonal. Refer to Figure 3.4.1. We apply Equation (2). Thus,

$$x^2 + (x + 3)^2 = (2x - 3)^2$$
$$x^2 + x^2 + 6x + 9 = 4x^2 - 12x + 9$$
$$-2x^2 + 18x = 0$$
$$x^2 - 9x = 0$$

$$x(x - 9) = 0$$
$$x = 0 \quad \text{or} \quad x - 9 = 0$$
$$x = 9$$

Thus, the width of the rectangle is 9 inches, and because $x + 3 = 9 + 3 = 12$, the length is 12 inches.

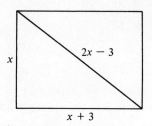

Figure 3.4.1

Example 6:   Points A and B are 200 miles apart. An airplane flies from A to B at a constant speed. For the return trip from B to A the plane increases its speed by 30 miles per hour, and thus reduces the time required for the trip by 20 minutes. What is the speed of the plane while traveling from A to B?

Solution: Let r miles per hour be the rate of the plane while traveling from A to B, and let $r + 30$ miles per hour be the rate of the plane for the return trip from B to A. Because the distance between A and B is given, we use the formula $t = d/r$ to find the number of hours required to complete the trip in each direction, and we construct the following table.

	Miles $\div$	Miles per Hour $=$	Hours
A to B	200	r	$\dfrac{200}{r}$
B to A	200	$r + 30$	$\dfrac{200}{r + 30}$

Because the time for the return trip is 20 minutes less than the time for the trip from A to B and because 20 minutes equals $\frac{1}{3}$ hour, the expression in the table that represents the time from B to A is $\frac{1}{3}$ less than the expression that represents the time from A to B. Thus,

$$\frac{200}{r + 30} = \frac{200}{r} - \frac{1}{3}$$

We use the Cross Product Method to eliminate the fractions.

$$\frac{200}{r+30} = \frac{600-r}{3r}$$

$$600r = (r+30)(600-r)$$

$$600r = 600r - r^2 + 18{,}000 - 30r$$

$$r^2 + 30r - 18{,}000 = 0$$

$$(r-120)(r+150) = 0$$

$$r - 120 = 0 \qquad \text{or} \qquad r + 150 = 0$$

$$r = 120 \qquad\qquad\qquad r = -150$$

Because the rate must be positive, we disregard $r = -150$. The speed of the plane while traveling from A to B is 120 miles per hour.

EXERCISES 3.4

For Exercises 1–20 use the method of factoring to find the solution set.

1. $x^2 - 5x + 6 = 0$
2. $x^2 + 2x - 8 = 0$
3. $3x^2 - x = 0$
4. $2x^2 + x = 0$
5. $2x^2 + 5x = 3$
6. $6x^2 = x + 1$
7. $(x+2)^2 = 6x + 7$
8. $(x+4)(x+1) = 10$
9. $(2x+1)(x+1) = x(x+5)$
10. $(x+5)(x+3) + 1 = 0$
11. $x + 3 = \dfrac{4}{x}$
12. $2x + \dfrac{9}{x} = 9$
13. $\dfrac{x+3}{2x-1} = 3x + 1$
14. $\dfrac{x-1}{x+2} = \dfrac{3x-1}{x+3}$
15. $\dfrac{1}{x} - \dfrac{3}{x-2} = 4$
16. $\dfrac{1}{x+1} + \dfrac{1}{6} = \dfrac{1}{x}$
17. $\dfrac{3x+8}{x^2+2x} = \dfrac{x-4}{x+2}$
18. $\dfrac{x+5}{x^2+4x+4} = \dfrac{x+1}{x+2}$
19. $\dfrac{x^2-8}{x^2-4} = \dfrac{1}{x+2} + \dfrac{1}{x-2}$
20. $\dfrac{3x}{x^2+x-2} + \dfrac{x}{x+2} = \dfrac{1}{1-x}$

For Exercises 21–24 solve for x.

21. $ax^2 + bx = 0$
22. $x^2 - 3ax = 4a^2$
23. $3x^2 = 2ax + a^2$
24. $4a^2x^2 = 4abx - b^2$

For Exercises 25–36 use the solution of an equation to answer the stated question.

25. If an object is thrown upward with initial speed k feet per second, after t seconds it is h feet above its starting point, with $h = kt - 16t^2$. If a ball is thrown up-

ward with initial speed 80 feet per second, how long will it take for the ball to rise to a height of 96 feet?

26. How long will it take the ball in Exercise 25 to return to its starting point?

27. If E volts is the electromotive force, I amperes is the current, and R ohms is the resistance, then P watts is the power in an electrical circuit, with $P = EI - RI^2$. What is the current in a circuit in which the resistance is 2 ohms, the electromotive force is 12 volts, and the power is 18 watts?

28. If the unit price of a commodity is P dollars, the total revenue from sales is R dollars, with $R = P(200 - 4P)$. What price will yield a total revenue of $2400?

29. The length of a rectangle is 2 inches greater than its width, and its area is $19\frac{1}{4}$ square inches. What are the dimensions of the rectangle?

30. A ladder is 13 feet long, and the foot of the ladder is 5 feet from the wall. How far up the wall does the ladder reach?

31. The width of a rectangle is $\frac{3}{4}$ of its length, and the diagonal is 2 centimeters more than the length. What are the dimensions of the rectangle?

32. Two ships leave the same point at the same time. One ship heads north, and the other ship heads west with a speed that is 2 miles per hour faster than the ship heading north. After 3 hours the ships are 30 miles apart. What is the speed of each ship?

33. A motorboat travels 24 miles upstream in a river and then 24 miles back downstream in a total of 5 hours. If the speed of the river current is 2 miles per hour, how fast does the boat travel in still water?

34. If a cyclist increases his speed by 3 miles per hour, he can reduce the time required for a 6-mile trip by 10 minutes. What is the slower speed?

35. A pipe can fill a tank in 2 minutes less time than it takes a drain to empty the tank. If both the pipe and the drain are open, it takes 24 minutes to fill the tank. How long will it take to fill the tank if the drain is closed?

36. An open bin has a square base, rectangular sides, and a depth of 4 feet. The material for the bottom costs 20 cents per square foot, and the material for the sides costs 10 cents per square foot. What is the volume of the bin if the total cost of materials is 13 dollars?

3.5 Second Degree Equations with Irrational Solutions

The solution set for a second degree equation can be found by factoring and applying Theorem 3.4.1 only when each solution is a rational number. To find solutions that are irrational numbers, we must use techniques other than factoring.

Consider the equation $x^2 = 5$. Although we cannot find the solution set by factoring (with integer coefficients), from the definition of square root we see that either $x = \sqrt{5}$ or $x = -\sqrt{5}$, which we may also indicate by writing $x = \pm\sqrt{5}$. In general, $a = \pm\sqrt{b}$ means either $a = \sqrt{b}$ or $a = -\sqrt{b}$, and we have the following theorem.

3.5.1   *Theorem:* **Square Root**

If $b \geq 0$, then $a^2 = b$ if and only if $a = \pm\sqrt{b}$.

Example 1: Find the solution set.

(a) $3x^2 = x^2 + 7$ (b) $x^2 + 6x = 1$

Solution: We apply the Square Root Theorem.

(a) First, we solve the equation for x^2.

$$3x^2 = x^2 + 7$$
$$2x^2 = 7$$
$$x^2 = \tfrac{7}{2}$$

Then we apply Theorem 3.5.1.

$$x = \pm\sqrt{\tfrac{7}{2}}$$

The solution set is $\{\sqrt{\tfrac{7}{2}}, -\sqrt{\tfrac{7}{2}}\}$.

(b) Because the equation contains both x^2 and x, we cannot solve for x^2. However, if we add 9 to both sides, this will "complete the square," because $x^2 + 6x + 9 = (x + 3)^2$. Thus,

$$x^2 + 6x = 1$$
$$x^2 + 6x + 9 = 1 + 9$$
$$(x + 3)^2 = 10$$

Now we may apply the Square Root Theorem with $a = x + 3$. Thus,

$$x + 3 = \pm\sqrt{10}$$
$$x = -3 \pm \sqrt{10}$$

The solution set is $\{-3 + \sqrt{10}, -3 - \sqrt{10}\}$.

If a second degree equation does not contain a first degree term, as in Example 1(a), we may always solve for x^2 and then apply the Square Root Theorem to find the solution set. If a second degree equation also contains a first degree term, as in Example 1(b), we may always complete the square and then apply the Square Root Theorem. To complete the square for an expression of the form $x^2 + bx$, we add $(b/2)^2$, because

$$x^2 + bx + \left(\frac{b}{2}\right)^2 = \left(x + \frac{b}{2}\right)^2$$

Example 2: Find the solution set by completing the square.
(a) $x^2 = 3x + 1$ (b) $2x^2 + 4x = 1$

Solution:
(a) First, we separate the constant term from the terms that contain x.

$$x^2 = 3x + 1$$
$$x^2 - 3x = 1$$

To complete the square, we add $(-\frac{3}{2})^2$ to both sides.

$$x^2 - 3x + (-\tfrac{3}{2})^2 = 1 + (-\tfrac{3}{2})^2$$
$$(x - \tfrac{3}{2})^2 = \tfrac{13}{4}$$
$$x - \tfrac{3}{2} = \pm\sqrt{\tfrac{13}{4}}$$
$$x = \tfrac{3}{2} \pm \sqrt{\tfrac{13}{4}}$$
$$x = \frac{3 \pm \sqrt{13}}{2}$$

The solution set is $\left\{\dfrac{3 + \sqrt{13}}{2}, \dfrac{3 - \sqrt{13}}{2}\right\}$.

(b) To complete the square, the expression on the left must be of the form $x^2 + bx$. Because the coefficient of x^2 is 2, we divide on both sides by 2.

$$2x^2 + 4x = 1$$
$$x^2 + 2x = \tfrac{1}{2}$$

To complete the square, we add $(\frac{2}{2})^2 = 1$ to both sides.

$$x^2 + 2x + 1 = \tfrac{1}{2} + 1$$
$$(x + 1)^2 = \tfrac{3}{2}$$
$$x + 1 = \pm\sqrt{\tfrac{3}{2}}$$
$$x = -1 \pm \sqrt{\tfrac{3}{2}}$$

The solution set is $\{-1 + \sqrt{\tfrac{3}{2}}, -1 - \sqrt{\tfrac{3}{2}}\}$.

The following steps can be followed to find the solution set by completing the square for any second degree equation in x.

1. Multiply on both sides by the reciprocal of the coefficient of x^2, and write the equation in the form $x^2 + bx = c$.
2. Complete the square by adding $(b/2)^2$ to both sides. Write the expression on the left in the form $(x + b/2)^2$, and simplify the constant on the right side.
3. Apply the Square Root Theorem to take the square roots of each side.
4. Solve the resulting first degree equations for x.

The equation $x^2 = -5$ does not have a real solution, because the square of any real number is greater than or equal to zero. If $-a$ is any negative number, then the solution set for the equation $x^2 = -a$ is $\varnothing$, the empty set.

If $a \neq 0$, the equation

$$ax^2 + bx + c = 0$$

is a second degree equation with unknown variable x. We solve the equation for x by completing the square. First, we multiply on both sides by $1/a$ and separate the constant term from the terms that contain x. This results in

$$x^2 + \frac{b}{a}x = -\frac{c}{a}$$

To complete the square, we add $(b/2a)^2$ to both sides and then simplify.

$$x^2 + \frac{b}{a}x + \left(\frac{b}{2a}\right)^2 = -\frac{c}{a} + \left(\frac{b}{2a}\right)^2$$

$$\left(x + \frac{b}{2a}\right)^2 = -\frac{c}{a} + \frac{b^2}{4a^2}$$

$$\left(x + \frac{b}{2a}\right)^2 = \frac{b^2 - 4ac}{4a^2}$$

Next, we apply the Square Root Theorem and solve for x.

$$x + \frac{b}{2a} = \frac{\pm\sqrt{b^2 - 4ac}}{2a}$$

$$x = \frac{-b \pm \sqrt{b^2 - 4ac}}{2a} \qquad (1)$$

Equation (1) is called the **Quadratic Formula**, and it can be used to find the solution set for any second degree equation. If the expression $b^2 - 4ac$ that appears under the radical sign has a negative value, then the solution set is $\varnothing$, because the square root of a negative number is not real. If $b^2 - 4ac = 0$, there is only one solution, because $\pm\sqrt{0} = 0$. If $b^2 - 4ac > 0$, the solution set contains two real numbers. We have proved the following theorem.

3.5.2   Theorem: Quadratic Formula

If $a \neq 0$ and if $b^2 - 4ac \geq 0$, then the solution set of the equation $ax^2 + bx + c = 0$ is

$$\left\{ \frac{-b + \sqrt{b^2 - 4ac}}{2a}, \frac{-b - \sqrt{b^2 - 4ac}}{2a} \right\}$$

Example 3: Use the Quadratic Formula to find the solution set.
(a) $3x(2 - x) = 1$ (b) $2x^2 + \frac{7}{2}x - 1 = 0$

Solution:
(a) First we write the equation in the form $ax^2 + bx + c = 0$.

$$3x(2 - x) = 1$$
$$6x - 3x^2 = 1$$
$$-3x^2 + 6x - 1 = 0$$

Because the coefficient of x^2 is a negative number, we multiply on both sides by -1. Thus,

$$3x^2 - 6x + 1 = 0$$

Now we use the Quadratic Formula with $a = 3$, $b = -6$, and $c = 1$. Thus,

$$x = \frac{-b \pm \sqrt{b^2 - 4ac}}{2a}$$

$$x = \frac{-(-6) \pm \sqrt{(-6)^2 - 4(3)(1)}}{2(3)}$$

$$x = \frac{6 \pm \sqrt{24}}{6}$$

Next, we simplify the result. We cannot cancel 6 because the numerator is not in factored form. However, $\sqrt{24} = \sqrt{4}\sqrt{6} = 2\sqrt{6}$. Thus,

$$x = \frac{6 \pm 2\sqrt{6}}{6}$$

$$= \frac{2(3 \pm \sqrt{6})}{2(3)}$$

$$= \frac{3 \pm \sqrt{6}}{3}$$

The solution set is $\left\{ \frac{3 + \sqrt{6}}{3}, \frac{3 - \sqrt{6}}{3} \right\}$.

(b) First, we eliminate the fraction.

$$2x^2 + \tfrac{7}{2}x - 1 = 0$$

$$4x^2 + 7x - 2 = 0 \tag{2}$$

We use the Quadratic Formula with $a = 4$, $b = 7$, and $c = -2$. Thus,

$$x = \frac{-b \pm \sqrt{b^2 - 4ac}}{2a}$$

$$= \frac{-7 \pm \sqrt{7^2 - 4(4)(-2)}}{2(4)}$$

$$= \frac{-7 \pm \sqrt{81}}{8}$$

We simplify the result.

$$x = \frac{-7 + \sqrt{81}}{8} \quad \text{or} \quad x = \frac{-7 - \sqrt{81}}{8}$$

$$= \frac{-7 + 9}{8} \qquad\qquad = \frac{-7 - 9}{8}$$

$$= \tfrac{1}{4} \qquad\qquad\qquad = -2$$

The solution set is $\{\tfrac{1}{4}, -2\}$.

Because the solution set for the equation in Example 3(b) contains rational numbers, we can also find the solution set by factoring. Indeed, a factored form of Equation (2) is

$$(4x - 1)(x + 2) = 0$$

Thus,

$$4x - 1 = 0 \quad \text{or} \quad x + 2 = 0$$

$$x = \tfrac{1}{4} \qquad\qquad x = -2$$

which agrees with the result obtained by using the Quadratic Formula.

Example 4:   Solve for x.

(a) $x^2 = ax^2 + b$ 　　　　　　　　 **(b)** $x = \dfrac{y}{x + y}$

Solution:
(a) We cannot solve for x by taking the square root of each side because both sides of the equation contain x. However, because the equation does not contain the first power of x, we may first solve for x^2 and then apply the Square Root Theorem.

$$x^2 = ax^2 + b$$
$$x^2 - ax^2 = b$$
$$x^2(1 - a) = b$$
$$x^2 = \frac{b}{1 - a}$$
$$x = \pm\sqrt{\frac{b}{1 - a}}$$

(b) First, we eliminate the fraction.

$$x = \frac{y}{x + y}$$
$$x^2 + xy = y$$
$$x^2 + xy - y = 0$$

Because the equation contains both x^2 and x, we apply the Quadratic Formula. We have $a = 1$. Because the coefficient of x is y, we take $b = y$. Because the term that does not contain x is $-y$, we take $c = -y$. Thus,

$$x = \frac{-b \pm \sqrt{b^2 - 4ac}}{2a}$$
$$x = \frac{-y \pm \sqrt{y^2 - 4(1)(-y)}}{2(1)}$$
$$x = \frac{-y \pm \sqrt{y^2 + 4y}}{2}$$

Example 5:   An unframed painting is 30 centimeters by 50 centimeters. We want to enclose the painting with a frame of uniform width in such a way that the area of the frame is 1200 square centimeters. How wide should we make the frame?

Solution: Let x centimeters be the width of the frame. Refer to Figure 3.5.1. We are given that the inner dimensions of the frame are 30 centimeters and

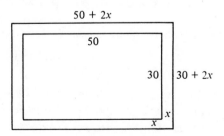

Figure 3.5.1

50 centimeters. Thus, $(30 + 2x)$ centimeters and $(50 + 2x)$ centimeters are the outer dimensions of the frame. The area of the frame equals the area of the outer rectangle minus the area of the inner rectangle. The area of the outer rectangle is $(30 + 2x)(50 + 2x)$ square centimeters, and the area of the inner rectangle is $(30)(50)$ square centimeters. Because we are given that 1200 square centimeters is the area of the frame,

$$(30 + 2x)(50 + 2x) - (30)(50) = 1200$$
$$1500 + 60x + 100x + 4x^2 - 1500 = 1200$$
$$4x^2 + 160x = 1200$$
$$x^2 + 40x = 300$$

Because we can complete the square without using fractions, we apply this method to solve the equation. We add $(\frac{40}{2})^2 = 400$ to both sides.

$$x^2 + 40x + 400 = 300 + 400$$
$$(x + 20)^2 = 700$$
$$x + 20 = \pm\sqrt{700}$$
$$x = -20 \pm \sqrt{700}$$

Because $-20 - \sqrt{700}$ is a negative number and the width of the frame is not negative, we disregard this solution. Because $-20 + \sqrt{700} \approx 6.46$, we conclude that the width of the frame is 6.46 centimeters.

EXERCISES 3.5

For Exercises 1–6 find the solution set by using the Square Root Theorem.

1. $5x^2 - 7 = x^2 + 4$

2. $3x(x + 2) = 6x + 1$

3. $\frac{x^2}{2} + 3 = 4x^2 - 5$

4. $\frac{x}{3x - 4} = \frac{x + 2}{2 - x}$

5. $(2x + 3)(2x - 1) = x(x + 4) - 3$

6. $5x^2 + 4 = x^2 + 1$

For Exercises 7–16 find the solution set by completing the square.

7. $x^2 - 6x + 2 = 0$

8. $x^2 + 10x + 15 = 0$

9. $x^2 + 5x = 1$

10. $x^2 - 7x = 3$

11. $x^2 + 4x + 5 = 0$

12. $x^2 - 8x + 20 = 0$

13. $3x^2 = 6x + 2$

14. $2x^2 + 8x = 5$

15. $2x^2 + 5x = 3$

16. $3x^2 = 4x + 4$

For Exercises 17–28 find the solution set by using the Quadratic Formula.

17. $x^2 + 5x + 2 = 0$ **18.** $x^2 + x - 3 = 0$

19. $2x^2 - 7x + 1 = 0$ **20.** $3x^2 - 5x - 4 = 0$

21. $5x^2 = 4x + 2$ **22.** $7x^2 + 2 = 8x$

23. $3(2x^2 - 1) = 7x$ **24.** $24x(x + 1) = 8x^2 - 9$

25. $3x(x + 3) = x^2 + x - 2$ **26.** $(2x + 1)^2 = 12x + 5$

27. $\dfrac{3x^2}{2} + 2x = \dfrac{x^2}{4} + 3$ **28.** $x(x + 2) = \dfrac{4x - 1}{7}$

For Exercises 29–32 solve for x.

29. $ax^2 = x^2 + c^2$ **30.** $\dfrac{a^2 x^2 + b^2}{x^2} = b^2$

31. $2x = \dfrac{y}{x - y}$ **32.** $x(x + y) = (2x - y)^2$

For Exercises 33–34 solve for the indicated variable.

33. $r = \dfrac{s}{s - r}$; for r **34.** $(r + s)^2 = rs(s + 2)$; for s

For Exercises 35–40 use the solution of an equation to answer the stated question.

35. If dropped from rest, an object will fall s feet in t seconds, with $s = 16t^2$. How long will it take an object to fall 500 feet?

36. If thrown upward with initial velocity v meters per second, an object will be s meters above its starting point after t seconds, with $s = vt - 5t^2$. If a shell is fired upward with muzzle speed 100 meters per second, how long will it take for the shell to rise to a height of 450 meters?

37. Find the dimensions of a rectangle whose area is 200 square centimeters if the length is 5 centimeters more than the width.

38. Find the dimensions of a rectangle if the length is 2 inches more·than the width and the diagonal is 3 inches more than the length.

39. A rectangular yard is 40 feet by 60 feet, and the yard contains a swimming pool with a concrete deck of uniform width on all sides of the pool. The area of the deck is the same as the area of the pool. What is the width of the deck?

40. A motorboat takes 15 minutes longer to go 6 miles upstream in a river than to return the same distance downstream. If the speed of the boat in still water is 8 miles per hour, what is the speed of the river current?

3.6   Equations with Radicals

The solution set for the equation $\sqrt{x} = 3$ is $\{9\}$, because 9 is the only number whose principal square root is 3. Moreover, if we square both sides of the equation $\sqrt{x} = 3$, the result is $x = 9$. However, squaring both sides of an equation does not always result in an equivalent equation. Consider the equation

$$x = 2 \tag{1}$$

If we square both sides, the result is

$$x^2 = 4 \tag{2}$$

The solution set for Equation (1) is $\{2\}$, but the solution set for Equation (2) is $\{2, -2\}$. Thus, Equation (1) is not equivalent to Equation (2). However, note that $\{2\}$, the solution set of Equation (1), is a subset of $\{2, -2\}$, the solution set of Equation (2). In general, we have the following theorem.

3.6.1   Theorem: Squaring

If we square the expression on each side of an equation, the solution set of the original equation is a subset of the solution set of the resulting equation.

Example 1:   Find the solution set: $x - 2 = \sqrt{x + 10}$.

Solution: We eliminate the radical by squaring both sides.

$$x - 2 = \sqrt{x + 10}$$
$$(x - 2)^2 = (\sqrt{x + 10})^2$$
$$x^2 - 4x + 4 = x + 10$$
$$x^2 - 5x - 6 = 0$$
$$(x - 6)(x + 1) = 0$$
$$x - 6 = 0 \quad \text{or} \quad x + 1 = 0$$
$$x = 6 \qquad\qquad x = -1$$

Thus, the solution set of the original equation is a subset of $\{6, -1\}$. We test each member of this set to see whether or not it is a solution of the original equation.

$$x - 2 = \sqrt{x + 10} \qquad\qquad x - 2 = \sqrt{x + 10}$$
$$6 - 2 = \sqrt{6 + 10} \quad (x \longleftarrow 6) \qquad -1 - 2 = \sqrt{-1 + 10} \quad (x \longleftarrow -1)$$
$$4 = \sqrt{16} \qquad\qquad\qquad -3 = \sqrt{9}$$
$$\text{TRUE} \qquad\qquad\qquad\qquad \text{FALSE}$$

Because $\sqrt{9}$ represents the *principal* square root of 9, $\sqrt{9} \neq -3$. Thus, the replacement -1 does not satisfy the original equation, and we reject $x = -1$. The solution set for the original equation is $\{6\}$.

Example 2:   Find the solution set: $\sqrt{2x + 6} - x = 3$.

Solution: We cannot eliminate the radical by squaring both sides. By the Binomial Square Theorem, $(a + b)^2 = a^2 + 2ab + b^2$, we have

$$(\sqrt{2x + 6} - x)^2 = (\sqrt{2x + 6})^2 + 2\sqrt{2x + 6}(-x) + (-x)^2$$

However, if we first separate the term that contains the radical from the other terms and then square both sides, we eliminate the radical.

$$\sqrt{2x + 6} - x = 3$$
$$\sqrt{2x + 6} = x + 3$$
$$(\sqrt{2x + 6})^2 = (x + 3)^2$$
$$2x + 6 = x^2 + 6x + 9$$
$$0 = x^2 + 4x + 3$$
$$0 = (x + 1)(x + 3)$$

$$x + 1 = 0 \qquad \text{or} \qquad x + 3 = 0$$
$$x = -1 \qquad\qquad\qquad x = -3$$

We test each of the possible solutions in the original equation.

$$\sqrt{2x + 6} - x = 3$$
$$\sqrt{2(-1) + 6} - (-1) = 3 \qquad (x \longleftarrow -1)$$
$$\sqrt{4} + 1 = 3$$
$$3 = 3$$

$$\sqrt{2x + 6} - x = 3$$
$$\sqrt{2(-3) + 6} - (-3) = 3 \qquad (x \longleftarrow -3)$$
$$\sqrt{0} + 3 = 3$$
$$3 = 3$$

Because both -1 and -3 satisfy the original equation, the solution set is $\{-1, -3\}$.

Example 3:   Find the solution set: $x + 3\sqrt{x - 1} + 1 = 0$.

Solution: First, we separate the term that contains the radical from the other terms, and then we eliminate the radical by squaring both sides.

$$x + 3\sqrt{x - 1} + 1 = 0$$
$$x + 1 = -3\sqrt{x - 1}$$
$$(x + 1)^2 = (-3\sqrt{x - 1})^2$$
$$x^2 + 2x + 1 = 9(x - 1)$$
$$x^2 + 2x + 1 = 9x - 9$$
$$x^2 - 7x + 10 = 0$$
$$(x - 2)(x - 5) = 0$$
$$x - 2 = 0 \quad \text{or} \quad x - 5 = 0$$
$$x = 2 \qquad\qquad x = 5$$

We test each of the possible solutions in the original equation.

$$x + 3\sqrt{x - 1} + 1 = 0$$
$$2 + 3\sqrt{2 - 1} + 1 = 0 \qquad (x \longleftarrow 2)$$
$$6 = 0$$

FALSE

$$x + 3\sqrt{x - 1} + 1 = 0$$
$$5 + 3\sqrt{5 - 1} + 1 = 0 \qquad (x \longleftarrow 5)$$
$$12 = 0$$

FALSE

Because neither of the possible solutions satisfies the original equation, we conclude that its solution set is $\varnothing$, the empty set.

Example 4: Find the solution set:

$$\sqrt{2x + 5} - \sqrt{x + 3} = 2$$

Solution: First, we separate one of the terms that contains a radical from the other terms and then square both sides.

$$\sqrt{2x + 5} - \sqrt{x + 3} = 2$$
$$\sqrt{2x + 5} = \sqrt{x + 3} + 2$$
$$(\sqrt{2x + 5})^2 = (\sqrt{x + 3} + 2)^2$$
$$2x + 5 = (\sqrt{x + 3})^2 + 2\sqrt{x + 3}(2) + 2^2$$
$$2x + 5 = x + 3 + 4\sqrt{x + 3} + 4$$
$$2x + 5 = 4\sqrt{x + 3} + x + 7$$

Next, we separate the remaining term that contains a radical from the other terms and then square both sides.

$$x - 2 = 4\sqrt{x + 3}$$
$$(x - 2)^2 = (4\sqrt{x + 3})^2$$
$$x^2 - 4x + 4 = 16(x + 3)$$
$$x^2 - 4x + 4 = 16x + 48$$
$$x^2 - 20x - 44 = 0$$
$$(x - 22)(x + 2) = 0$$
$$x - 22 = 0 \qquad \text{or} \qquad x + 2 = 0$$
$$x = 22 \qquad\qquad\qquad x = -2$$

We test each possible solution in the original equation.

$$\sqrt{2x + 5} - \sqrt{x + 3} = 2$$
$$\sqrt{2(22) + 5} - \sqrt{22 + 3} = 2 \qquad (x \longleftarrow 22)$$
$$\sqrt{49} - \sqrt{25} = 2$$
$$2 = 2$$

TRUE

$$\sqrt{2x + 5} - \sqrt{x + 3} = 2$$
$$\sqrt{2(-2) + 5} - \sqrt{-2 + 3} = 2 \qquad (x \longleftarrow -2)$$
$$\sqrt{1} - \sqrt{1} = 2$$
$$0 = 2$$

FALSE

The solution set is {22}.

Because there is only one real cube root of a real number, if we cube both sides of an equation, the resulting equation is equivalent to the original equation. Thus, we find the solution set for an equation that contains the cube root radical by cubing both sides; it is not necessary to test each solution, as we must do after squaring both sides.

Example 5:   Find the solution set: $\sqrt[3]{x^2 - 1} = 2$.

Solution: To eliminate the cube root radical, we cube both sides.

$$\sqrt[3]{x^2 - 1} = 2$$
$$(\sqrt[3]{x^2 - 1})^3 = 2^3$$
$$x^2 - 1 = 8$$
$$x^2 = 9$$
$$x = \pm 3$$

The solution set is {3, −3}.

Example 6: Solve for t: $s = t + \sqrt{t^2 + t}$.

Solution: First, we eliminate the radical.

$$s = t + \sqrt{t^2 + t}$$
$$s - t = \sqrt{t^2 + t}$$
$$(s - t)^2 = (\sqrt{t^2 + t})^2$$
$$s^2 - 2st + t^2 = t^2 + t$$
$$s^2 = t + 2st$$
$$s^2 = t(1 + 2s)$$
$$\frac{s^2}{1 + 2s} = t$$
$$t = \frac{s^2}{1 + 2s}$$

EXERCISES 3.6

For Exercises 1–34 find the solution set.

1. $\sqrt{3x + 10} = 4$

2. $\sqrt{2x + 8} = 3$

3. $2x = \sqrt{6x}$

4. $2\sqrt{x} = x$

5. $5 + \sqrt{x} = 0$

6. $1 + \sqrt{3x} = 0$

7. $x = \sqrt{x + 6}$

8. $2x = \sqrt{x + 3}$

9. $x + 3 = \sqrt{x + 5}$

10. $\sqrt{6 - x} = x + 6$

11. $2\sqrt{x} = x - 3$

12. $x + 4 = 3\sqrt{x + 2}$

13. $x + \sqrt{2x - 1} = 2$

14. $\sqrt{2x - 5} + 2 = x$

15. $6x = 1 + \sqrt{2x + 3}$

16. $3x = 2 - \sqrt{3x + 10}$

17. $2(1 - \sqrt{x + 2}) = 3x$

18. $2x = -5 + 3\sqrt{x + 2}$

19. $\sqrt{x + 5} = \sqrt{x} + 1$

20. $\sqrt{x - 7} = \sqrt{x} - 1$

21. $3 + \sqrt{x - 6} = \sqrt{x + 9}$

22. $1 + \sqrt{x + 2} = \sqrt{x + 7}$

23. $\sqrt{2x + 4} = 1 - \sqrt{x + 3}$

24. $\sqrt{2x + 3} = 2 + \sqrt{x + 2}$

25. $\sqrt{2x - 3} - \sqrt{x - 1} = 2$

26. $\sqrt{2x - 9} + \sqrt{x - 5} = 1$

27. $\dfrac{\sqrt{x + 3}}{x} = -2$

28. $\dfrac{\sqrt{x + 4}}{x - 1} = 2$

29. $\dfrac{2}{\sqrt{3x + 4}} = \dfrac{1}{\sqrt{x}}$

30. $\dfrac{1}{\sqrt{x - 1}} = \dfrac{\sqrt{x + 2}}{2}$

31. $\sqrt[3]{2x - 1} = 3$

32. $\sqrt[3]{x^2 + 2x} = 2$

33. $x^{2/3} = 4$

34. $x^{2/3} + 4x^{1/3} = 0$

For Exercises 35–38 solve for the indicated variable.

35. $y = x + \sqrt{x^2 - 4}$;   for x **36.** $r = \dfrac{1}{\sqrt{s+1}}$;   for s

37. $s = \dfrac{\sqrt{t^2 + 1}}{t}, t > 0$;   for t **38.** $t = r + \sqrt{r^2 - r}$;   for r

For Exercises 39–40 use the solution of an equation to answer the stated question.

39. The total cost of producing n items is c dollars, with $c = n + \sqrt{6n + 1}$. How many items can be produced for 15 dollars?

40. If an object is given an initial downward velocity of v_0 feet per second and allowed to fall for a distance of s feet, its velocity will be v feet per second, with $v = \sqrt{64s + v_0^2}$. What is the initial velocity if the object attains a velocity of 64 feet per second after falling for 60 feet?

3.7   Other Types of Equations

If a and b are real numbers, then $b^3 = a$ if and only if $b = \sqrt[3]{a}$. Thus, we may find the solution set for an equation of the form $x^3 = a$ by taking the cube root of both sides.

Example 1:   Find the solution set for

$$3x^3 - 1 = x^3 + 7$$

Solution: We solve the equation for x^3 and then take the cube root of both sides.

$$3x^3 - 1 = x^3 + 7$$
$$2x^3 = 8$$
$$x^3 = 4$$
$$x = \sqrt[3]{4}$$

The solution set is $\{\sqrt[3]{4}\}$.

Example 2:   Find the solution set for

$$x^3 = 3x^2 + 4x$$

Solution: Because the equation contains powers of x other than x^3, we cannot write the equation in the form $x^3 = a$ and take the cube root of both sides. However, we may use factoring to find the solution set. First, we write the equation in zero form.

$$x^3 = 3x^2 + 4x$$
$$x^3 - 3x^2 - 4x = 0$$
$$x(x^2 - 3x - 4) = 0$$

Thus,

$$x = 0 \quad \text{or} \quad x^2 - 3x - 4 = 0$$
$$(x - 4)(x + 1) = 0$$
$$x - 4 = 0 \quad \text{or} \quad x + 1 = 0$$
$$x = 4 \qquad\qquad x = -1$$

The solution set is $\{0, 4, -1\}$.

Example 3: Find the solution set for

$$x^4 - 2x^2 = 3$$

Solution: We write the equation in zero form and then factor.

$$x^4 - 2x^2 = 3$$
$$x^4 - 2x^2 - 3 = 0$$
$$(x^2 - 3)(x^2 + 1) = 0$$

Thus,

$$x^2 - 3 = 0 \qquad\qquad \text{or} \quad x^2 + 1 = 0$$
$$x^2 = 3 \qquad\qquad\qquad x^2 = -1$$
$$x = \pm\sqrt{3}$$

Because the square of a real number is not negative, there are no real solutions for the equation $x^2 = -1$. Thus, the solution set is $\{\sqrt{3}, -\sqrt{3}\}$.

Example 4: Find the solution set for

$$4x = \sqrt[3]{x}$$

Solution: First, we eliminate the radical by cubing both sides.

$$4x = \sqrt[3]{x}$$
$$64x^3 = x$$
$$64x^3 - x = 0$$
$$x(64x^2 - 1) = 0$$

Thus,

$$x = 0 \quad \text{or} \quad 64x^2 - 1 = 0$$
$$x^2 = \tfrac{1}{64}$$
$$x = \pm\tfrac{1}{8}$$

The solution set is $\{0, \tfrac{1}{8}, -\tfrac{1}{8}\}$.

Example 5: Find the solution set for

$$x^3 + 3x^2 - x - 3 = 0$$

Solution: We factor by grouping terms.

$$x^3 + 3x^2 - x - 3 = 0$$
$$x^2(x + 3) + (-1)(x + 3) = 0$$
$$(x^2 - 1)(x + 3) = 0$$

Thus,

$$x^2 - 1 = 0 \quad\text{or}\quad x + 3 = 0$$
$$x^2 = 1 \qquad\qquad x = -3$$
$$x = \pm 1$$

The solution set is $\{1, -1, -3\}$.

Because x^4 is the square of x^2, the equation

$$3x^4 - 2x^2 + 5 = 0 \tag{1}$$

is said to be a quadratic equation in x^2. Indeed, if we replace x^2 by u in Equation (1), the result is the quadratic equation

$$3u^2 - 2u + 5 = 0$$

In general, an equation of the form $au^2 + bu + c = 0$ is quadratic in form if a, b, and c are any constants, with $a \neq 0$, and u is any expression that contains one variable. Equations that are quadratic in form can be solved by applying the techniques of Sections 3.4–3.6.

Example 6: Find the solution set for

$$x^{1/2} - 5x^{1/4} + 6 = 0$$

Solution: Because $x^{1/2} = (x^{1/4})^2$, the equation is a quadratic in $x^{1/4}$. We let $u = x^{1/4}$. Thus, $u^2 = x^{1/2}$, and we substitute into the given equation.

$$x^{1/2} - 5x^{1/4} + 6 = 0$$
$$u^2 - 5u + 6 = 0$$
$$(u - 2)(u - 3) = 0$$
$$u - 2 = 0 \quad\text{or}\quad u - 3 = 0$$
$$u = 2 \qquad\qquad u = 3$$

Because $u = x^{1/4}$, we have

$$x^{1/4} = 2 \qquad\qquad x^{1/4} = 3$$

If we square both sides and then square both sides again, we obtain the fourth power of both sides. Thus,

$$(x^{1/4})^4 = 2^4 \qquad\qquad (x^{1/4})^4 = 3^4$$
$$x = 16 \qquad\qquad x = 81$$

Because we squared both sides, we must test each of the possible solutions in the original equation.

$$x^{1/2} - 5x^{1/4} + 6 = 0$$
$$16^{1/2} - 5 \cdot 16^{1/4} + 6 = 0 \quad (x \longleftarrow 16)$$
$$4 - 5 \cdot 2 + 6 = 0$$
$$0 = 0$$
$$x^{1/2} - 5x^{1/4} + 6 = 0$$
$$81^{1/2} - 5 \cdot 81^{1/4} + 6 = 0 \quad (x \longleftarrow 81)$$
$$9 - 5 \cdot 3 + 6 = 0$$
$$0 = 0$$

Because both 16 and 81 satisfy the original equation, the solution set is $\{16, 81\}$.

EXERCISES 3.7

For Exercises 1–42 find the solution set.

1. $x^3 = 64$
2. $x^3 + 8 = 0$
3. $8x^3 + 1 = 0$
4. $64x^3 = 27$
5. $2x^3 + 1 = x^3 + 3$
6. $x^3 - 1 = 3x^3 + 5$
7. $x^3 = 16x$
8. $4x^3 = x$
9. $x^3 + 8x^2 = 0$
10. $2x^3 = 3x^2$
11. $x^3 + 3x^2 + 2x = 0$
12. $x^3 = 2x^2 + 3x$
13. $2x^3 + 5x^2 = 3x$
14. $3x^3 + 5x^2 = 2x$
15. $x^3 + 2x^2 - x = 0$
16. $x^3 - 4x^2 + x = 0$
17. $x^4 - 5x^2 + 4 = 0$
18. $x^4 - 10x^2 + 9 = 0$
19. $x^4 + 3 = 4x^2$
20. $x^4 + 8 = 6x^2$
21. $x^4 + 2x^2 = 8$
22. $x^4 = x^2 + 6$
23. $16x^4 = x^2$
24. $8x^4 = x$
25. $16x^4 - 1 = 0$
26. $2x^4 + 3x^3 = 0$
27. $x = \sqrt[3]{x}$
28. $2x = \sqrt[3]{2x}$
29. $3x = \sqrt[3]{3x^2}$
30. $x + 1 = \sqrt[3]{3x + 1}$
31. $x^3 + 2x^2 - x - 2 = 0$
32. $x^3 - 3x^2 - x + 3 = 0$
33. $x^3 + x^2 - 2x - 2 = 0$
34. $x^3 + 2x^2 - 5x - 10 = 0$
35. $x^3 + 3x^2 + 3x + 1 = 0$
36. $x^3 - 6x^2 + 12x - 8 = 0$
37. $x^{2/3} - 5x^{1/3} + 6 = 0$
38. $x^{2/3} - 2x^{1/3} - 8 = 0$

39. $x^{1/2} - x^{1/4} - 6 = 0$

40. $2x^{1/2} + x^{1/4} - 1 = 0$

41. $x^2 + \dfrac{12}{x^2} = 7$

42. $\dfrac{2x - 1}{x} = \dfrac{2x^2}{x + 1}$

3.8 First Degree Inequalities

Any sentence whose connective is $<$, $\leq$, $>$, or $\geq$ is called an **inequality**. Consider the inequality

$$2x + 3 < 8 \tag{1}$$

If x is replaced by 2 in Inequality (1), the result is

$$2 \cdot 2 + 3 < 8$$
$$7 < 8$$

which is a true statement. Thus, the number 2 is said to satisfy Inequality (1), and 2 is a solution of the inequality. On the other hand, the number 3 does not satisfy Inequality (1), because the false statement $9 < 8$ results when x is replaced by 3.

Any replacement for the variable in an inequality with one variable that results in a true statement is said to **satisfy** the inequality, and the replacement is called a **solution** of the inequality. The set that contains all the numbers that are solutions of an inequality, and only those numbers that are solutions of the inequality, is called the **solution set** of the inequality. If two inequalities have the same solution set, they are **equivalent inequalities**.

Consider the true statement $-2 < 3$. If we add 4 to both the left and right expressions, we have $-2 + 4 < 3 + 4$, which is also a true statement, because $2 < 7$ is true. Moreover, if we add -3 to both sides of $-2 < 3$, the result is $-2 + (-3) < 3 + (-3)$, which is also true, because it is true that $-5 < 0$. We may always add the same number, whether that number is positive or negative, to both sides of an inequality.

Suppose we multiply both sides of the true statement $-2 < 3$ by 5. The result is $-2 \cdot 5 < 3 \cdot 5$, which is a true statement, because $-10 < 15$ is true. However, if we multiply both sides of the true statement $-2 < 3$ by -5, the result is $(-2)(-5) < 3(-5)$, which is a false statement, because $10 < -15$ is false. Note that the multiplier 5 is a positive number, whereas the multiplier -5 is a negative number. Moreover, the false statement $10 < -15$ that results when we multiply by the negative number becomes a true statement if we replace the connective $<$ by the connective $>$. That is, $10 > -15$ is true. In general, we may multiply both sides of an inequality by any positive number, but we must reverse the sense of the connective when we multiply both sides by a negative number.

3.8.1   Theorem: *Equivalent Inequalities*

(i)   If we replace any expression in an inequality by an equivalent expression, the resulting inequality is equivalent to the original inequality.

(ii) If we add or subtract the same expression on both sides of an inequality, the resulting inequality is equivalent to the original inequality.

(iii) If we multiply or divide on both sides of an inequality by the same positive number, the resulting inequality is equivalent to the original inequality.

(iv) If we multiply or divide on both sides of an inequality by the same negative number and also reverse the sense of the connective, the resulting inequality is equivalent to the original inequality.

The solution set for a first degree inequality is an interval of numbers. The steps for finding the interval that satisfies a first degree inequality are similar to the steps for solving a first degree equation, except that we must reverse the sense of the connective whenever we multiply or divide both sides by a negative number.

Example 1:   Find the solution set.

$$3x + 1 < 5x - 7$$

Solution:

$$3x + 1 < 5x - 7$$
$$(3x + 1) + (-5x) < (5x - 7) + (-5x)$$
$$-2x + 1 < -7$$
$$(-2x + 1) + (-1) < (-7) + (-1)$$
$$-2x < -8$$
$$(-1)(-2x) > (-1)(-8) \qquad (2)$$
$$2x > 8$$
$$\tfrac{1}{2}(2x) > \tfrac{1}{2} \cdot 8$$
$$x > 4$$

The solution set is $\{x : x > 4\}$, and the graph of this interval is shown in Figure 3.8.1. Note that on step (2) in the solution we reverse the sense of the connective because the multiplier -1 is a negative number.

Figure 3.8.1

Alternate Solution:

$$3x + 1 < 5x - 7$$

$$(3x + 1) + (-3x) < (5x - 7) + (-3x)$$

$$1 < 2x - 7$$

$$1 + 7 < (2x - 7) + 7$$

$$8 < 2x$$

$$\tfrac{1}{2} \cdot 8 < \tfrac{1}{2}(2x)$$

$$4 < x$$

$$x > 4 \qquad\qquad (3)$$

The solution set is $\{x: x > 4\}$. Note that we reverse the sense of the connective in step (3) because $a < b$ if and only if $b > a$.

Example 2: Find the solution set.

$$\frac{x + 1}{-3} \geq x - 3$$

Solution: First, we eliminate the fraction. Because the multiplier is -3, a negative number, we reverse the sense of the connective.

$$\frac{x + 1}{-3} \geq x - 3$$

$$(-3)\frac{x + 1}{-3} \leq (-3)(x - 3)$$

$$x + 1 \leq -3x + 9$$

$$4x + 1 \leq 9$$

$$4x \leq 8$$

$$x \leq 2$$

The solution set is $\{x: x \leq 2\}$ and the graph is Figure 3.8.2.

Figure 3.8.2

Example 3: Find the solution set.

$$1 < 2x + 1 < 7$$

Solution: We reduce the middle expression to x. First, we add -1 to each of the three expressions and simplify.

$$1 < 2x + 1 < 7$$
$$0 < 2x \quad\quad < 6$$

Next, we divide each of the three expressions by 2 and simplify.

$$0 < x < 3$$

The solution set is $\{x: 0 < x < 3\}$ and the graph is Figure 3.8.3.

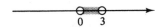

Figure 3.8.3

The inequality $|x| < 3$ is satisfied by any positive number between 0 and 3. Moreover, any negative number between -3 and 0 is a solution. For example, if x is replaced by -2 in $|x| < 3$, the result is $|-2| < 3$, which is a true statement. However, a negative number that is less than -3, for example -4, does not satisfy $|x| < 3$, because it is false that $|-4| < 3$. We conclude that the solution set for $|x| < 3$ is the interval $\{x: -3 < x < 3\}$. In general, we have the following theorem.

3.8.2   *Theorem*

If $b > 0$, then

$$|a| < b \quad\quad \text{if and only if} \quad\quad -b < a < b$$

Example 4: Find the solution set.

$$|x + 2| < 3$$

Solution: We apply Theorem 3.8.2 with $a = x + 2$ and $b = 3$. Thus, we replace the given inequality by a continued inequality.

$$|x + 2| < 3$$
$$-3 < x + 2 < 3$$
$$-5 < x < 1$$

The solution set is $\{x: -5 < x < 1\}$, whose graph is Figure 3.8.4.

Figure 3.8.4

The inequality $|x| > 3$ is satisfied by any positive number greater than 3 and by any negative number less than -3. For example, -4 is a solution of $|x| > 3$ because $|-4| > 3$ is a true statement. However, a negative number between -3 and 0 does not satisfy $|x| > 3$. For example, -2 is not a solution because $|-2| > 3$ is a false statement. We conclude that the solution set for $|x| > 3$ is $\{x: x > 3\} \cup \{x: x < -3\}$, the union of two intervals. We cannot use a continued inequality to represent this union. In particular, we cannot use $3 < x < -3$ because it is false that $3 < -3$. In general, we have the following theorem.

3.8.3   Theorem

If $b > 0$, then

$$|a| > b \quad \text{if and only if} \quad a > b \text{ or } a < -b$$

Example 5:   Find the solution set.

$$|2x - 3| \geq 1$$

Solution: We apply Theorem 3.8.3 with $a = 2x - 3$ and $b = 1$. Thus, either

$$
\begin{array}{ccc}
2x - 3 \geq 1 & \text{or} & 2x - 3 \leq -1 \\
2x \geq 4 & & 2x \leq 2 \\
x \geq 2 & & x \leq 1
\end{array}
$$

The solution set is $\{x: x \geq 2\} \cup \{x: x \leq 1\}$. The graph is Figure 3.8.5.

Figure 3.8.5

EXERCISES 3.8

For Exercises 1–12 find the solution set and sketch its graph.

1. $x + 1 < 4$	**2.** $x - 1 < 3$	**3.** $x - 1 > 1$
4. $x + 1 > 2$	**5.** $-x > 1$	**6.** $-x < -2$
7. $-2x < -6$	**8.** $-3x > 12$	**9.** $x + 1 \leq 3x - 1$
10. $2x - 1 \geq 3x + 1$	**11.** $2 - x \geq 2x + 5$	**12.** $1 - 3x \leq x + 5$

For Exercises 13–26 find the solution set.

13. $3x + 1 > 0$ **14.** $2x - 3 \leq 0$

15. $5 - 2x \geq 0$ **16.** $1 - 5x < 0$

17. $3(x + 1) < 5x + 3$ **18.** $2(x - 3) > 3(x - 2)$

19. $2(3x + 2) > 3(2x + 1)$ **20.** $3(4x + 1) < 12x$

21. $\dfrac{x}{3} - x \leq 1$ **22.** $\dfrac{x}{2} - 3x > 2$

23. $\dfrac{2x - 1}{-2} < x$ **24.** $\dfrac{x + 5}{-5} \geq x + 1$

25. $\dfrac{x + 3}{-4} \geq \dfrac{x + 2}{-3}$ **26.** $\dfrac{x - 1}{-2} < \dfrac{x - 2}{-3}$

For Exercises 27–34 find the solution set and draw its graph.

27. $-1 < x + 3 < 2$ **28.** $0 \leq x + 1 \leq 5$ **29.** $-1 \leq 2x - 1 < 3$

30. $-5 < 2x + 1 \leq 3$ **31.** $|x| \leq 2$ **32.** $|x| < 1$

33. $|x| > 1$ **34.** $|x| \geq 2$

For Exercises 35–44 find the solution set.

35. $|x + 1| < 3$ **36.** $|x - 1| < 2$ **37.** $|x - 2| > 1$

38. $|x + 2| > 3$ **39.** $|x - 1| \geq 2$ **40.** $|x - 2| \leq 1$

41. $|2x + 3| \leq 3$ **42.** $|3x - 2| \geq 1$ **43.** $|x| < -1$

44. $|x| > -2$

For Exercises 45–46 use the solution set for an inequality to answer the stated question.

45. After t seconds the velocity of a ball that is thrown upward with initial velocity 80 feet per second will be v feet per second, with $v = 80 - 32t$. What is the time interval during which the velocity is between 16 and 64 feet per second?

46. If F degrees is the temperature using the Fahrenheit scale and C degrees is the temperature using the Celsius scale, then $C = \frac{5}{9}(F - 32)$. If the temperature is between 20°C and 30°C, what is the corresponding interval on the Fahrenheit scale?

3.9 Second Degree Inequalities (optional)

In this section we develop a technique for finding the solution set of an inequality that contains a second degree polynomial. The first two examples illustrate the method when it is possible to solve by factoring.

Example 1:   Find the solution set for

$$x^2 - 2x > 8$$

Solution: First we write the given inequality in zero form and then factor.

$$x^2 - 2x > 8$$
$$x^2 - 2x - 8 > 0$$
$$(x + 2)(x - 4) > 0 \qquad (1)$$

We note that the factor $x + 2$ has value zero when $x = -2$, and the factor $x - 4$ has value zero when $x = 4$. We use the numbers -2 and 4 to subdivide the number line into three subintervals, as indicated in Table 3.9.1. The factor $x + 2$ has a negative value if $x < -2$, and it has a positive value when $x > -2$, as indicated in the table. The factor $x - 4$ has a negative value if $x < 4$, and it has a positive value if $x > 4$. Because the product of two negative numbers is positive, the product $(x + 2)(x - 4)$ has a positive value if $x < -2$, as indicated in the table. Because the product of one positive number and one negative number is negative, the product $(x + 2)(x - 4)$ has a negative value if $-2 < x < 4$, as indicated in the table. And because the product of two positive numbers is positive, the product $(x + 2)(x - 4)$ has a positive value if $x > 4$. Inequality (1) is satisfied whenever the product $(x + 2)(x - 4)$ has a positive value. From Table 3.9.1 we conclude that the solution set is

$$\{x : x < -2\} \cup \{x : x > 4\}$$

The graph of this set is shown in Figure 3.9.1.

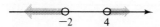

Figure 3.9.1

Table 3.9.1.

	$x < -2$	$x = -2$	$-2 < x < 4$	$x = 4$	$x > 4$
$x + 2$	$-$	0	$+$	$+$	$+$
$x - 4$	$-$	$-$	$-$	0	$+$
$(x + 2)(x - 4)$	$+$	0	$-$	0	$+$

Example 2:   Find the solution set.

$$x^2 \leq 3x$$

Solution: First we write the given inequality in zero form and then factor.

$$x^2 \le 3x$$

$$x^2 - 3x \le 0$$

$$x(x - 3) \le 0 \qquad\qquad (2)$$

Because the factor x has value zero when $x = 0$ and the factor $x - 3$ has value zero when $x = 3$, we use the numbers 0 and 3 to subdivide the number line into subintervals. Table 3.9.2 indicates the sign of each factor and of the product of the two factors for each of the subintervals. Because Inequality (2) is satisfied whenever the product $x(x - 3)$ is either negative or has value 0, from Table 3.9.2 we conclude that the solution set is

$$\{x: 0 \le x \le 3\}$$

The graph of the set is shown in Figure 3.9.2.

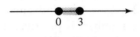

$$0 \quad 3$$

Figure 3.9.2

Table 3.9.2.

	$x < 0$	$x = 0$	$0 < x < 3$	$x = 3$	$x > 3$
x	$-$	0	$+$	$+$	$+$
$x - 3$	$-$	$-$	$-$	0	$+$
$x(x - 3)$	$+$	0	$-$	0	$+$

When it is not possible to factor the expression that appears in the zero form of a quadratic inequality, we may find the solution set by completing the square and then taking the principle square root of both sides. However, we must remember that $\sqrt{x^2} = |x|$. The following two examples illustrate the method.

Example 3:   Find the solution set for

$$x^2 - 10 < 0$$

Solution: First, we solve for x^2. Thus,

$$x^2 - 10 < 0$$

$$x^2 < 10$$

Next, we take the principal square root of both sides.

$$\sqrt{x^2} < \sqrt{10}$$
$$|x| < \sqrt{10}$$

By Theorem 3.8.2 the above is equivalent to

$$-\sqrt{10} < x < \sqrt{10}$$

Thus, the solution set is

$$\{x: -\sqrt{10} < x < \sqrt{10}\}$$

and the graph of the set is shown in Figure 3.9.3.

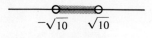

$$-\sqrt{10} \qquad \sqrt{10}$$

Figure 3.9.3

Example 4:   Find the solution set for $4x - x^2 \leq 1$.

Solution: Because the coefficient of x^2 is a negative number, we first multiply both sides by -1 and reverse the sense of the connective.

$$4x - x^2 \leq 1$$
$$x^2 - 4x \geq -1.$$

Next, we complete the square and then take the principal square root of both sides. Adding 4 to both sides, we have

$$x^2 - 4x + 4 \geq -1 + 4$$
$$(x - 2)^2 \geq 3$$
$$\sqrt{(x - 2)^2} \geq \sqrt{3}$$
$$|x - 2| \geq \sqrt{3}$$

Now, by Theorem 3.8.3, we must solve two separate inequalities.

$$x - 2 \geq \sqrt{3} \qquad \text{or} \qquad x - 2 \leq -\sqrt{3}$$
$$x \geq 2 + \sqrt{3} \qquad\qquad\qquad x \leq 2 - \sqrt{3}$$

Hence, the solution set is

$$\{x: x \geq 2 + \sqrt{3}\} \cup \{x: x \leq 2 - \sqrt{3}\}$$

and the graph of the set is shown in Figure 3.9.4.

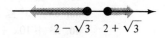

$$2 - \sqrt{3} \quad 2 + \sqrt{3}$$

Figure 3.9.4

Example 5: Find the solution set for $x^2 + 2x + 2 > 0$.

Solution:

$$x^2 + 2x + 2 > 0$$
$$x^2 + 2x + 1 > -1$$
$$(x + 1)^2 > -1$$

Because the square of any real number is greater than or equal to zero, the above inequality is satisfied by every real number. The solution set is R.

EXERCISES 3.9

For Exercises 1–20 use factoring to find the solution set. For Exercises 1–12 also sketch the graph.

1. $x^2 + 3x < 0$ **2.** $x^2 - 2x > 0$

3. $x^2 - 4 > 0$ **4.** $x^2 - 9 < 0$

5. $4x - x^2 < 0$ **6.** $3x - x^2 > 0$

7. $x(1 - x) > x - 1$ **8.** $(x + 2)(x + 8) < 2x(x + 5)$

9. $x^2 + 15 \le 8x$ **10.** $x^2 + 2x \le 8$

11. $x^2 - x \ge 6$ **12.** $x^2 \ge 2 - x$

13. $2x(x + 1) < 3x$ **14.** $3x(x + 1) < 2x$

15. $(2x)^2 < 1 - 5x^2$ **16.** $1 - 7x^2 < (3x)^2$

17. $2x^2 + 5x > 3$ **18.** $3x^2 + 5x + 2 < 0$

19. $7x > 6x^2 + 2$ **20.** $2x < 3 - 8x^2$

For Exercises 21–40 find the solution set by completing the square and then taking the principal square root of both sides. For Exercises 21–28 also sketch the graph.

21. $2x^2 < x^2 + 25$ **22.** $x(x + 3) > 3x + 1$

23. $10 - x^2 < 1$ **24.** $8 - x^2 > 4$

25. $(x + 1)^2 \ge 2(x + 2)$ **26.** $(x - 2)^2 \le 9 - 4x$

27. $2x^2 - 7 \le 0$ **28.** $10 - 3x^2 \le 0$

29. $x^2 + 4 < 0$ **30.** $x^2 + 1 > 0$

31. $x^2 - 2x < 1$ **32.** $x^2 + 2x < 2$

33. $x^2 + 4x + 1 > 0$ **34.** $x^2 - 4x + 2 > 0$

35. $x^2 \ge 6x - 7$ **36.** $x^2 \le 8x - 11$

37. $8x - x^2 \ge 10$ **38.** $6x - x^2 \le 2$

39. $x^2 - 6x + 12 > 0$ **40.** $x^2 + 10x + 30 < 0$

REVIEW EXERCISES 3

For Exercises 1–26 find the solution set of the given equation.

1. $2x(x - 3) = (x + 5)(2x - 1)$

2. $x - [3x - (x - 2)] = x + 2$

3. $3x^2 = 8x + 7$

4. $(3x + 1)^2 = 5x^2 + 6x + 4$

5. $x^2 + 24x + 74 = 0$

6. $12x^2 + 44x - 45 = 0$

7. $\dfrac{2x - 1}{5} + x = \dfrac{x + 2}{2}$

8. $\dfrac{x}{6} + \dfrac{x + 2}{4} = \dfrac{x - 1}{3}$

9. $\dfrac{2x + 1}{x - 2} + 3 = \dfrac{x + 3}{x - 2}$

10. $\dfrac{2x + 1}{x + 3} = \dfrac{x + 5}{x + 1}$

11. $3 - \dfrac{x + 5}{x + 2} = \dfrac{1}{x}$

12. $\dfrac{5}{x - 3} = \dfrac{x}{x + 1} - 1$

13. $\dfrac{x + 14}{x^2 + 6x} = \dfrac{3}{2x} + \dfrac{2}{x + 6}$

14. $\dfrac{x}{x - 1} + \dfrac{3}{x + 2} = \dfrac{2x + 1}{x^2 + x - 2}$

15. $x = 1 + \sqrt{x + 1}$

16. $3\sqrt{x + 1} = x + 3$

17. $2\sqrt{2x + 3} = \sqrt{2x + 15}$

18. $\sqrt{x + 5} = 1 + \sqrt{x + 2}$

19. $\sqrt{2x} - \sqrt{x + 2} = 4$

20. $\sqrt{x - 1} = x - \sqrt{2x - 1}$

21. $1 - x^3 = 7x^3 - 2$

22. $x^3 + 4x^2 = 5x$

23. $x^4 - 10x^2 + 24 = 0$

24. $2x^3 + x^2 - 4x - 2 = 0$

25. $x + 2 = \sqrt[3]{7x + 8}$

26. $x^{4/3} - 5x^{2/3} + 4 = 0$

For Exercises 27–32 find the solution set of the given inequality and sketch the graph.

27. $5 - 3x \le x - 3$

28. $\dfrac{3x + 2}{-2} + x \ge \dfrac{x - 1}{4}$

29. $|x - 3| < 2$

30. $|2x + 1| > 3$

31. $(x + 2)^2 > 7x + 4$

32. $x(x - 2) < 8$

For Exercises 33–38 find the solution set of the given inequality.

33. $\dfrac{x + 6}{-2} > x - 3$

34. $(x + 2)(x - 4) < (x - 1)^2$

35. $6x^2 + 1 < 5x$

36. $2(x + 1)^2 > x + 2$

37. $2x^2 - 1 > x^2 + 4$

38. $x^2 < 2(x + 1)$

For Exercises 39–44 solve for the indicated variable.

39. $A = P(1 + rt)$; for t.

40. $s = s_0 + v_0 t - \frac{1}{2}gt^2$; for v_0

41. $S = \dfrac{a - br}{1 - r}$; for r

42. $R = \dfrac{R_1 R_2}{R_1 + R_2}$; for R_1

43. $P = 2\pi\sqrt{\dfrac{L}{g}}$; for L

44. $s = vt + at^2$; for t

For Exercises 45–56 use the solution of an equation to answer the stated question.

45. If a projectile is fired upward from the ground with a speed of v meters per second, after t seconds it is at a height of s meters, with $s = vt - 5t^2$. With what muzzle speed must a bullet be fired upward if it remains in the air for 8 seconds?

46. If a force of F_1 units is applied to one side of a lever at a distance of d_1 units from the fulcrum and a force of F_2 units is applied on the other side of the lever at a distance of d_2 units from the fulcrum, then the lever is in equilibrium if and only if $F_1 d_1 = F_2 d_2$. Where should the fulcrum be placed on a 6-foot crowbar so that a 200-pound man just balances a weight of 1600 pounds?

47. If $2000 more is invested at 8% per annum than is invested at 10% per annum and if the total simple interest paid on both investments is $2500 per year, how much is invested at each rate?

48. How many milliliters of 80% alcohol must be added to 30 milliliters of 10% alcohol to make a mixture that is 40% alcohol?

49. Two ships leave at noon and head in opposite directions, with one ship traveling 3 miles per hour faster than the other. After one hour the faster ship reverses its direction and overtakes the slower ship at 8 P.M. How far from the starting point are the ships at 8 P.M.?

50. A cyclist can travel $2\frac{1}{2}$ times as fast when going downhill as when going uphill. The road to the top of Mount Stag is 16 miles long, and it takes the cyclist 4 hours to complete the round trip. How fast does the cyclist travel when going downhill?

51. If cashews sell for $3.50 per pound and peanuts sell for $2.00 per pound, how many pounds of each should be used to make 20 pounds of a mix that sells for $2.50 per pound?

52. If a runner increases his speed by 2 meters per second, he can reduce the time required to run 200 meters by 5 seconds. How long does it take him to run 200 meters at the slower speed?

53. It takes the experienced worker only $\frac{2}{3}$ as much time to complete a job as it takes his helper to do the same job. If it takes 8 hours to complete the job when working together, how long does it take for the helper to do the job when working alone?

54. If the drain is closed, it takes 2 hours to fill a pool with a certain pipe. After the pipe has been running for 3 hours, it is discovered that the drain is open. The drain is closed, and then it takes the pipe an additional $1\frac{1}{2}$ hours to fill the pool. How long does it take to empty the pool if the drain is open and the pipe is shut off?

55. We want to use 80 feet of new fencing to enclose a rectangular plot of ground that already has a fence on one side. What should be the dimensions of the rectangle if its area is 400 square feet and neither dimension exceeds 40 feet?

56. What is the area of a rectangle if the length is 1 centimeter more than the width and the diagonal is twice the width?

4

graphs of equations and inequalities with two variables

4.1 Sets of Ordered Pairs

If x and y are two real numbers, then "the ordered pair x and y" is represented by (x, y). The ordered pair $(2, 3)$ is not the same as the ordered pair $(3, 2)$. In general, $(a, b) = (c, d)$ if and only if $a = c$ and $b = d$. Note that parentheses are used to indicate an ordered pair, and braces are used to indicate a set. The ordered pair $(2, 3)$ is not the same as the set $\{2, 3\}$.

Consider two number lines—one a horizontal line called the **x-axis** with positive direction to the right, and the other a vertical line called the **y-axis** with positive direction upward—which intersect at their origins. The plane determined by these two axes is called the **coordinate plane**. Corresponding to each ordered pair of real numbers there is one and only one point in the coordinate plane. The ordered pair $(2, 3)$ corresponds to the point shown in Figure 4.1.1. This point is the intersection of two lines. One line is perpendicular to the x-axis at the point 2, and the other line is perpendicular to the y-axis at the point 3. Thus, the number 2 is called the **x-coordinate** of the point, and the number 3 is called the **y-coordinate** of the point. In general, the point corresponding to the **ordered pair** (a, b), which we refer to as "the point (a, b)," is the intersection of a vertical line that is perpendicular to the x-axis

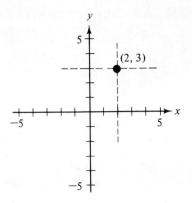

Figure 4.1.1

at the point a and a horizontal line that is perpendicular to the y-axis at the point b. The number a is called the x-coordinate of the point (a, b), and the number b is called the y-coordinate of the point (a, b).

If S is a set whose members are ordered pairs of real numbers, then the **graph** of S is the set of all points in the coordinate plane that correspond to the members of S. If S contains only a few ordered pairs, we may draw the graph of S by "plotting" the points that correspond to the ordered pairs.

Example 1:   Draw the graph of the set

$$\{(-3, 2), (0, 4), (-1, -3), (2, -4)\}$$

Solution: We plot the point corresponding to each ordered pair in the set. The graph is shown in Figure 4.1.2.

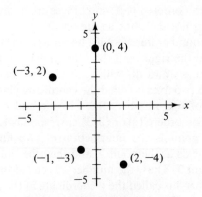

Figure 4.1.2

The ordered pair (3, 1) is a solution for the equation

$$x + y = 4 \qquad (1)$$

because a true statement results if x is replaced by 3 and y is replaced by 1 in the equation. Similarly, the ordered pairs (4, 0), (5, −1), and (−2, 6) are solutions of Equation (1) because each of these pairs satisfies the equation. Indeed, there are infinitely many ordered pairs that are solutions of Equation (1). On the other hand, the ordered pair (2, 3) is not a solution of Equation (1) because a false statement results if x is replaced by 2 and y is replaced by 3 in the equation. In general, the ordered pair (a, b) is a **solution** for an equation with variables x and y if and only if a true statement results when x is replaced by a and y is replaced by b in the equation. Most equations with two variables are satisfied by infinitely many ordered pairs. The set that contains all of the ordered pairs that are solutions for an equation with two variables is called the **solution set** of the equation. And the graph of the solution set of the equation is called the graph of the equation.

Example 2:   Sketch the graph of the equation

$$y = -2x + 4 \qquad (2)$$

Solution: We make several replacements for x, chosen arbitrarily for convenience, and for each replacement we use Equation (2) to calculate the value of y.

The results of the calculations are given in Table 4.1.1. Next, we plot the points that correspond to the solutions given in the table. See Figure 4.1.3. Because the points fall in a straight line, we assume that all of the solutions of the equation correspond to points on the line. Thus, we draw the line that contains the points, and this line is the graph of the equation.

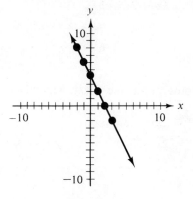

Figure 4.1.3

Table 4.1.1

x	3	2	1	0	−1	−2
y	−2	0	2	4	6	8

The equation of Example 2 is called a **linear equation** because its graph is a straight line. In Section 4.2 we prove that the graph of every first degree equation with variables x and y is a line. We state the theorem now.

4.1.1   Theorem: *Linear Equation*

If A and B are not both 0, then the graph of the equation

$$Ax + By = C$$

is a straight line.

Example 3:   Sketch the graph of the equation

$$2x - y = 2y + 6$$

Solution: First, we add $-2y$ to both sides of the given equation.

$$2x - y = 2y + 6$$
$$2x - 3y = 6$$

By the Linear Equation Theorem the graph is a straight line. Because a line is determined by two points, we can sketch the line after plotting only two points. First, we replace x by 0 in the equation and then solve for y.

$$2x - 3y = 6$$
$$2 \cdot 0 - 3y = 6 \qquad (x \longleftarrow 0)$$
$$-3y = 6$$
$$y = -2$$

Thus, $(0, -2)$ is a point on the line. Next, we replace y by 0 in the equation and solve for x.

$$2x - 3y = 6$$
$$2x - 3 \cdot 0 = 6 \qquad (y \longleftarrow 0)$$
$$2x = 6$$
$$x = 3$$

Thus, (3, 0) is a point on the line. We plot the points (0, −2) and (3, 0) and draw the line that contains these two points. See Figure 4.1.4.

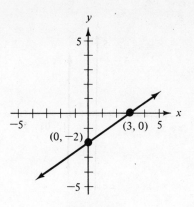

Figure 4.1.4

The point (3, 0) in Figure 4.1.4 is called the *x*-intercept point of the line, and the number 3 is called the *x*-intercept of the line. The point (0, −2) is called the *y*-intercept point, and the number −2 is called the *y*-intercept of the line. In general, if a line intersects the *x*-axis at the point (*a*, 0), then the number *a* is called the **x-intercept** of the line; and if a line intersects the *y*-axis at the point (0, *b*), then the number *b* is called the **y-intercept** of the line. As we illustrated in Example 3, to find the *x*-intercept we replace *y* by 0 and solve the equation for *x*; to find the *y*-intercept we replace *x* by 0 and solve the equation for *y*. Sometimes the graph of a linear equation can be quickly sketched by plotting only its *x*- and *y*-intercept points.

Example 4:   Sketch the graph of the indicated set.

(a) $\{(x, y): x = 2\}$ (b) $\{(x, y): y = -3\}$

Solution:

(a) The set contains all the ordered pairs (x, y) that satisfy the equation $x = 2$. Because the equation $x = 2$ is equivalent to

$$x + 0 \cdot y = 2 \qquad (3)$$

the Linear Equation Theorem applies. Thus, the graph is a straight line. Furthermore, because the ordered pair (2, 0) satisfies Equation (3), then (2, 0) is the *x*-intercept point of the line. We cannot find a *y*-intercept point. If *x* is replaced by 0 in Equation (3), the result is 0 = 2, which is impossible. However, the line contains the points (2, 1), (2, 2), (2, 3), and so on, because each of these ordered pairs is a solution of Equation (3). We conclude that the line is parallel to the y-axis. See Figure 4.1.5.

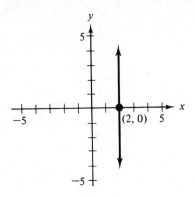

Figure 4.1.5

(b) The given equation is equivalent to

$$0 \cdot x + y = -3 \qquad (4)$$

Thus, the Linear Equation Theorem applies, and the graph is a straight line. The y-intercept point is $(0, -3)$ because $(0, -3)$ satisfies Equation (4). If we replace y by 0 in Equation (4), we get the impossible result $0 = -3$. Therefore, the line does not have an x-intercept point. We conclude that the line is parallel to the x-axis. See Figure 4.1.6.

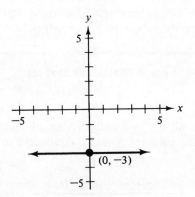

Figure 4.1.6

As we illustrated in Example 4, the graph of $\{(x, y): x = a\}$ is a vertical line that is perpendicular to the x-axis at the point a (and thus parallel to the *y*-axis). The graph of $\{(x, y): y = b\}$ is a horizontal line that is perpendicular to the *y*-axis at the point *b* (and thus parallel to the *x*-axis).

Example 5:   Sketch the graph of the equation $y = |x| - 2$.

Solution: Because $|x|$ is not a first degree polynomial, the Linear Equation Theorem does not apply. However, we may apply the definition for absolute value (1.3.1). Thus, $|x| = x$ if $x \geq 0$, and $|x| = -x$ if $x < 0$. Therefore, the given equation is equivalent to

$$y = x - 2 \quad \text{if} \quad x \geq 0 \tag{5}$$

and

$$y = -x - 2 \quad \text{if} \quad x < 0 \tag{6}$$

We make several replacements for *x*, and for each replacement we calculate the value of *y*. If $x \geq 0$, we use Equation (5) to find *y*, and if $x < 0$, we use Equation (6) to find *y*. The results of the calculations are given in Table 4.1.2. We plot the points from the table and draw the graph of the equation. See Figure 4.1.7. Note that the graph is the union of two half-lines. The half-line to the right of the *y*-axis is the graph of Equation (5), and the half-line to the left of the *y*-axis is the graph of Equation (6).

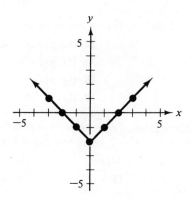

Figure 4.1.7

Table 4.1.2

x	3	2	1	0	−1	−2	−3
y	1	0	−1	−2	−1	0	1

EXERCISES 4.1

For Exercises 1–8 draw the graph of the indicated set.

1. $\{(3, 1), (-2, 2)\}$ **2.** $\{(1, -4), (-3, -1)\}$

3. $\{(2, 0), (0, -4)\}$ **4.** $\{(0, 3), (-1, 0)\}$

5. $\{(0, 0), (-1, -4), (5, 1)\}$ **6.** $\{(2, 4), (0, -2), (-3, 4)\}$

7. $\{(-3, 0), (2, -5), (-4, 4), (0, 1)\}$ **8.** $\{(0, 0), (-2, -5), (3, -3), (4, 0)\}$

For Exercises 9–14 make a table of ordered pairs that satisfy the equation, with x chosen from the set $\{2, 1, 0, -1, -2\}$; plot the points; and sketch the graph of the equation.

9. $y = x + 1$ **10.** $y = x - 1$ **11.** $y = 2x - 1$

12. $y = 2x + 1$ **13.** $y = 2 - x$ **14.** $y = 1 - 2x$

For Exercises 15–22 plot each intercept point, and then sketch the graph of the equation.

15. $x + 2y = 4$ **16.** $4x + y = 4$

17. $3x - y = 6$ **18.** $x - 2y = 6$

19. $2x - 3y + 6 = 0$ **20.** $4x - 3y + 12 = 0$

21. $2x - y = 4x + 3y + 8$ **22.** $3(x + y) + 4 = y - x$

For Exercises 23–30 sketch the graph of the indicated set.

23. $\{(x, y): x + y = 0\}$ **24.** $\{(x, y): 2x - y = 0\}$

25. $\{(x, y): y = 5 - 3x\}$ **26.** $\{(x, y): x = 2y + 3\}$

27. $\{(x, y): x + 4 = 0\}$ **28.** $\{(x, y): 2 - y = 0\}$

29. $\{(x, y): 4x - 3y = 10\}$ **30.** $\{(x, y): 2x + 5y + 9 = 0\}$

For Exercises 31–36 make a table of ordered pairs that satisfy the equation, with x chosen from the set $\{3, 2, 1, 0, -1, -2, -3\}$; plot the points; and sketch the graph.

31. $y = |x|$ **32.** $y = -|x|$ **33.** $y = |x| + 1$

34. $y = |x| - 3$ **35.** $y = |x - 2|$ **36.** $y = |x + 1|$

4.2 Lines

Figure 4.2.1 shows the line L that contains the points $A = (1, 2)$ and $B = (6, 5)$. The difference of the x-coordinates is called the change in x and is represented by $\Delta x = 6 - 1 = 5$. The difference of the y-coordinates is called the change in y and is represented by $\Delta y = 5 - 2 = 3$. And the ratio $\frac{\Delta y}{\Delta x}$ is called the **slope** of the line segment AB. It can be shown that $\frac{3}{5}$ is the

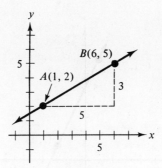

Figure 4.2.1

slope of any line segment that is contained in line L, and thus $\frac{3}{5}$ is called the slope of line L. In general, we make the following definition.

> ### 4.2.1 Definition: *Slope*
>
> If a line contains the points (x_1, y_1) and (x_2, y_2) and if $x_1 \neq x_2$, then the slope of the line, designated by m, is given by
>
> $$m = \frac{\Delta y}{\Delta x} = \frac{y_2 - y_1}{x_2 - x_1}$$

Example 1: Find the slope of the line that contains the points $(-1, 7)$ and $(2, 1)$.

Solution: We apply Definition 4.2.1 with $(x_1, y_1) = (-1, 7)$ and $(x_2, y_2) = (2, 1)$. Thus, the slope is given by

$$m = \frac{1 - 7}{2 - (-1)} = \frac{-6}{3} = -2$$

Alternate Solution: We apply Definition 4.2.1 with $(x_1, y_1) = (2, 1)$ and $(x_2, y_2) = (-1, 7)$. Thus,

$$m = \frac{7 - 1}{-1 - 2} = \frac{6}{-3} = -2$$

When the slope of a line is a positive number, the line is inclined upward, as in Figure 4.2.1, which illustrates a line with slope $\frac{3}{5}$. When the slope of a line is a negative number, the line is inclined downward, as in Figure 4.2.2, which illustrates the line of Example 1 with slope -2. The slope of a horizontal line is 0. For example, the horizontal line illustrated in Figure 4.1.6

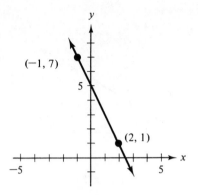

Figure 4.2.2

contains the points $(0, -3)$ and $(1, -3)$. Thus, its slope is given by

$$m = \frac{(-3) - (-3)}{1 - 0} = \frac{0}{1} = 0$$

The slope of a vertical line is not defined. For example, the vertical line illustrated in Figure 4.1.5 contains the points $(2, 0)$ and $(2, 1)$. Because the x-coordinate of point $(2, 0)$ is the same as the x-coordinate of point $(2, 1)$, $x_1 = x_2$, and thus Definition 4.2.1 does not apply. If we attempt to use the formula given in the definition, the fraction has denominator zero, which is impossible. The absolute value of the slope of a line is a measure of the steepness of the line. Note that the line of Figure 4.2.2 is more steeply inclined than the line of Figure 4.2.1. Furthermore, the absolute value of the slope of the steeper line is 2, a number that is larger than $\frac{2}{3}$, which is the slope of the line that is less steeply inclined.

In Section 4.1 we learned to sketch the graph of a given linear equation. We may now reverse the process. Given a description of the line we may find an equation whose graph is the given line. Suppose we wish to find an equation for the line that contains the point $(3, 1)$ and that has slope 2. Figure 4.2.3 shows a sketch of the line. Let (x, y) be any point on the line except the point $(3, 1)$. We apply Definition 4.2.1 with $(x_1, y_1) = (3, 1)$, $(x_2, y_2) = (x, y)$, and $m = 2$. Thus, the formula

$$m = \frac{y_2 - y_1}{x_2 - x_1}$$

becomes

$$2 = \frac{y - 1}{x - 3} \tag{1}$$

Equation (1) is satisfied by any point (x, y) on the line except $(3, 1)$. The point $(3, 1)$ does not satisfy Equation (1) because the fraction has denominator 0 if x is replaced by 3. However, if we multiply on both sides of Equation (1) by

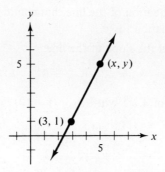

Figure 4.2.3

$x - 3$, we obtain

$$y - 1 = 2(x - 3)$$

which is an equation that is satisfied by every point on the line, and thus is an equation of the line.

We may generalize the above procedure. If a line contains the point (x_0, y_0) and has slope m, then we may apply Definition 4.2.1 with $(x_1, y_1) = (x_0, y_0)$ and $(x_2, y_2) = (x, y)$. Thus, the formula of the definition becomes

$$m = \frac{y - y_0}{x - x_0}$$

Eliminating the fraction, we obtain

$$y - y_0 = m(x - x_0)$$

We have proved the following theorem.

4.2.2   Theorem: *Point-Slope*

An equation of the line that contains the point (x_0, y_0) and that has slope m is given by

$$y - y_0 = m(x - x_0)$$

Example 2:   Find an equation of the line that contains the point $(-1, 2)$ and that has slope $-\frac{1}{3}$.

Solution: We apply Theorem 4.2.2 with $(x_0, y_0) = (-1, 2)$ and $m = -\frac{1}{3}$. Thus, an equation of the line is

$$y - 2 = -\tfrac{1}{3}[x - (-1)]$$
$$y - 2 = -\tfrac{1}{3}(x + 1)$$

Example 3:   Find an equation of the line that contains the points $(0, 2)$ and $(1, 5)$, and solve the equation for y.

Solution: First, we find the slope of the line.

$$m = \frac{5-2}{1-0} = 3$$

Next, we apply Theorem 4.2.2 with $(x_0, y_0) = (0, 2)$ and $m = 3$. Thus, an equation of the line is

$$y - 2 = 3(x - 0)$$
$$y = 3x + 2 \tag{2}$$

Alternate Solution: After finding the slope of the line, we apply Theorem 4.2.2 with $(x_0, y_0) = (1, 5)$ and $m = 3$. Thus, an equation of the line is

$$y - 5 = 3(x - 1)$$
$$y - 5 = 3x - 3$$
$$y = 3x + 2$$

which agrees with the result obtained in Equation (2).

In Example 3 we are given a line with slope 3 and y-intercept 2. Note that the numbers 3 and 2 appear as coefficients in Equation (2). Suppose that a line has slope m and y-intercept b. Then the line contains the point $(0, b)$, and we may apply Theorem 4.2.2 with $(x_0, y_0) = (0, b)$ to obtain an equation of the line. We have

$$y - b = m(x - 0)$$
$$y = mx + b$$

We have proved the following theorem.

4.2.3   Theorem: Slope-Intercept

An equation of the line with slope m and y-intercept b is given by

$$y = mx + b$$

Example 4:   Find the slope and y-intercept of the line $2x - 3y = 6$.

Solution: We apply Theorem 4.2.3. First, we solve the equation for y.

$$2x - 3y = 6$$
$$-3y = -2x + 6$$
$$3y = 2x - 6$$
$$y = \tfrac{2}{3}x - 2$$

Comparing this equation with the equation $y = mx + b$ of Theorem 4.2.3, we conclude that $m = \frac{2}{3}$ and $b = -2$. That is, the slope of the line is $\frac{2}{3}$, the coefficient of x when the equation is solved for y, and the y-intercept is -2, the constant term when the equation is solved for y.

We use Theorem 4.2.3 to prove the Linear Equation Theorem (4.1.1). Consider the equation

$$Ax + By = C \tag{3}$$

where A and B are not both 0. If $B \neq 0$, we can solve the equation for y, as follows.

$$By = -Ax + C$$

$$y = -\frac{A}{B}x + \frac{C}{B} \tag{4}$$

Comparing Equation (4) with the equation $y = mx + b$, we conclude that the graph of Equation (4) is a line with slope $-A/B$ and y-intercept C/B. If $B = 0$, then $A \neq 0$, because A and B are by hypothesis not both 0. Thus, Equation (3) is

$$Ax + 0 \cdot y = C$$

$$Ax = C$$

$$x = \frac{C}{A} \tag{5}$$

The graph of Equation (5) is a vertical line that is perpendicular to the x-axis at the point C/A. Because Equation (3) is either equivalent to Equation (4) or equivalent to Equation (5), we conclude that the graph of Equation (3) is a straight line if A and B are not both 0.

We have considered three forms for an equation of a line.

---

1. Standard form: $Ax + By = C$
2. Slope-intercept form: $y = mx + b$
3. Point-slope form: $y - y_0 = m(x - x_0)$

The slope-intercept form is used to find the slope and y-intercept of a line whose equation is given, as in Example 4. The point-slope form is used to find an equation of a line if we are given the coordinates of a point on the line and the slope of the line, as in Example 2. The standard form is used when sketching the graph of a linear equation and is used in Chapter 5, when solving systems of linear equations.

Example 5:　Find an equation in standard form for the line that has x-intercept -3 and that has the same y-intercept as the line $x + 3y = 6$.

Solution:　First, we find the y-intercept of the given line

$$x + 3y = 6$$

We let $x = 0$ and solve the equation for y.

$$0 + 3y = 6$$
$$y = 2$$

Thus, the y-intercept is 2, and the line whose equation we seek contains the point $(0, 2)$. Because the required line has x-intercept -3, this line contains the point $(-3, 0)$. We use the two points $(0, 2)$ and $(-3, 0)$ to find the slope of the required line.

$$m = \frac{2 - 0}{0 - (-3)} = \frac{2}{3}$$

We apply the Slope-Intercept Theorem with the point $(0, 2)$ and slope $\frac{2}{3}$. Thus, an equation of the line is

$$y = \tfrac{2}{3}x + 2$$

We eliminate the fractions and then write the equation in a standard form. Multiplying on both sides by 3, we obtain

$$3y = 2x + 6$$
$$-2x + 3y = 6$$

EXERCISES 4.2

For Exercises 1–8 find the slope of the line that contains the given points, if the slope is defined.

1. $(1, 1), (5, 3)$　　　**2.** $(2, 2), (1, -1)$　　　**3.** $(4, 0), (0, 3)$

4. $(0, -2), (3, 0)$　　　**5.** $(-2, 3), (1, -3)$　　　**6.** $(4, -1), (-2, 2)$

7. $(-3, -1), (-3, 2)$　　**8.** $(2, -1), (-1, -1)$

For Exercises 9–14 find an equation of the line that contains the given point and has the given slope.

9. $(2, 3); m = 2$　　　　　　　　**10.** $(-1, 4); m = -3$

11. $(-5, 0); m = -\tfrac{1}{2}$　　　　　**12.** $(0, -2); m = \tfrac{2}{3}$

13. $(1, -2); m = 0$　　　　　　　**14.** $(3, 1);$ slope not defined

For Exercises 15–20 find an equation of the line that contains the given points. Solve the equation for y, if possible.

15. $(1, 3), (-1, 5)$ **16.** $(0, 3), (-3, 0)$ **17.** $(-5, 2), (1, 4)$
18. $(1, 3), (3, 2)$ **19.** $(1, 3), (1, 0)$ **20.** $(-2, 2), (1, 2)$

For Exercises 21–28 find the slope and y-intercept of the given line, if possible.

21. $2x - y = 3$ **22.** $x + 3y = 6$
23. $3x + 2y + 8 = 0$ **24.** $5x - 4y + 6 = 0$
25. $2x + y = 2x - y + 1$ **26.** $2(y - x) = 5y - 2x$
27. $3(x + y) = 3y + 2$ **28.** $y - 2x = 3x + y$

For Exercises 29–36 find an equation for the line that is described. Write the equation in a standard form that does not contain fractions.

29. The line has x-intercept 2 and slope 1.
30. The line has x-intercept 3 and y-intercept -1.
31. The line has x-intercept -2 and y-intercept 4.
32. The line has x-intercept -1 and slope -2.
33. The line contains the point $(2, -3)$ and has the same slope as the line $x - 2y = 3$.
34. The line contains the point $(-3, 1)$ and has the same y-intercept as the line $2x + y = 3$.
35. The line has y-intercept -2 and has the same x-intercept as the line $2x + y + 6 = 0$.
36. The line has the same x-intercept as the line $3x + 2y = 4$ and the same slope as the line $2x + y = 2$.

4.3 Parabolas

The graph of every first degree equation in x and y is a straight line. The graph of a second degree equation in x and y, however, is not a line. For certain second degree equations the graph is a curve called a **parabola**.

Example 1: Sketch the graph of the equation

$$y = x^2 - 2x$$

Solution: Because the given equation is not a first degree equation, the graph is not a line. We make several replacements for x, and for each replacement we use the given equation to calculate y. Table 4.3.1 shows the results of the calculations. Next, we plot the point corresponding to each pair (x, y) in the table. Finally, we draw a smooth curve that contains the points. See Figure 4.3.1.

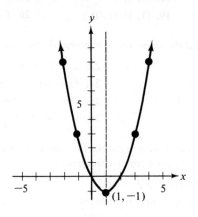

Figure 4.3.1

Table 4.3.1

x	4	3	2	1	0	−1	−2
y	8	3	0	−1	0	3	8

The curve in Figure 4.3.1 is a parabola. The point $(1, -1)$ is called the **vertex** of the parabola, and the vertical line $x = 1$ that contains the vertex is called the **axis** of the parabola. The parabola is symmetric with respect to its axis.

Example 2:   Sketch the graph of the equation

$$x^2 + y = 5$$

Solution: First, we solve the equation for y.

$$x^2 + y = 5$$

$$y = -x^2 + 5 \tag{1}$$

Next, we make replacements for x and use Equation (1) to calculate y. The results of the calculations are shown in Table 4.3.2. Finally, we plot the point corresponding to each pair (x, y) in the table and draw a smooth curve that contains the points. See Figure 4.3.2. Again, the graph is a parabola. The vertex of the parabola is the point (0, 5), and the axis of the parabola is the *y*-axis.

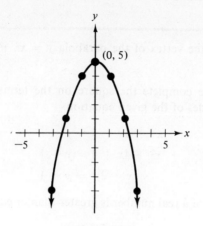

Figure 4.3.2

Table 4.3.2

x	3	2	1	0	−1	−2	−3
y	−4	1	4	5	4	1	−4

The examples have illustrated the following theorem, which is proved in more advanced courses.

4.3.1   Theorem: *Parabola*

If $a \neq 0$, the graph of the equation

$$y = ax^2 + bx + c$$

is a parabola with vertical axis.

If a parabola lies above its vertex, as in Figure 4.3.1, then the *y*-coordinate of its vertex is the smallest value of *y* for any pair (x, y) that satisfies an equation of the parabola. On the other hand, if a parabola lies below its vertex, as in Figure 4.3.2, then the y-coordinate of its vertex is the largest value of y for any pair (x, y) that satisfies an equation of the parabola. We use these facts to find the vertex of a parabola.

Example 3: Find the vertex of the parabola $y = x^2 + 4x + 3$ and sketch the graph.

Solution: First, we complete the square on the terms that contain x by adding 1 to both sides of the given equation.

$$x^2 + 4x + 3 = y \qquad (2)$$
$$x^2 + 4x + 4 = y + 1$$
$$(x + 2)^2 = y + 1 \qquad (3)$$

Because the square of a real number is greater than or equal to zero, we have

$$(x + 2)^2 \geq 0 \qquad (4)$$

We substitute from Equation (3) into Inequality (4). Thus,

$$y + 1 \geq 0$$
$$y \geq -1$$

Because -1 is the smallest value of y, we conclude that the parabola lies above its vertex and, furthermore, that -1 is the y-coordinate of the vertex. To find the x-coordinate of the vertex, we replace y by -1 in Equation (3) and solve for x. We have

$$(x + 2)^2 = 0$$
$$x = -2$$

Thus $(-2, -1)$ is the vertex of the parabola. Note that the coordinates of the vertex can be found by setting each member of Equation (3) equal to zero and then solving the two equations for x and y, respectively.

To sketch the graph we find the x-intercepts. We let $y = 0$ in Equation (2) and solve for x. Thus,

$$x^2 + 4x + 3 = 0$$
$$(x + 1)(x + 3) = 0$$
$$x = -1 \qquad x = -3$$

Hence, the x-intercept points are $(-1, 0)$ and $(-3, 0)$. We plot the vertex and the x-intercept points and sketch the curve. See Figure 4.3.3.

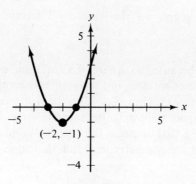

Figure 4.3.3

The following steps are used to find the vertex of a parabola with vertical axis.

1. Separate the terms that contain x from those that do not contain x and complete the square on the terms that contain x.
2. Set each side of the above equation equal to zero and solve the resulting equations for x and y, respectively. The vertex is $(\bar{x}, \bar{y})$, where $\bar{x}$ and $\bar{y}$ are the solutions just found.

Example 4: Find the vertex of the parabola $y = -x^2 + 2x - 3$, and sketch the graph.

Solution: First, we complete the square.

$$y = -x^2 + 2x - 3 \tag{5}$$
$$x^2 - 2x = -y - 3$$
$$x^2 - 2x + 1 = -y - 3 + 1$$
$$(x - 1)^2 = -y - 2 \tag{6}$$

Next, we set each member of Equation (6) equal to zero and solve

$$(x - 1)^2 = 0 \qquad -y - 2 = 0$$
$$x = 1 \qquad y = -2$$

Thus, the vertex is $(1, -2)$.

To sketch the graph we also find the intercept points. If $y = 0$ in Equation (6), then

$$(x - 1)^2 = -2$$

which is impossible, because the square of a real number cannot be negative. We conclude that the curve does not have an x-intercept point. If $x = 0$ in Equation (5), then $y = -3$. Thus, $(0, -3)$ is the y-intercept point. A parabola is symmetric with respect to its axis. Because the vertex is $(1, -2)$, the axis is the vertical line $x = 1$ that contains the vertex. We plot the vertex and the y-intercept point and use symmetry to sketch the curve. See Figure 4.3.4.

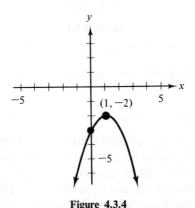

Figure 4.3.4

Example 3 illustrated that when $a > 0$, the parabola $y = ax^2 + bx + c$ lies above its vertex, as shown in Figure 4.3.3. On the other hand, when $a < 0$, the parabola $y = ax^2 + bx + c$ lies below its vertex, as shown in Figure 4.3.4. We can use Equation (6) to prove that the parabola of Example 4 does in fact lie below its vertex. Because the square of a real number is nonnegative, we have

$$(x - 1)^2 \geq 0 \qquad (7)$$

Substituting from Equation (6) into Inequality (7), we obtain

$$-y - 2 \geq 0$$
$$-y \geq 2$$
$$y \leq -2$$

Thus, -2 is the largest value of y for any pair (x, y) that satisfies Equation (6), and hence the parabola lies below its vertex.

The following theorem results if we interchange x and y in the statement of Theorem 4.3.1.

4.3.2   Theorem: **Parabola**

If $a \neq 0$, the graph of the equation

$$x = ay^2 + by + c$$

is a parabola with horizontal axis.

Example 5:   Sketch the graph of the equation

$$2x - y^2 + 4 = 0$$

Solution: We solve the given equation for x.

$$2x - y^2 + 4 = 0$$
$$2x = y^2 - 4$$
$$x = \tfrac{1}{2}y^2 - 2$$

From Theorem 4.3.2 we conclude that the graph is a parabola with horizontal axis. To find the vertex of this parabola, we complete the square on the terms that contain y.

$$2x - y^2 + 4 = 0$$
$$2x + 4 = y^2 \qquad\qquad (8)$$

Because Equation (8) does not contain the first power of y, the square is complete. We set each member of Equation (8) equal to zero and solve.

$$2x + 4 = 0 \qquad\quad y^2 = 0$$
$$x = -2 \qquad\quad y = 0$$

Thus, the vertex is $(-2, 0)$. To find the y-intercept, we let $x = 0$ in Equation (8). We obtain

$$4 = y^2$$
$$y = \pm 2$$

Thus, there are two y-intercept points, $(0, 2)$ and $(0, -2)$. We plot the vertex and the y-intercept points and use the fact that the axis is horizontal to sketch the curve. See Figure 4.3.5 on the next page.

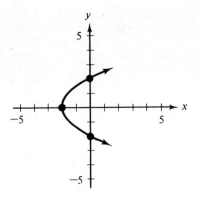

Figure 4.3.5

Example 6: If an object is thrown upward from ground level with initial speed 160 feet per second, after t seconds it will be s feet above the ground, with $s = -16t^2 + 160t$. What is the highest point reached by the object, and how long does it take to reach that point?

Solution: We complete the square on the terms that contain t.

$$s = -16t^2 + 160t$$

$$\frac{s}{-16} = t^2 - 10t$$

$$\frac{-s}{16} + 25 = t^2 - 10t + 25$$

$$\frac{-s + 400}{16} = (t - 5)^2 \tag{9}$$

Because $(t - 5)^2 \geq 0$, from Equation (9) it follows that

$$\frac{-s + 400}{16} \geq 0$$

$$-s + 400 \geq 0$$

$$s \leq 400$$

Thus, the highest point reached is 400 feet above the ground. Moreover, if $s = 400$, by substitution in Equation (9) we have

$$0 = (t - 5)^2$$

$$t = 5$$

Hence, it takes 5 seconds to reach the highest point. See Figure 4.3.6.

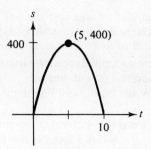

Figure 4.3.6

EXERCISES 4:3

For Exercises 1–10 make a table of ordered pairs that satisfy the equation, with x chosen from the set {3, 2, 1, 0, −1, −2, −3}; *plot the points; and sketch the graph of the equation.*

1. $y = x^2$
2. $y = -x^2$
3. $y = x^2 + 2$
4. $y = x^2 - 3$
5. $y = x^2 + 2x$
6. $y = x^2 - 3x$
7. $x^2 + y = 6$
8. $x^2 + y = 3$
9. $x^2 - 3x + y = 0$
10. $x^2 + 2x + y = 0$

For Exercises 11–30 find the vertex of the parabola, plot the vertex and each intercept point, and sketch the graph of the equation.

11. $y = 4 - x^2$ **12.** $y = x^2 - 1$
13. $y = x^2 - 4x$ **14.** $y = x^2 + 4x$
15. $x^2 + y = 2x$ **16.** $x^2 = 4x - y$
17. $x^2 - 4y = 4$ **18.** $x^2 + 4x + 4y = 0$
19. $y = x^2 + 6x + 8$ **20.** $y = x^2 - 6x + 5$
21. $3y = x^2 + 4x - 5$ **22.** $2y = x^2 - 2x - 3$
23. $y = x^2 + 3x - 4$ **24.** $y = x^2 - 5x + 4$
25. $y = x^2 + 4x + 5$ **26.** $y = -x^2 + 4x - 4$
27. $x + y^2 + 4y = 0$ **28.** $x - y^2 + 4 = 0$
29. $2x = y^2 + 2y - 3$ **30.** $4x + y^2 = 4y + 5$

For Exercises 31–34 use the coordinates of the vertex of a parabola to answer the stated question.

31. If the price of each item is P dollars, the total revenue from sales is R dollars, with $R = P(100 - P)$. What is the greatest possible total revenue, and what price should be set to earn the greatest possible revenue?

32. If n units are produced, the average cost per unit is c dollars, with $100c = n^2 - 40n + 700$. What is the smallest possible average unit cost, and how many units should be produced to make the average unit cost a minimum?

33. If a bullet is fired upward with initial speed 60 meters per second, after t seconds the bullet is s meters above the ground, with $s = -5t^2 + 60t$. What is the maximum height reached by the bullet, and how long does it take to reach that height?

34. If a ball is rolled upward on an inclined plane with initial speed 14 feet per second, after t seconds the ball is s feet beyond its starting point, with $s = -2t^2 + 14t$. How far does the ball roll upward before starting to roll back downward, and how long does it take to reach its highest point on the plane?

4.4 Circles, Ellipses, and Hyperbolas

In this section we study the graphs of equations of the form

$$Ax^2 + By^2 = C \tag{1}$$

Because $(-x)^2 = x^2$ and $(-y)^2 = y^2$, for every pair (x, y) that satisfies Equation (1), there are also the pairs $(-x, y)$, $(x, -y)$ and $(-x, -y)$ that satisfy the equation. Figure 4.4.1 illustrates that the points (x, y) and $(-x, y)$

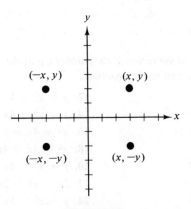

Figure 4.4.1

are symmetric with respect to the y-axis; the points (x, y) and $(x, -y)$ are symmetric with respect to the x-axis; and the points (x, y) and $(-x, -y)$ are symmetric with respect to the origin. Therefore, the graph of Equation (1) is symmetric with respect to both axes and the origin, and we may sketch the graph by drawing the part that is in the quadrant where $x \geq 0$ and $y \geq 0$ and by using symmetry to complete the sketch.

Example 1:   Sketch the graph of the equation $x^2 + y^2 = 25$.

Solution: First, we solve the equation for y.

$$x^2 + y^2 = 25$$
$$y^2 = 25 - x^2$$
$$y = \pm\sqrt{25 - x^2} \qquad (2)$$

Because the graph is symmetric with respect to both axes, we plot points only for $x \geq 0$ and $y \geq 0$ and use symmetry to complete the sketch. Thus, we make nonnegative replacements for x and use the positive square root in Equation (2) to calculate y. Table 4.4.1 shows the results of the calculations. In the table we have given decimal approximations for irrational square roots. For example, when $x = 1$, then $y = \sqrt{24} \approx 4.9$. Next, we plot the points from the table, draw a smooth curve through the points, and use symmetry to complete the sketch. See Figure 4.4.2. The graph is a **circle** with center at the origin and radius 5. Note that we cannot replace x by a number larger than 5 in Equation (2) because such a replacement results in a negative number under the radical sign.

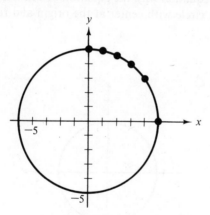

Figure 4.4.2

Table 4.4.1

x	0	1	2	3	4	5
y	5	4.9	4.6	4	3	0

The following theorem is a generalization of the result of Example 1.

4.4.1   Theorem: Circle

If $C > 0$, the graph of the equation

$$x^2 + y^2 = C$$

is a circle with center at the origin and radius $\sqrt{C}$.

Example 2:   Sketch the graph of the equation

$$4x^2 = 49 - 4y^2$$

Solution: We apply Theorem 4.4.1.

$$4x^2 = 49 - 4y^2$$
$$4x^2 + 4y^2 = 49$$
$$x^2 + y^2 = \tfrac{49}{4}$$

By comparing this equation with the equation of Theorem 4.4.1, we conclude that the graph is a circle with center at the origin and radius $\sqrt{\tfrac{49}{4}} = \tfrac{7}{2}$. See Figure 4.4.3.

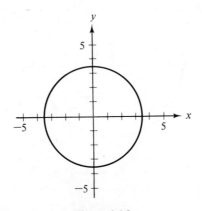

Figure 4.4.3

Example 3:   Sketch the graph of the equation

$$x^2 + 4y^2 = 36$$

Solution: Because the coefficient of x^2 is not the same as the coefficient of y^2, we cannot write the equation in the form $x^2 + y^2 = C$. Thus, Theorem

4.4.1 does not apply, and the graph is not a circle. We solve the equation for y.

$$x^2 + 4y^2 = 36$$
$$4y^2 = 36 - x^2$$
$$2y = \pm\sqrt{36 - x^2}$$
$$y = \frac{\pm\sqrt{36 - x^2}}{2} \tag{3}$$

Because the graph is symmetric with respect to both axes, we plot points only for $x \geq 0$ and $y \geq 0$ and use symmetry to complete the sketch. We make nonnegative replacements for x and use Equation (3) with positive square root to calculate y. Table 4.4.2 gives the results of the calculations, where we have given decimal approximations for irrational square roots. For example, when $x = 4$, then $y = \frac{1}{2}\sqrt{20} \approx 2.2$. We plot the points from the table, draw a smooth curve through the points, and use symmetry to complete the sketch. See Figure 4.4.4. The curve is called an **ellipse**. Note that we cannot replace x by a number larger than 6 in Equation (3) because such a replacement results in a negative number under the radical sign.

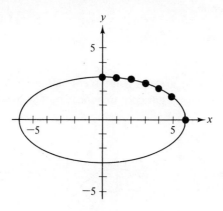

Figure 4.4.4

Table 4.4.2

x	0	1	2	3	4	5	6
y	3	2.9	2.8	2.6	2.2	1.7	0

The following theorem is a generalization of the result of Example 3.

4.4.2   Theorem: *Ellipse*

If $A > 0$, $B > 0$, $C > 0$, and $A \neq B$, then the graph of the equation

$$Ax^2 + By^2 = C$$

is an ellipse with center at the origin.

Example 4:   Sketch the graph of the equation $9x^2 + 4y^2 = 144$.

Solution: By comparing the given equation with Theorem 4.4.2, we conclude that the graph is an ellipse with center at the origin. We plot the x- and y-intercept points and use them to sketch the graph.

If $x = 0$, the given equation becomes

$$4y^2 = 144$$
$$y^2 = 36$$
$$y = \pm 6$$

Thus, $(0, 6)$ and $(0, -6)$ are the y-intercept points. Furthermore, if $y = 0$, the given equation becomes

$$9x^2 = 144$$
$$x^2 = 16$$
$$x = \pm 4$$

Thus, $(4, 0)$ and $(-4, 0)$ are the x-intercept points. We plot the intercept points and draw the ellipse that contains these points. See Figure 4.4.5.

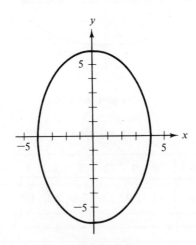

Figure 4.4.5

Example 5: Sketch the graph of the equation $x^2 - y^2 = 4$.

Solution: Because the coefficients of x^2 and y^2 are not both positive, the graph is neither an ellipse nor a circle. We solve the equation for y.

$$x^2 - y^2 = 4$$

$$y^2 = x^2 - 4$$

$$y = \pm\sqrt{x^2 - 4} \tag{4}$$

Because the graph is symmetric with respect to both axes, we plot points only for $x \geq 0$ and $y \geq 0$ and use symmetry to complete the sketch. Note that we cannot replace x by a number between 0 and 2 in Equation (4) because such a replacement results in a negative number under the radical sign. Thus, we choose $x \geq 2$ and use the positive square root in Equation (4) to calculate y. Table 4.4.3 gives the results of the calculations, where decimal approximations have been given for irrational square roots. We plot the points from the table and use symmetry to complete the sketch. See Figure 4.4.6. The curve is called a **hyperbola**. Note that there is no largest possible replacement for x in Equation (4). Any replacement for x with $x > 2$ results in a positive number under the radical sign. Thus, the graph of the equation is unbounded, which we indicate in Figure 4.4.6 by the use of arrows.

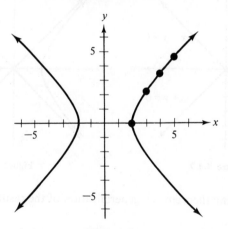

Figure 4.4.6

Table 4.4.3

x	2	3	4	5	6	7
y	0	2.2	3.5	4.6	5.7	6.7

If the constant term is replaced by 0 in the equation of Example 5, the result is

$$x^2 - y^2 = 0 \tag{5}$$

or, equivalently,

$$(x - y)(x + y) = 0$$
$$x - y = 0 \quad \text{or} \quad x + y = 0 \tag{6}$$

Because the graph of each equation in (6) is a line, we conclude that the graph of Equation (5) is the union of the lines. See Figure 4.4.7. Furthermore, if the hyperbola of Example 5, which is shown in Figure 4.4.6, and the lines of Equation (5) are drawn on the same coordinate plane, we have the result illustrated in Figure 4.4.8. For replacements of x with large absolute value, the points on the hyperbola nearly coincide with those on the lines. Thus, we say that the curve "approaches" the lines, and each line is called an **asymptote** of the curve. Every hyperbola has two asymptotes, and equations for the asymptotes are found by replacing the constant term in the equation of the hyperbola by 0.

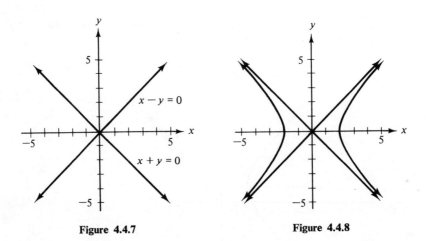

Figure 4.4.7   Figure 4.4.8

The following theorem is a generalization of the result of Example 5.

4.4.3   Theorem: Hyperbola

If $A > 0$, $B > 0$, and $C > 0$, the graph of the equation

$$Ax^2 - By^2 = C$$

and the equation

$$-Ax^2 + By^2 = C$$

is a hyperbola whose asymptotes are the lines

$$Ax^2 - By^2 = 0$$

Example 6: Sketch the graph of the equation $y^2 - 4x^2 = 3$.

Solution: Because the conditions of Theorem 4.4.3 are satisfied, the graph is a hyperbola. First, we sketch the asymptotes. We replace the constant term by 0 and solve the resulting equation for y. Thus,

$$y^2 - 4x^2 = 0$$
$$y^2 = 4x^2$$
$$y = \pm 2x$$

Thus, one asymptote is the line that contains the origin and has slope 2, and the other asymptote is the line that contains the origin and has slope -2. See Figure 4.4.9. We use broken lines to sketch the asymptotes because the lines are not part of the graph of the given equation. We are using the lines merely as a guide for drawing the hyperbola.

Next, we find the intercept points. If $x = 0$ in the given equation, the result is

$$y^2 = 3$$
$$y = \pm\sqrt{3}$$
$$y = \pm 1.7$$

Thus, the y-intercept points are $(0, 1.7)$ and $(0, -1.7)$. If $y = 0$ in the given equation, the result is

$$-4x^2 = 3$$
$$x^2 = -\tfrac{3}{4}$$

which is impossible, because the square of a real number cannot be negative. We conclude that the hyperbola does not have an x-intercept point. We plot the y-intercept points and use symmetry and the asymptotes to sketch the hyperbola, which is shown in Figure 4.4.9.

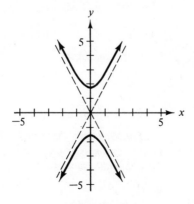

Figure 4.4.9

We summarize. If $C > 0$, the graph of the equation

$$Ax^2 + By^2 = C$$

is:

1. A circle if A and B are both positive, with $A = B$, as in $2x^2 + 2y^2 = 15$
2. An ellipse if A and B are both positive, with $A \neq B$, as in $3x^2 + 4y^2 = 20$
3. A hyperbola if A and B have opposite signs, as in $x^2 - 3y^2 = 12$ or $5y^2 - 5x^2 = 1$.

The circle, ellipse, parabola, and hyperbola are called **conic sections**, because each of these curves is the intersection of a plane with a right circular cone that has two nappes. See Figure 4.4.10. There are many applications of conic sections. The orbits of satellites and of the planets are ellipses. Arches of bridges are sometimes elliptical or parabolic in shape. The path of a projectile is a parabola. Parabolas are used in the design of headlight reflectors and radar antennas. Hyperbolas are used to locate the source of a sound.

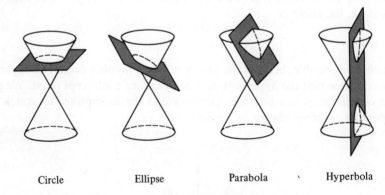

Circle   Ellipse   Parabola   Hyperbola

Figure 4.4.10

EXERCISES 4.4

For Exercises 1–6 make a table of ordered pairs that satisfy the equation, with $x \geq 0$ and $y \geq 0$; plot the points; and use symmetry to sketch the graph of the equation. Use decimal approximations for irrational square roots.

1. $x^2 + y^2 = 36$ 2. $x^2 + y^2 = 30$ 3. $2x^2 + y^2 = 50$
4. $x^2 + 4y^2 = 25$ 5. $4y^2 - x^2 = 4$ 6. $2x^2 - y^2 = 8$

For Exercises 7–12 plot each intercept point and sketch the circle or ellipse that is the graph of the equation.

7. $x^2 + 4y^2 = 64$ **8.** $x^2 + y^2 = 16$ **9.** $4x^2 + 4y^2 = 81$

10. $4x^2 + y^2 = 36$ **11.** $9x^2 + 4y^2 = 100$ **12.** $9x^2 + 16y^2 = 144$

For Exercises 13–20 find an equation for each asymptote, sketch each asymptote, plot each intercept point, and sketch the hyperbola that is the graph of the equation.

13. $x^2 - y^2 = 1$ **14.** $y^2 - x^2 = 4$ **15.** $x^2 - 4y^2 = 16$

16. $y^2 - 4x^2 = 1$ **17.** $y^2 - 4x^2 = 6$ **18.** $x^2 - 4y^2 = 9$

19. $4y^2 - 9x^2 = 36$ **20.** $4x^2 - 9y^2 = 20$

For Exercises 21–30 give the name of the curve that is the graph of the equation. Do not sketch the graph.

21. $y^2 = 10 - 2x^2$ **22.** $2x^2 = 15 - 2y^2$ **23.** $x^2 = y^2 + 5$

24. $5x^2 = 2 + 3y^2$ **25.** $3y^2 = 20 - 3x^2$ **26.** $x^2 = 5 - 3y^2$

27. $4x = x^2 + y$ **28.** $4y^2 = 4x^2 - 7$ **29.** $2y^2 = 7 + 3x^2$

30. $3y = 2x + y^2$

For Exercises 31–38 give the name of the curve that is the graph of the equation, plot the intercept points, sketch the asymptotes, and sketch the graph.

31. $4y^2 = 36 - 9x^2$ **32.** $4y^2 = 16 + x^2$ **33.** $x^2 - y^2 + 9 = 0$

34. $y^2 = 4(16 - x^2)$ **35.** $2x^2 = y^2 + 8$ **36.** $4x^2 = 81 - 9y^2$

37. $x^2 = 4(4 - y^2)$ **38.** $y^2 - x^2 + 3 = 0$

4.5   Graphs of Inequalities (optional)

The graph of the equation $y = mx + b$ is a straight line. Because the y-coordinates of points on the y-axis increase as we move upward on the y-axis, every point in the coordinate plane that lies above the line $y = mx + b$ satisfies the inequality

$$y > mx + b \tag{1}$$

and every point in the coordinate plane that lies below the line $y = mx + b$ satisfies the inequality

$$y < mx + b \tag{2}$$

Therefore, the graph of Inequality (1) is the half-plane that lies above the line $y = mx + b$, as indicated by shading in Figure 4.5.1. We use a broken line to indicate that the boundary line $y = mx + b$ is not included in the graph. And the graph of Inequality (2) is the half-plane that lies below the line $y = mx + b$, as indicated by shading in Figure 4.5.2.

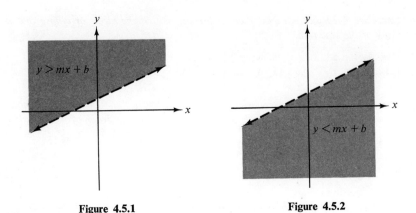

Figure 4.5.1   Figure 4.5.2

Example 1:   Sketch the graph of the inequality.

(a) $x + y < 3$ **(b)** $2x - y \leq 4$

Solution:

(a) First, we solve the inequality for y. Thus,

$$x + y < 3$$
$$y < -x + 3 \tag{3}$$

Because the connective in Inequality (3) is "less than," we conclude that the graph is a half-plane that lies below a line. The boundary line is obtained by replacing $<$ by $=$ in the given inequality. Thus, the boundary line is the line whose equation is

$$x + y = 3 \tag{4}$$

Line (4) has x-intercept 3 and y-intercept 3. Figure 4.5.3 shows the graph of the given inequality. Note the broken line which indicates that the boundary line itself is not part of the graph.

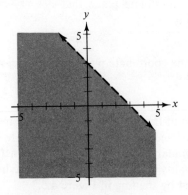

Figure 4.5.3

(b) First, we solve the inequality for y. Thus,

$$2x - y \leq 4$$
$$-y \leq -2x + 4$$
$$y \geq 2x - 4$$

Thus, either

$$y = 2x - 4 \tag{5}$$

or

$$y > 2x - 4 \tag{6}$$

The graph of Equation (5) is the line that contains the points $(0, -4)$ and $(2, 0)$. Because the connective in Inequality (6) is "greater than," the graph of (6) is the half-plane that lies above line (5). The graph of the original inequality is the union of line (5) and half-plane (6), as illustrated in Figure 4.5.4. Note the use of a solid line to indicate that the boundary line is included as part of the graph.

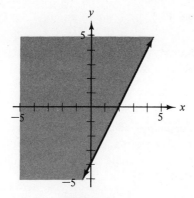

Figure 4.5.4

Example 2:   Sketch the graph of the inequality.
(a) $x^2 - y < 4$ **(b)** $x - y^2 \leq 0$

Solution:
(a) First, we solve the inequality for y.

$$x^2 - y < 4$$
$$-y < -x^2 + 4$$
$$y > x^2 - 4 \tag{7}$$

Because the connective in Inequality (7) is "greater than," the graph is the region that lies above the boundary curve

$$y = x^2 - 4 \tag{8}$$

Equation (8) is obtained by replacing $>$ by $=$ in Inequality (7). The graph of Equation (8) is a parabola with vertex at $(0, -4)$ and with x-intercepts 2 and -2. Figure 4.5.5 shows the graph of the given inequality. The boundary curve is not included, so it is drawn as a broken curve.

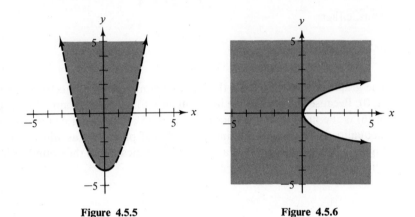

Figure 4.5.5   Figure 4.5.6

(b) Because the inequality contains y^2, we cannot solve it uniquely for y. Therefore, we solve for x.

$$x - y^2 \leq 0$$
$$x \leq y^2 \tag{9}$$

Because the x-coordinates of points on the x-axis increase as we move toward the right on the x-axis and because Inequality (9) contains the connective "less than," we conclude that the graph of (9) contains all points that are to the left of the boundary curve

$$x = y^2 \tag{10}$$

The graph of Equation (10) is a parabola with vertex at the origin, with axis horizontal, and that contains the point $(1, 1)$.

Figure 4.5.6 shows the graph of the given inequality. Because the given inequality contains the equals sign, the graph includes the boundary curve, as indicated by the use of a solid curve in the figure.

Example 3:   Sketch the graph of the inequality.
(a) $x^2 + y^2 \leq 9$ **(b)** $x^2 + 4y^2 > 16$

Solution:
(a) Because the inequality contains both x^2 and y^2, we cannot solve the inequality for either x or y. However, the graph is some region that is bounded by the curve

$$x^2 + y^2 = 9 \tag{11}$$

The graph of Equation (11) is a circle with center at the origin and radius 3. The graph of the inequality

$$x^2 + y^2 < 9 \qquad (12)$$

is either the region that is inside the circle or the region that is outside the circle. The point $(0, 0)$ is inside the circle, and $(0, 0)$ satisfies Inequality (12). The point $(4, 0)$ is outside the circle (because the radius is 3 and $4 > 3$), and $(4, 0)$ does not satisfy Inequality (12). We conclude that the graph of the given inequality is the set of all points that are either on the circle or inside the circle. See Figure 4.5.7.

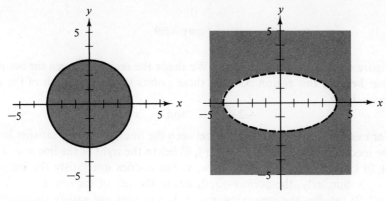

Figure 4.5.7 **Figure 4.5.8**

(b) The graph is some region that is bounded by the curve

$$x^2 + 4y^2 = 16$$

which is an ellipse with center at the origin, x intercepts ± 4, and y intercepts ± 2. See Figure 4.5.8. Because the point $(5, 0)$, which is outside the ellipse, satisfies the inequality

$$x^2 + 4y^2 > 16$$

and the point $(0, 0)$, which is inside the ellipse, does not satisfy the inequality, we conclude that the graph of the inequality is the region that is outside the ellipse but not on the ellipse.

Example 4: Sketch the graph of the set

$$\{(x, y): -2 \le x < 3\}$$

Solution: The boundary of the region that is the graph consists of the vertical lines whose equations are

$$x = -2 \quad \text{and} \quad x = 3$$

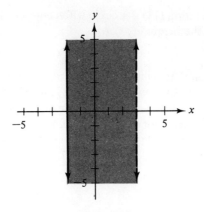

Figure 4.5.9

Figure 4.5.9 illustrates the graph. We shade the region between the boundary lines because this region contains those points that satisfy both of the given inequalities

$$-2 < x \quad \text{and} \quad x < 3 \tag{13}$$

For example, the point $(0, 0)$ lies between the lines, and $(0, 0)$ satisfies both of the inequalities in (13). The point $(4, 0)$ lies to the right of the line $x = 3$; and $(4, 0)$ satisfies the inequality $-2 < x$, but it does not satisfy the inequality $x < 3$. Similarly, the point $(-3, 0)$ lies to the left of the line $x = -2$; and $(-3, 0)$ satisfies the inequality $x < 3$, but it does not satisfy the inequality $-2 < x$. Note that in Figure 4.5.9 the boundary line $x = -2$ is included in the graph, but the boundary line $x = 3$ is not included.

EXERCISES 4.5

For Exercises 1–26 sketch the graph of the given inequality. Give the coordinates of each intercept point of the line or curve that is the boundary of the region. Use a solid line or curve to indicate that the boundary is included in the graph; use a broken line or curve to indicate that the boundary is not included in the graph.

1. $y > x - 4$	**2.** $y < x - 1$	**3.** $y \leq 2 - x$
4. $y \geq x + 1$	**5.** $x + 2y > 4$	**6.** $2x + y < 2$
7. $3x - y + 3 \geq 0$	**8.** $x - 2y - 4 < 0$	**9.** $x + y < 0$
10. $x - y \geq 0$	**11.** $y \leq x^2$	**12.** $x \geq y^2$
13. $x + y^2 \leq 4$	**14.** $x^2 + 4y \leq 4$	**15.** $y > x^2 + 2x$
16. $y < x^2 - 4x$	**17.** $x^2 - y > x + 2$	**18.** $x^2 - 6 < x + y$
19. $x^2 + y^2 \geq 4$	**20.** $x^2 + y^2 \leq 16$	**21.** $4x^2 + y^2 \leq 64$

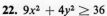

22. $9x^2 + 4y^2 \geq 36$ **23.** $16x^2 + 25y^2 > 100$ **24.** $9x^2 + 16y^2 < 225$

25. $x^2 - y^2 < 4$ **26.** $y^2 - x^2 > 1$

For Exercises 27–34 sketch the graph of the indicated set. Follow the instructions for Exercises 1–26 for the boundary.

27. $\{(x, y): x \geq 1\}$ **28.** $\{(x, y): y < 4\}$

29. $\{(x, y): -1 < y < 3\}$ **30.** $\{(x, y): -2 \leq x \leq 1\}$

31. $\{(x, y): |x| \leq 2\}$ **32.** $\{(x, y): |y| > 1\}$

33. $\{(x, y): y \geq |x|\}$ **34.** $\{(x, y): x \leq |y|\}$

REVIEW EXERCISES 4

For Exercises 1–4 plot each intercept point, and sketch the graph of the equation.

1. $3x - 4y = 12$ **2.** $2x + 3y + 6 = 0$

3. $y = 3 - 2x$ **4.** $4y = x + 5$

For Exercises 5–8 sketch the graph of the indicated set.

5. $\{(x, y): x + 2y = 0\}$ **6.** $\{(x, y): 3x - 4y = 0\}$

7. $\{(x, y): y + 2 = 0\}$ **8.** $\{(x, y): 3 - x = 0\}$

For Exercises 9–10 find the slope of the line that contains the given points.

9. $(-2, 1), (2, -4)$ **10.** $(6, -1), (2, -3)$

For Exercises 11–12 find the slope and y-intercept of the given line.

11. $4x - 3y + 6 = 0$ **12.** $3(2x - y) = 2(3x + 1)$

For Exercises 13–18 find an equation of the line that contains the given points and has the given slope. Write the equation in a standard form that does not contain fractions.

13. $(-2, 5); m = 3$ **14.** $(3, -1); m = -\frac{2}{3}$

15. $(1, -2), (-1, 2)$ **16.** $(3, 1), (-2, -3)$

17. The line has y-intercept $\frac{2}{3}$ and has the same x-intercept as the line $2x + y + 4 = 0$.

18. The line contains the origin, and the slope of the line is not defined.

For Exercises 19–22 find the coordinates of the vertex of the given parabola.

19. $y = x^2 + 6x + 11$ **20.** $y = -x^2 + 10x - 40$

21. $y = -2x(x - 16)$ **22.** $y = x^2 + 5x + 1$

For Exercises 23–26 plot the vertex and each intercept point, and sketch the graph of the equation.

23. $4y = x^2 - 16$ **24.** $2y = 4x - x^2$

25. $x = y^2 + 4y$ **26.** $3x + y^2 = 0$

For Exercises 27–30 plot each intercept point, sketch each asymptote, and sketch the graph of the equation.

27. $4x^2 + 9y^2 = 144$ **28.** $6x^2 + 4y^2 = 96$

29. $9x^2 - 4y^2 = 36$ **30.** $4x^2 - y^2 + 4 = 0$

For Exercises 31–34 give the name of the curve that is the graph of the equation. Do not sketch the graph.

31. $4y^2 = 6 - 4x^2$ **32.** $4y^2 = 10 - 3x$

33. $2x^2 = 3y^2 + 12$ **34.** $3x^2 = 5 - 2y^2$

For Exercises 35–40 plot each intercept point of the boundary, and sketch the graph of the inequality.

35. $2x - y < 2$ **36.** $x + 2y + 4 < 0$

37. $x^2 + y \le 1$ **38.** $y^2 - 4x \ge 4$

39. $x^2 + y^2 \ge 16$ **40.** $x^2 - y^2 \le 1$

For Exercises 41–42 sketch the graph of the indicated set.

41. $\{(x, y): y = |x - 1|\}$ **42.** $\{(x, y): |2x - 1| < 3\}$

5

systems
of equations

5.1 Solving by the Elimination Method

Consider the two linear equations

$$x + y = 10 \tag{1}$$
$$x - y = 4 \tag{2}$$

The ordered pair (7, 3) is a solution of the system of two equations because (7, 3) satisfies both Equation (1) and Equation (2). On the other hand, (8, 2), which satisfies Equation (1), is not a solution of the system because (8, 2) does not satisfy Equation (2). The ordered pair (a, b) is a **solution** of a system of two equations with two variables if and only if (a, b) satisfies both equations of the system. The set of ordered pairs that contains all the solutions for a system of two equations with two variables is called the **solution set** for the system. Two systems of equations are **equivalent systems** if the systems have the same solution set.

Example 1: Find the solution set for the following system.

$$x + 2y = 4 \tag{3}$$
$$3x - 2y = 4 \tag{4}$$

Solution: Because the coefficient of y in Equation (3) is the opposite of the coefficient of y in Equation (4), we can "eliminate" y from the system by adding the corresponding expressions in the two equations.

$$\begin{array}{ll} x + 2y = 4 & \text{[Eq. (3)]} \\ \underline{3x - 2y = 4} & \text{[Eq. (4)]} \\ 4x \quad\ = 8 & \text{[Eq. (3) plus Eq. (4)]} \end{array}$$

Solving for x, we have

$$x = 2$$

Next, we replace x by 2 in Equation (3) and solve for y.

$$\begin{array}{ll} x + 2y = 4 & \text{[Eq. (3)]} \\ 2 + 2y = 4 & [x \longleftarrow 2] \\ y = 1 \end{array}$$

We conclude that (2, 1) is the only solution of the system, and thus $\{(2, 1)\}$ is the solution set. In Figure 5.1.1 we show the lines that are the graphs of Equations (3) and (4). The lines intersect at the point (2, 1), which is the solution of the system.

Check: We replace x by 2 and y by 1 in both Equations (3) and (4).

$$\begin{array}{ll} x + 2y = 4 & \text{[Eq. (3)]} \\ 2 + 2\cdot 1 = 4 & [x \longleftarrow 2;\ y \longleftarrow 1] \\ 4 = 4 \end{array}$$

$$\begin{array}{ll} 3x - 2y = 4 & \text{[Eq. (4)]} \\ 3\cdot 2 - 2\cdot 1 = 4 & [x \longleftarrow 2;\ y \longleftarrow 1] \\ 6 - 2 = 4 \\ 4 = 4 \end{array}$$

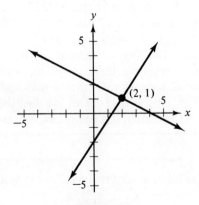

Figure 5.1.1

Example 2: Find the solution set for the following system.

$$2x + y = 5 \tag{5}$$

$$5x - 3y = 18 \tag{6}$$

Solution: We cannot eliminate y by adding the given equations because the sum of y and $-3y$ is not 0. However, if we first multiply on both sides of Equation (5) by 3 and then add the equations, we eliminate y.

$$
\begin{array}{ll}
6x + 3y = 15 & \text{[3 times Eq. (5)]} \\
5x - 3y = 18 & \text{[Eq. (6)]} \\
\hline
11x \quad\;\; = 33 & \text{[Sum]} \\
x \quad\;\; = 3 &
\end{array}
$$

Next, we let $x = 3$ in Equation (5) and solve for y. We have

$$2 \cdot 3 + y = 5$$

$$y = -1$$

The solution set is $\{(3, -1)\}$.

Example 3: Find the solution set for the following system.

$$2(x + 3y) = y + 3 \tag{7}$$

$$\frac{3x + 9y}{2} = y + 2 \tag{8}$$

Solution: First we write each equation in a standard form.

$$
\begin{array}{ll}
2(x + 3y) = y + 3 & \text{[Eq. (7)]} \\
2x + 6y = y + 3 & \\
2x + 5y = 3 & \tag{7$'$} \\
\dfrac{3x + 9y}{2} = y + 2 & \text{[Eq. (8)]} \\
3x + 9y = 2y + 4 & \\
3x + 7y = 4 & \tag{8$'$}
\end{array}
$$

We want to eliminate either x or y from the system of Equations (7$'$) and (8$'$). To eliminate x, we want the coefficient of x in Equation (8$'$) to be the opposite of the coefficient of x in Equation (7$'$). Therefore, we multiply on both sides of Equation (7$'$) by 3, and we multiply on both sides of Equation (8$'$) by -2.

$$
\begin{array}{ll}
6x + 15y = 9 & \text{[3 times Eq. (7$'$)]} \\
-6x - 14y = -8 & \text{[-2 times Eq. (8$'$)]} \\
\hline
y = 1 & \text{[Sum]}
\end{array}
$$

Next, we let $y = 1$ in Equation (7'). This results in

$$2x + 5 \cdot 1 = 3$$
$$2x = -2$$
$$x = -1$$

Thus, the solution set is $\{(-1, 1)\}$. Note that the x-coordinate of the solution is written first, notwithstanding the fact that we found y first.

Example 4: Find the solution set for the following system.

$$x^2 + y^2 = 10 \qquad (9)$$
$$x^2 - y^2 = 8 \qquad (10)$$

Solution: We eliminate y by adding.

$$
\begin{array}{lll}
x^2 + y^2 = 10 & \text{[Eq. (9)]} \\
\underline{x^2 - y^2 = 8} & \text{[Eq. (10)]} \\
2x^2 = 18 & \text{[Sum]} \\
x^2 = 9 \\
x = \pm 3
\end{array}
$$

First, we let $x = 3$ in Equation (9). Thus,

$$3^2 + y^2 = 10$$
$$y^2 = 1$$
$$y = \pm 1$$

Therefore, both $(3, 1)$ and $(3, -1)$ are solutions of the system. Next, we let $x = -3$ in Equation (9). Thus,

$$(-3)^2 + y^2 = 10$$
$$y^2 = 1$$
$$y = \pm 1$$

Hence, both $(-3, 1)$ and $(-3, -1)$ are solutions of the system. The solution set is $\{(3, 1), (3, -1), (-3, 1), (-3, -1)\}$. Figure 5.1.2 illustrates the graph of Equation (9), which is a circle, and the graph of Equation (10), which is a hyperbola, and the four points of intersection of the two curves.

Example 5: Find the solution set for the following system.

$$x - 2y = 2$$
$$-x + 2y = 4$$

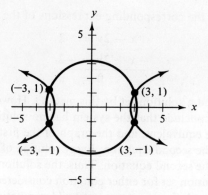

Figure 5.1.2

Solution: We add the corresponding expressions of the given equations.

$$x - 2y = 2$$
$$-x + 2y = 4$$
$$\overline{ 0 = 6}$$

Because $0 = 6$ is false, we conclude that the system does not have a solution. Thus, its solution set is $\varnothing$, the empty set. Figure 5.1.3 illustrates that the graphs of the given equations are parallel lines, and thus there is not a point of intersection. The equations in this system are said to be **inconsistent** because the system does not have a solution.

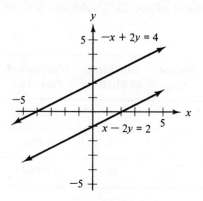

Figure 5.1.3

Example 6: Find the solution set for the following system.

$$x - 2y = 2$$
$$-x + 2y = -2$$

Solution: We add the corresponding expressions of the given equations.

$$x - 2y = 2$$
$$-x + 2y = -2$$
$$0 = 0$$

Thus, we cannot find a solution set by this method. However, because $0 = 0$ is true, we do not conclude that the system has no solution. In fact, the two given equations are equivalent, and the graph of the first equation coincides with the graph of the second equation. Every solution of the first equation is also a solution of the second equation. Thus, the solution set of the system is the same as the solution set for either equation considered alone. Because we cannot list all the solutions, we use set-builder notation to represent the solution set. It is either

$$\{(x, y): x - 2y = 2\}$$

or

$$\{(x, y): -x + 2y = -2\}$$

because these two sets are the same. The equations in this system are said to be **dependent**.

Example 7:   How many milliliters of 6% acid solution and how many milliliters of 12% acid solution must be mixed to make 60 milliliters of 8% acid solution?

Solution: Let x milliliters be the volume of the 6% solution, and let y milliliters be the volume of the 12% solution. We construct the following table.

Percent Acid	×	Milliliters of Mixture	=	Milliliters of Pure Acid
6%		x		$(0.06)x$
12%		y		$(0.12)y$
8%		60		$(0.08)(60)$

Because the whole equals the sum of its parts, the sum of the first two expressions in the table that represent volume equals the third expression that represents volume. Thus,

$$x + y = 60 \tag{11}$$

and
$$(0.06)x + (0.12)y = (0.08)(60) \tag{12}$$
We eliminate the fractions in Equation (12) and simplify the result.
$$6x + 12y = 480$$
$$x + 2y = 80 \tag{12'}$$
To eliminate x, we multiply on both sides of Equation (11) by -1 and then add the resulting equation to Equation (12').

$$
\begin{array}{ll}
-x - y = -60 & \text{[-1 times Eq. (11)]} \\
\underline{x + 2y = 80} & \text{[Eq. (12')]} \\
y = 20 & \text{[Sum]}
\end{array}
$$

If $y = 20$ in Equation (11), we have
$$x + 20 = 60$$
$$x = 40$$

Therefore, we must mix 40 milliliters of 6% acid solution and 20 milliliters of 12% acid solution.

EXERCISES 5.1

For Exercises 1–8 use the Elimination Method to find the solution set of the system of equations. Check your answer by substituting the solution into each equation of the system.

1. $x + y = 3$
$x - y = -1$

2. $2x + y = -1$
$-2x + 3y = 5$

3. $x + y = 1$
$3x + 2y = 5$

4. $2x + y = 2$
$x + 3y = -4$

5. $3x - 4y = 12$
$2x + 3y = 8$

6. $5x + 2y = -4$
$2x + 3y = -6$

7. $3x + y - 3 = 0$
$5x - 3y + 2 = 0$

8. $2x + 7y - 1 = 0$
$5x - 2y + 4 = 0$

For Exercises 9–16 use the Elimination Method to find the solution set of the system of equations.

9. $3x - y = 1$
$\tfrac{1}{2}x - y = -4$

10. $\tfrac{1}{2}x + \phantom{\tfrac{1}{2}}y = -1$
$2x - \tfrac{1}{2}y = 5$

11. $\tfrac{1}{3}x + 2y = 1$
$\phantom{\tfrac{1}{3}}x + \tfrac{1}{2}y = -\tfrac{5}{2}$

12. $\tfrac{1}{4}x - \tfrac{1}{3}y = 1$
$\tfrac{1}{2}x + \tfrac{1}{6}y = \tfrac{1}{3}$

13. $\dfrac{x}{2} + \dfrac{y}{3} = 0$

$\dfrac{3x}{4} - \dfrac{y}{6} = 8$

14. $x - \dfrac{5y}{3} = 1$

$\dfrac{3x - 1}{4} - y = 2$

15. $\dfrac{x}{6} - \dfrac{y - 6}{2} = 2$

$\dfrac{x}{3} + 3y = 10$

16. $3x + \dfrac{y}{3} = 10$

$7x - \dfrac{y - 1}{4} = 2$

For Exercises 17–20 use the Elimination Method to find the solution set of the system of equations. Check your answer by sketching the graphs of both equations on the same coordinate plane.

17. $x^2 + y^2 = 25$
$2x^2 - y^2 = 2$

18. $x^2 + 4y^2 = 8$
$2x^2 + y^2 = 9$

19. $x^2 + y^2 = 4$
$4x^2 + y^2 = 16$

20. $x^2 - y^2 = -8$
$2x^2 + y^2 = 11$

For Exercises 21–24 use the Elimination Method to find the solution set of the system of equations.

21. $2x^2 - y^2 = 4$
$3x^2 + 2y^2 = 20$

22. $x^2 + 3y^2 = 25$
$2x^2 - 3y^2 = 50$

23. $x^2 - 2y^2 + 14 = 0$
$3x^2 - y^2 - 3 = 0$

24. $x^2 + y^2 - 10 = 0$
$3x^2 + 2y^2 - 29 = 0$

For Exercises 25–30 find the solution set of the system of equations. Identify each system that is inconsistent and each system that is dependent.

25. $2x - 4y = 3$
$3x - 6y = 2$

26. $2x + 6y = 4$
$3x + 9y = 6$

27. $4x - 6y = 8$
$-2x + 3y = -4$

28. $2x + 3y = 0$
$4x + 3y = 0$

29. $3x - 2y = 0$
$2x + y = 0$

30. $4x - 2y = 3$
$-6x + 3y = 2$

For Exercises 31–34 use the solution of a system of two linear equations to answer the stated question.

31. A dairy wants to produce 200 gallons of milk with 4% butterfat by mixing cream that is 61% butterfat and skim milk that is 1% butterfat. How much skim milk and how much cream should be used?

32. A total $25,000 is invested, partly in a savings account that pays 5% per year and the rest in bonds that pay 8% per year. The interest paid per year on the bonds is $80 less than the interest paid per year on the savings account. How much is invested in the savings account, and how much is invested in bonds?

33. A trip that is 15 miles upstream in a river takes $2\frac{1}{2}$ hours, whereas a trip that is 12 miles downstream takes $1\frac{1}{3}$ hours. What is the speed of the boat in still water, and what is the speed of the river current?

34. Two ships bound in opposite directions pass at sea, and after 30 minutes they are 25 miles apart. Then the faster ship turns back, and after 5 hours it overtakes the slower ship. What is the speed of each ship?

5.2 Solving by the Method of Determinants

Sometimes the Elimination Method for solving a system of equations is difficult to apply. Consider the system

$$5x + 3y = 6 \tag{1}$$

$$4x + 7y = -2 \tag{2}$$

To eliminate y, we multiply Equation (1) by 7 and Equation (2) by -3. Thus,

$$
\begin{array}{ll}
35x + 21y = 42 & \text{[7 times Eq. (1)]} \\
\underline{-12x - 21y = 6} & \text{[-3 times Eq. (2)]} \\
23x = 48 & \text{[Sum]} \\
x = \frac{48}{23} &
\end{array}
$$

Next, we let $x = \frac{48}{23}$ in Equation (1) and solve for y.

$$5(\tfrac{48}{23}) + 3y = 6$$

$$\tfrac{240}{23} + 3y = 6$$

$$3y = 6 - \tfrac{240}{23}$$

$$3y = -\tfrac{102}{23}$$

$$y = -\tfrac{34}{23}$$

Thus, the solution set is $\{(\frac{48}{23}, -\frac{34}{23})\}$.

In order to minimize the calculations necessary to solve a linear system of equations, we introduce **determinants**. The rectangular array of numbers

$$\begin{bmatrix} 3 & 2 \\ 5 & 7 \end{bmatrix}$$

is called a **matrix** with two rows and two columns. The elements 3 and 7 are said to be on the **first diagonal** of the matrix, and the elements 5 and 2 are on the **second diagonal**. The determinant of the matrix is given by

$$\begin{vmatrix} 3 & 2 \\ 5 & 7 \end{vmatrix} = 3 \cdot 7 - 5 \cdot 2 = 11$$

In general, the determinant of a matrix with two rows and two columns is indicated by using vertical bars about the array, and the determinant of the matrix is the number found by taking the product of the elements in the first diagonal minus the product of the elements on the second diagonal.

5.2.1   Definition: Determinant

$$\begin{vmatrix} a_1 & b_1 \\ a_2 & b_2 \end{vmatrix} = a_1 b_2 - a_2 b_1$$

Example 1: Calculate the simplest form of

$$\begin{vmatrix} -3 & -2 \\ 2 & 4 \end{vmatrix}$$

Solution: We apply Definition 5.2.1. Thus,

$$\begin{vmatrix} -3 & -2 \\ 2 & 4 \end{vmatrix} = (-3)(4) - (2)(-2)$$
$$= -12 - (-4)$$
$$= -8$$

We use determinants to find the solution of the system (1) and (2) that we first considered.

$$5x + 3y = 6 \qquad\qquad (1)$$
$$4x + 7y = -2 \qquad\qquad (2)$$

By using the Elimination Method, we found $x = \frac{48}{23}$ and $y = -\frac{34}{23}$. The matrix whose elements are the coefficients of x and y in the system is called the **coefficient matrix** of the system. First, we calculate the determinant of the coefficient matrix.

$$D = \begin{vmatrix} 5 & 3 \\ 4 & 7 \end{vmatrix} = 5 \cdot 7 - 4 \cdot 3 = 23$$

We note that $D = 23$ is the denominator of the fractions that we found when solving the system. Next, we replace the elements in the first column of the coefficient matrix, which are the coefficients of x, by the constant terms of the system of equations and calculate the determinant of the resulting matrix.

$$D_x = \begin{vmatrix} 6 & 3 \\ -2 & 7 \end{vmatrix} = 6 \cdot 7 - (-2)(3) = 48$$

We note that

$$x = \frac{D_x}{D} = \frac{48}{23}$$

agrees with the above value of x. Finally, we replace the elements in the second column of the coefficient matrix, which are the coefficients of y, by the constant terms of the system of equations and calculate the determinant of the resulting matrix.

$$D_y = \begin{vmatrix} 5 & 6 \\ 4 & -2 \end{vmatrix} = (5)(-2) - 4 \cdot 6 = -34$$

We note that

$$y = \frac{D_y}{D} = \frac{-34}{23}$$

agrees with the above value for y.

This method of solving a system of linear equations by using determinants is called **Cramer's Rule**. We now state and prove this rule.

5.2.2   Theorem: *Cramer's Rule*

For the system of linear equations

$$a_1 x + b_1 y = c_1 \tag{3}$$

$$a_2 x + b_2 y = c_2 \tag{4}$$

let

$$D = \begin{vmatrix} a_1 & b_1 \\ a_2 & b_2 \end{vmatrix} \qquad D_x = \begin{vmatrix} c_1 & b_1 \\ c_2 & b_2 \end{vmatrix} \qquad D_y = \begin{vmatrix} a_1 & c_1 \\ a_2 & c_2 \end{vmatrix}$$

If $D \neq 0$, then the solution set of the system is $\{(x, y)\}$, where

$$x = \frac{D_x}{D} \qquad y = \frac{D_y}{D}$$

PROOF: To eliminate y from the system, we multiply on both sides of Equation (3) by b_2 and on both sides of Equation (4) by $-b_1$. Thus,

$$a_1 b_2 x + b_1 b_2 y = c_1 b_2 \qquad [b_2 \text{ times Eq. (3)}]$$

$$\underline{-a_2 b_1 x - b_1 b_2 y = -c_2 b_1} \qquad [-b_1 \text{ times Eq. (4)}]$$

$$(a_1 b_2 - a_2 b_1)x = c_1 b_2 - c_2 b_1 \qquad [\text{Sum}]$$

$$x = \frac{c_1 b_2 - c_2 b_1}{a_1 b_2 - a_2 b_1} \tag{5}$$

Furthermore, we have

$$D_x = \begin{vmatrix} c_1 & b_1 \\ c_2 & b_2 \end{vmatrix} = c_1 b_2 - c_2 b_1 \tag{6}$$

and

$$D = \begin{vmatrix} a_1 & b_1 \\ a_2 & b_2 \end{vmatrix} = a_1 b_2 - a_2 b_1 \tag{7}$$

By substituting from Equations (6) and (7) into Equation (5), we obtain

$$x = \frac{D_x}{D}$$

To complete the proof, we eliminate x from the original system and solve the resulting equation for y. The steps are similar to the above and are omitted.

Example 2: Use Cramer's Rule to find the solution set for the system of equations.

$$3x = 2(2y + 1) \tag{8}$$

$$x + y = \frac{-2x + 1}{3} \tag{9}$$

Solution: First, we write each equation in a standard form.

$$3x = 2(2y + 1) \quad \text{[Eq. (8)]}$$

$$3x = 4y + 2$$

$$3x - 4y = 2 \tag{8'}$$

$$x + y = \frac{-2x + 1}{3} \quad \text{[Eq. (9)]}$$

$$3x + 3y = -2x + 1$$

$$5x + 3y = 1 \tag{9'}$$

We apply Cramer's Rule for the system

$$3x - 4y = 2 \quad \text{[Eq. (8')]}$$

$$5x + 3y = 1 \quad \text{[Eq. (9')]}$$

Thus,

$$D = \begin{vmatrix} 3 & -4 \\ 5 & 3 \end{vmatrix} = 3 \cdot 3 - 5(-4) = 29$$

$$D_x = \begin{vmatrix} 2 & -4 \\ 1 & 3 \end{vmatrix} = 2 \cdot 3 - 1(-4) = 10$$

$$D_y = \begin{vmatrix} 3 & 2 \\ 5 & 1 \end{vmatrix} = 3 \cdot 1 - 5 \cdot 2 = -7$$

Therefore,

$$x = \frac{D_x}{D} = \frac{10}{29} \qquad y = \frac{D_y}{D} = \frac{-7}{29}$$

The solution set is $\{(\frac{10}{29}, -\frac{7}{29})\}$.

Example 3:   Use Cramer's Rule to find the solution set for the system

$$\frac{5}{x} - \frac{3}{y} = -1 \tag{10}$$

$$\frac{3}{x} + \frac{2}{y} = 1 \tag{11}$$

Solution: Because the given system is not a *linear* system, we must first make a change of variable in order to apply Cramer's Rule. Let

$$u = \frac{1}{x} \quad \text{and} \quad v = \frac{1}{y} \tag{12}$$

Substituting from Equations (12) into Equations (10) and (11), we obtain the linear system

$$5u - 3v = -1 \tag{10'}$$

$$3u + 2v = 1 \tag{11'}$$

We have

$$D = \begin{vmatrix} 5 & -3 \\ 3 & 2 \end{vmatrix} = 5 \cdot 2 - 3(-3) = 19$$

$$D_u = \begin{vmatrix} -1 & -3 \\ 1 & 2 \end{vmatrix} = (-1)(2) - 1(-3) = 1$$

$$D_v = \begin{vmatrix} 5 & -1 \\ 3 & 1 \end{vmatrix} = 5 \cdot 1 - 3(-1) = 8$$

Therefore,

$$u = \frac{D_u}{D} = \frac{1}{19} \quad \text{and} \quad v = \frac{D_v}{D} = \frac{8}{19} \tag{13}$$

Substituting from Equations (13) into Equations (12), we obtain

$$\frac{1}{19} = \frac{1}{x} \qquad \frac{8}{19} = \frac{1}{y}$$

$$x = 19 \qquad y = \frac{19}{8}$$

Thus, the solution set is $\{(19, \frac{19}{8})\}$.

Cramer's Rule cannot be used to find the solution set for a system of equations if the determinant of the coefficient matrix is 0. Consider the system of Example 5 in Section 5.1.

$$x - 2y = 2$$
$$-x + 2y = 4$$

We have

$$D = \begin{vmatrix} 1 & -2 \\ -1 & 2 \end{vmatrix} = (1)(2) - (-1)(-2) = 0$$

$$D_x = \begin{vmatrix} 2 & -2 \\ 4 & 2 \end{vmatrix} = (2)(2) - (4)(-2) = 12$$

$$D_y = \begin{vmatrix} 1 & 2 \\ -1 & 4 \end{vmatrix} = (1)(4) - (-1)(2) = 6$$

Because $D = 0$, then D_x/D is not defined, and thus Cramer's Rule does not apply. In Example 5 we showed that the system is inconsistent and the solution set is $\varnothing$.

Next, consider the system of Example 6 in Section 5.1.

$$x - 2y = 2$$
$$-x + 2y = -2$$

We have

$$D = \begin{vmatrix} 1 & -2 \\ -1 & 2 \end{vmatrix} = (1)(2) - (-1)(-2) = 0$$

$$D_x = \begin{vmatrix} 2 & -2 \\ -2 & 2 \end{vmatrix} = (2)(2) - (-2)(-2) = 0$$

$$D_y = \begin{vmatrix} 1 & 2 \\ -1 & -2 \end{vmatrix} = (1)(-2) - (-1)(2) = 0$$

Again, Cramer's Rule does not apply because D_x/D is not defined. In Example 6 we showed that the system is dependent and the solution set contains infinitely many ordered pairs.

Example 5 and Example 6 of Section 5.1 illustrate a general fact about linear systems that are either inconsistent or dependent.

---

1. If $D = 0$ and $D_x \neq 0$, the system is inconsistent and the solution set is $\varnothing$.
2. If $D = 0$ and $D_x = 0$, the system is dependent and the solution set contains infinitely many pairs.
3. If $D \neq 0$, the system is consistent and independent and the solution set contains one ordered pair.

Example 4: If a ball is rolled down an inclined plane with initial speed v feet per second, it will travel s feet during the first t seconds, where $s =$

$vt + kt^2$ and k is a constant. What is the initial speed of the ball if it rolls 2 feet during the first second and 3 feet during the next second?

Solution: Because the ball rolls 2 feet during the first second, we let $s = 2$ and $t = 1$ in the given formula. This results in

$$2 = v + k \qquad (14)$$

Because the ball rolls a total distance of 5 feet during the first 2 seconds, we let $s = 5$ and $t = 2$ in the formula. We have

$$5 = 2v + 4k \qquad (15)$$

We use Cramer's Rule to find v for the system (14) and (15).

$$D = \begin{vmatrix} 1 & 1 \\ 2 & 4 \end{vmatrix} = 2 \qquad D_v = \begin{vmatrix} 2 & 1 \\ 5 & 4 \end{vmatrix} = 3$$

Thus,

$$v = \frac{D_v}{D} = \frac{3}{2}$$

We conclude that the ball has initial speed $1\frac{1}{2}$ feet per second.

EXERCISES 5.2

For Exercises 1–6 calculate the simplest form of the indicated determinant.

1. $\begin{vmatrix} 2 & 3 \\ 5 & 7 \end{vmatrix}$ **2.** $\begin{vmatrix} -1 & 2 \\ 1 & 2 \end{vmatrix}$ **3.** $\begin{vmatrix} 3 & -1 \\ 5 & 2 \end{vmatrix}$

4. $\begin{vmatrix} -3 & 2 \\ -5 & 3 \end{vmatrix}$ **5.** $\begin{vmatrix} -2 & -3 \\ 0 & -4 \end{vmatrix}$ **6.** $\begin{vmatrix} -3 & 4 \\ 6 & -8 \end{vmatrix}$

For Exercises 7–10 set up the matrices that are used to define the determinants D, D_x, and D_y of Cramer's Rule. Do not calculate the determinants, and do not solve the system.

7. $3x + 5y = 2$
    $4x + 7y = 1$

8. $3x - y = 5$
    $2x + 3y = 0$

9. $4x - y = 0$
    $x - 6y + 3 = 0$

10. $x - 2y - 6 = 0$
    $3x + 4y + 5 = 0$

For Exercises 11–24 use Cramer's Rule to find the solution set of the system of equations.

11. $2x + 3y = 1$
    $3x + 7y = 3$

12. $x + 3y = 3$
    $2x - 4y = 1$

13. $x - 3y = -1$
    $2x - 5y = 3$

14. $3x - 2y = 1$
    $-2x + y = 4$

15. $3x + 4y = 6$
$\quad\ x - 2y = -3$

16. $3x + 7y = -1$
$\quad -6x + 3y = 2$

17. $-4x + 9y + 7 = 0$
$\quad\ 3x - 8y - 5 = 0$

18. $2x - y + 3 = 0$
$\quad\ 3x + 2y - 1 = 0$

19. $3x - y - 2 = 0$
$\quad -x + y + 1 = 0$

20. $x - 2y + 5 = 0$
$\quad 2x + y - 1 = 0$

21. $5x = 2(4y + 1)$
$\quad x + 4y = 0$

22. $5x = 3y$
$\quad 5y = 2(2 - x)$

23. $\dfrac{x}{2} + y = 4$

$\quad x - \dfrac{y}{3} = 2$

24. $\dfrac{x + 2}{3} = y$

$\quad \dfrac{3x + y}{5} = x$

For Exercises 25–30 make a change of variable that results in a system of linear equations, and then use Cramer's Rule to find the solution set.

25. $\dfrac{2}{x} + \dfrac{3}{y} = 1$

$\quad \dfrac{3}{x} + \dfrac{4}{y} = 2$

26. $\dfrac{1}{x} + \dfrac{2}{y} = -1$

$\quad \dfrac{3}{x} + \dfrac{1}{y} = 1$

27. $\dfrac{1}{x} - \dfrac{2}{y} = 3$

$\quad \dfrac{2}{x} - \dfrac{1}{y} = 2$

28. $\dfrac{2}{x} - \dfrac{1}{y} = 4$

$\quad \dfrac{3}{x} + \dfrac{5}{y} = 2$

29. $2x^2 + y^2 = 1$
$\quad 6x^2 + 5y^2 = 4$

30. $2x^2 - y^2 = 1$
$\quad x^2 + 4y^2 = 3$

For Exercises 31–34 use Cramer's Rule to determine whether the solution set for the system contains no pairs, one pair, or many pairs. Identify each system that is dependent and each system that is inconsistent.

31. $2x + 4y = 1$
$\quad 3x + 6y = 2$

32. $x - 4y = 2$
$\quad -2x + 8y = -4$

33. $4x - 6y = 2$
$\quad 6x - 9y = 3$

34. $x - 2y = 0$
$\quad 2x + y = 0$

For Exercises 35–38 use the solution of a system of equations to answer the stated question.

35. If the natural length of a spring is L_0 inches, a force of F pounds will stretch the spring to a length of L inches, where $L = L_0 + kF$ and k is a constant. If a force of 2 pounds stretches the spring to a length of 15 inches and a force of 5 pounds stretches the spring to a length of 24 inches, what is the natural length of the spring?

36. If an object is thrown upward from an initial height of s_0 meters with an initial velocity of v_0 meters per second, after t seconds the height of the object is s meters, with $s = s_0 + v_0 t - 5t^2$. If the object has a height of 50 meters after 2 seconds and a height of 55 meters after 3 seconds, what is the initial height and the initial velocity?

37. If a ball is rolled down an inclined plane with initial speed v_0 centimeters per second, it will roll s centimeters in t seconds, where $s = v_0 t + k t^2$ and k is a constant. What is the initial speed of the ball if it rolls 20 centimeters during the first 2 seconds and 30 centimeters during the next 2 seconds?

38. Two pipes can fill a pool in 10 minutes when they are used together. Pipe A is left on for 8 minutes, pipe B is left on for 20 minutes, and thus the pool is filled. How long would it take each pipe to fill the pool if used alone?

5.3 Solving by the Substitution Method

Another method that can be used to find the solution set for a system of equations is the **Substitution Method**, which we illustrate with the following example.

Example 1: Find the solution set for the system.

$$3x - y = 9 \tag{1}$$

$$5x + 4y = -2 \tag{2}$$

Solution: First, we solve Equation (1) for y.

$$y = 3x - 9 \tag{1'}$$

Next, we substitute from Equation (1') into Equation (2) and then solve for x.

$$5x + 4(3x - 9) = -2$$

$$5x + 12x - 36 = -2$$

$$17x \qquad = 34$$

$$x \qquad = 2$$

Finally, we let $x = 2$ in Equation (1') and calculate y.

$$y = 3(2) - 9 = -3$$

We conclude that the solution set is $\{(2, -3)\}$.

The following example illustrates a system that cannot be solved by using either Cramer's Rule or the Elimination Method. However, the Substitution Method may be used to find the solution set.

Example 2: Find the solution set for the system.

$$-x + y = 1 \tag{3}$$

$$x^2 + y^2 = 13 \tag{4}$$

Solution: Because the system is not a linear system, Cramer's Rule does not apply. Furthermore, we cannot eliminate either variable by adding a multiple of one equation to a multiple of the other. However, we may solve Equation (3) for y.

$$y = x + 1 \qquad (3')$$

Substituting from Equation (3′) into Equation (4), we obtain

$$
\begin{aligned}
x^2 + (x + 1)^2 &= 13 \\
x^2 + x^2 + 2x + 1 &= 13 \\
2x^2 + 2x - 12 &= 0 \\
x^2 + x - 6 &= 0 \\
(x - 2)(x + 3) &= 0 \\
x = 2 \quad \text{or} \quad x &= -3
\end{aligned}
$$

We let $x = 2$ in Equation (3′). Thus,

$$y = 2 + 1 = 3$$

and hence (2, 3) is a solution. Next, we let $x = -3$ in Equation (3′). We have

$$y = -3 + 1 = -2$$

and hence $(-3, -2)$ is a solution. The solution set is $\{(2, 3), (-3, -2)\}$. Figure 5.3.1 illustrates the graph of Equation (3), which is a line; the graph of Equation (4), which is a circle; and the two points of intersection.

Note that we must use Equation (3′) to find y. If we let $x = 2$ in Equation (4), the result is

$$
\begin{aligned}
2^2 + y^2 &= 13 \\
y^2 &= 9 \\
y &= \pm 3
\end{aligned}
$$

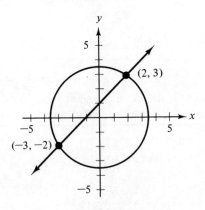

Figure 5.3.1

However, the ordered pair $(2, -3)$ is not a solution of the system because this pair does not satisfy Equation (3).

Example 3: Find the solution set for the system.

$$x + 2y = 1 \tag{5}$$

$$2x^2 - y^2 = 17 \tag{6}$$

Solution: First, we solve Equation (5) for x. We have

$$x = 1 - 2y \tag{5'}$$

Next, we substitute from Equation (5') into Equation (6).

$$2(1 - 2y)^2 - y^2 = 17$$

$$2(1 - 4y + 4y^2) - y^2 = 17$$

$$2 - 8y + 8y^2 - y^2 = 17$$

$$7y^2 - 8y - 15 = 0$$

$$(y + 1)(7y - 15) = 0$$

$$y + 1 = 0 \quad \text{or} \quad 7y - 15 = 0$$

$$y = -1 \qquad\qquad y = \tfrac{15}{7}$$

If $y = -1$ in Equation (5'), we have

$$x = 1 - 2(-1) = 3$$

If $y = \tfrac{15}{7}$ in Equation (5'), we have

$$x = 1 - 2(\tfrac{15}{7}) = -\tfrac{23}{7}$$

Thus, the solution set is $\{(3, -1), (-\tfrac{23}{7}, \tfrac{15}{7})\}$.

Example 4: Find the solution set for the system.

$$xy + 4 = 0 \tag{7}$$

$$y^2 - x^2 = 6 \tag{8}$$

Solution: First, we solve Equation (7) for y.

$$xy + 4 = 0$$

$$xy = -4$$

$$y = -\frac{4}{x} \tag{7'}$$

Next, we substitute from Equation (7') into Equation (8).

$$\left(-\frac{4}{x}\right)^2 - x^2 = 6$$

$$\frac{16}{x^2} - x^2 = 6$$

We multiply on both sides by x^2 to eliminate the fraction.

$$16 - x^4 = 6x^2$$

$$x^4 + 6x^2 - 16 = 0$$

$$(x^2 - 2)(x^2 + 8) = 0$$

$$x^2 - 2 = 0 \qquad \text{or} \qquad x^2 + 8 = 0$$

$$x^2 = 2 \qquad\qquad\qquad x^2 = -8$$

$$x = \pm\sqrt{2}$$

If $x = \sqrt{2}$ in Equation (7'), we have

$$y = -\frac{4}{\sqrt{2}} = -2\sqrt{2}$$

Thus, $(\sqrt{2}, -2\sqrt{2})$ is a solution. Furthermore, if $x = -\sqrt{2}$ in Equation (7'), we have

$$y = -\frac{4}{-\sqrt{2}} = 2\sqrt{2}$$

Thus, $(-\sqrt{2}, 2\sqrt{2})$ is also a solution. We ignore the result $x^2 = -8$ because the square of a real number is not negative. Therefore, the solution set is $\{(\sqrt{2}, -2\sqrt{2}), (-\sqrt{2}, 2\sqrt{2})\}$.

Example 5:   Find the solution set for the system.

$$x - y = 5 \qquad\qquad\qquad (9)$$

$$x^2 + y^2 = 9 \qquad\qquad\qquad (10)$$

Solution: Solving Equation (9) for x, we have

$$x = y + 5 \qquad\qquad\qquad (9')$$

Substituting from Equation (9') into Equation (10), we obtain

$$(y + 5)^2 + y^2 = 9$$

$$y^2 + 10y + 25 + y^2 = 9$$

$$2y^2 + 10y + 16 = 0$$

$$y^2 + 5y + 8 = 0$$

We apply the Quadratic Formula.

$$y = \frac{-5 \pm \sqrt{5^2 - 4 \cdot 1 \cdot 8}}{2 \cdot 1}$$

$$= \frac{-5 \pm \sqrt{-7}}{2}$$

Because the square root of a negative number is not real, we conclude that there are no ordered pairs of real numbers that satisfy the system. The solution set is $\varnothing$. Figure 5.3.2 illustrates the graphs. The line $x - y = 5$ does not intersect the circle $x^2 + y^2 = 9$.

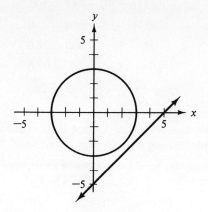

Figure 5.3.2

Example 6:   Find the lengths of the legs of a right triangle if the length of the hypotenuse is 25 centimeters and the perimeter is 60 centimeters.

Solution: Let x centimeters be the length of one leg and y centimeters be the length of the other leg. See Figure 5.3.3. Because 25 centimeters is the length of the hypotenuse, by the Pythagorean Theorem we have

$$x^2 + y^2 = 25^2 \qquad\qquad (11)$$

Because the perimeter is 60 centimeters, we also have

$$x + y + 25 = 60 \qquad\qquad (12)$$

First, we solve Equation (12) for y. Thus,

$$y = 35 - x \qquad\qquad (12')$$

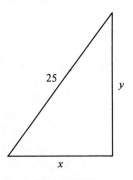

Figure 5.3.3

Next, we substitute from Equation (12′) into Equation (11).

$$x^2 + (35 - x)^2 = 25^2$$
$$x^2 + 1225 - 70x + x^2 = 625$$
$$2x^2 - 70x + 600 = 0$$
$$x^2 - 35x + 300 = 0$$
$$(x - 15)(x - 20) = 0$$
$$x = 15 \quad \text{or} \quad x = 20$$

If $x = 15$ in Equation (12′), we obtain $y = 20$. If $x = 20$ in Equation (12′), we obtain $y = 15$. We conclude that one leg is 15 centimeters long and the other leg is 20 centimeters long.

EXERCISES 5.3

For Exercises 1–4 use the Substitution Method to find the solution set of the system of linear equations.

1. $3x + 2y = 5$
   $2x + y = 1$

2. $2x + 3y = 1$
   $x + 2y = 2$

3. $-x + 2y = 4$
   $-2x + 3y = 2$

4. $4x - 5y = 1$
   $2x - y = 5$

For Exercises 5–8 use the Substitution Method to find the solution set of the system of equations. Check your answer by sketching the graphs of both equations on the same coordinate plane.

5. $y = x^2$
   $x + y = 2$

6. $y = 2x$
   $x^2 + 2y^2 = 9$

7. $y = 2x$
   $x^2 - y^2 = 4$

8. $y = -x + 4$
   $x^2 + y^2 = 8$

For Exercises 9–32 use the Substitution Method to find the solution set of the system of equations.

9. $x - 3y = 0$
   $x^2 - 4y^2 = 20$

10. $2x + y = 0$
   $x^2 + y^2 = 5$

11. $-3x^2 + y^2 = 6$
   $2x - y = 1$

12. $2x^2 - 7y^2 = -10$
   $x + 2y = 1$

13. $xy + 6 = 0$
   $2x + y = 1$

14. $x - 3y = 5$
   $xy = 2$

15. $x^2 - y = 0$
   $xy = 64$

16. $x - y^2 = 0$
   $xy + 8 = 0$

17. $x^2 + y = 0$
$\quad x + y^2 = 0$

18. $2x^2 + y = 0$
$\quad x - 2y^2 = 0$

19. $x + y = x^2$
$\quad y + 6 = 2x^2$

20. $x^2 + y = 8$
$\quad y + 10 = x^2$

21. $x^2 + y^2 = 5$
$\quad x + y^2 = 3$

22. $3x^2 - y^2 = -4$
$\quad x^2 + y = 8$

23. $3x - 2y = 1$
$\quad x^2 + y^2 = 2$

24. $2x + 3y = 2$
$\quad x^2 + y^2 = 1$

25. $x^2 + y^2 = 13$
$\quad xy = 6$

26. $x^2 - y^2 = 3$
$\quad xy + 2 = 0$

27. $x^2 - y^2 = 6$
$\quad xy + 4 = 0$

28. $x^2 + y^2 = 4$
$\quad xy = 2$

29. $y = x^3$
$\quad y = x$

30. $y = x^3$
$\quad y = 4x$

31. $y = x^3 - x^2$
$\quad y = 2x$

32. $y^2 = x^3$
$\quad y^2 = x$

For Exercises 33–34 use the solution of a system of equations to answer the stated question.

33. What are the dimensions of a rectangle if the length of the diagonal is 20 inches and the perimeter is 56 inches?

34. What are the lengths of the legs of a right triangle if the area of the triangle is 2 square centimeters and the length of the hypotenuse is $\sqrt{10}$ centimeters?

5.4 Systems of Three Equations with Three Variables

A solution for an equation that contains three variables x, y, and z is an **ordered triple** of numbers (a, b, c) such that the equation is satisfied if x is replaced by a, y is replaced by b, and z is replaced by c. For example, the ordered triple $(2, -1, 3)$ is a solution of the equation

$$3x + y - z = 2$$

because the result of replacing x by 2, y by -1, and z by 3 in the equation is

$$3(2) + (-1) - 3 = 2$$

or

$$2 = 2$$

A solution for a system of three equations with three variables is an ordered triple that satisfies all three equations. If a system of three equations in three variables has a unique solution, the solution can be found by applying variations of the methods that we have considered for solving a system of two equations in two variables.

The first example illustrates how to apply the Substitution Method to find a solution for a system of three first degree equations with three variables.

Example 1: Find a solution for the system.

$$x + y + z = 7 \tag{1}$$

$$2x + y - z = -6 \tag{2}$$

$$x - 3y + 2z = 5 \tag{3}$$

Solution: We apply the Substitution Method. First, we solve Equation (1) for z.

$$z = -x - y + 7 \tag{1'}$$

Next, we substitute from Equation (1') into Equation (2).

$$2x + y - (-x - y + 7) = -6$$

$$3x + 2y = 1 \tag{4}$$

Next, we substitute from Equation (1') into Equation (3).

$$x - 3y + 2(-x - y + 7) = 5$$

$$x + 5y = 9 \tag{5}$$

We solve the system of Equations (4) and (5). Solving Equation (5) for x, we have

$$x = -5y + 9 \tag{5'}$$

Substituting from Equation (5') into Equation (4), we obtain

$$3(-5y + 9) + 2y = 1$$

$$-13y + 27 = 1$$

$$-13y = -26$$

$$y = 2$$

We let $y = 2$ in Equation (5'). Thus,

$$x = -5(2) + 9 = -1$$

We let $x = -1$ and $y = 2$ in Equation (1'). Thus,

$$z = -(-1) - 2 + 7 = 6$$

Therefore, a solution for the system is $(-1, 2, 6)$.

When using the Substitution Method to find a solution for a system of three first degree equations, we may apply Cramer's Rule after obtaining a system of two equations in two variables if that is more convenient than continuing with the Substitution Method. The next example shows how to apply Cramer's Rule after first using the Elimination Method to obtain a system of two equations with two variables.

Example 2: Find a solution for the system.

$$-3x + 3y - 5z = 2 \tag{6}$$
$$5x - 3y + 2z = -1 \tag{7}$$
$$3x + 2y - 5z = 5 \tag{8}$$

Solution: Because the coefficient of y in Equation (7) is the opposite of the coefficient of y in Equation (6), it is easy to eliminate y from the first two equations.

$$
\begin{array}{llll}
-3x + 3y - 5z = & 2 & \text{[Eq. (6)]} \\
\underline{5x - 3y + 2z = -1} & & \text{[Eq. (7)]} \\
2x \qquad - 3z = & 1 & \text{[Sum]} & \tag{9}
\end{array}
$$

Next, we eliminate y from Equations (6) and (8).

$$
\begin{array}{llll}
-6x + 6y - 10z = & 4 & \text{[2 times Eq. (6)]} \\
\underline{-9x - 6y + 15z = -15} & & \text{[-3 times Eq. (8)]} \\
-15x \qquad + 5z = -11 & & \text{[Sum]} & \tag{10}
\end{array}
$$

Now we apply Cramer's Rule to find a solution for the system of Equations (9) and (10). Thus,

$$D = \begin{vmatrix} 2 & -3 \\ -15 & 5 \end{vmatrix} = -35 \qquad D_x = \begin{vmatrix} 1 & -3 \\ -11 & 5 \end{vmatrix} = -28$$

$$D_z = \begin{vmatrix} 2 & 1 \\ -15 & -11 \end{vmatrix} = -7$$

Therefore,

$$x = \frac{D_x}{D} = \frac{-28}{-35} = \frac{4}{5} \quad \text{and} \quad z = \frac{D_z}{D} = \frac{-7}{-35} = \frac{1}{5}$$

Finally, we let $x = \frac{4}{5}$ and $z = \frac{1}{5}$ in Equation (6) and solve for y.

$$-3(\tfrac{4}{5}) + 3y - 5(\tfrac{1}{5}) = 2$$
$$y = \tfrac{9}{5}$$

Therefore, a solution of the system is $(\frac{4}{5}, \frac{9}{5}, \frac{1}{5})$.

The next example illustrates the method that is easiest to apply when using a computer, because the steps are very systematic and repetitive.

Example 3:   Find a solution of the system

$$x - y - 2z = 1 \tag{11}$$
$$-2x + 3y + 6z = -1 \tag{12}$$
$$3x + 2y - 3z = 1 \tag{13}$$

Solution: We apply a variation of the Elimination Method. Because the coefficient of x in Equation (11) is 1, we can eliminate x from Equations (12) and (13) by adding an integer multiple of Equation (11) to Equation (12) and an integer multiple of Equation (11) to Equation (13). For Example, we eliminate x from Equation (12) by adding two times Equation (11) plus Equation (12).

$$2x - 2y - 4z = 2 \qquad \text{[2 times Eq. (11)]}$$
$$\underline{-2x + 3y + 6z = -1} \qquad \text{[Eq. (12)]}$$
$$y + 2z = 1 \qquad \text{[2 times Eq. (11) plus Eq. (12)]}$$

And we eliminate x from Eq. (13) by adding -3 times Equation (11) plus Equation (13). With practice you should be able to do the calculations mentally and write the resulting system as follows.

$$x - y - 2z = 1 \qquad \text{[Eq. (11)]} \tag{11}$$
$$y + 2z = 1 \qquad \text{[2 times Eq. (11) plus Eq. (12)]} \tag{14}$$
$$5y + 3z = -2 \qquad \text{[-3 times Eq. (11) plus Eq. (13)]} \tag{15}$$

Because the coefficient of y in Equation (14) is 1, we can eliminate y from Equation (15) by adding an integer multiple of Equation (14) to Equation (15). This results in the following system.

$$x - y - 2z = 1 \tag{11}$$
$$y + 2z = 1 \tag{14}$$
$$-7z = -7 \qquad \text{[-5 times Eq. (14) plus Eq. (15)]} \tag{16}$$

We divide on both sides of Eq. (16) by -7 and obtain the following system.

$$x - y - 2z = 1 \tag{11}$$
$$y + 2z = 1 \tag{14}$$
$$z = 1 \quad . \text{[$-\frac{1}{7}$ times Eq. (16)]} \tag{17}$$

The system of Equations (11), (14), and (17) is said to be in **upper triangular form** and is easily solved as follows. We let $z = 1$ in Equation (14) and solve for y.

$$y + 2(1) = 1$$
$$y = -1$$

We let $z = 1$ and $y = -1$ in Equation (11) and solve for x.

$$x - (-1) - 2(1) = 1$$
$$x \qquad\qquad = 2$$

Therefore, a solution of the system is $(2, -1, 1)$.

If we designate a z-axis that is perpendicular to both the x-axis and the y-axis, then there is a point in space that corresponds to every solution (x, y, z) of an equation with three variables. The graph of the solution set for a first degree equation in x, y, and z is a flat surface called a **plane**. Two such planes that are not parallel intersect in a straight line. A third plane that is not parallel to this line intersects the line in one point. The ordered triple corresponding to this point, which is a point on all three planes, is the solution for the system of three equations that correspond to the three planes.

Not every system of three first degree equations in three variables has a unique solution. If two of the planes are parallel or if one plane is parallel to the line of intersection of the other two planes, then there is no point that is common to all three planes and hence no solution for the system of equations. Such a system is said to be **inconsistent**. A system that has at least one solution is said to be **consistent**.

Example 4: Show that the system is inconsistent.

$$x - y + 2z = -1 \qquad\qquad (18)$$
$$-x + 2y + z = 1 \qquad\qquad (19)$$
$$-x + 3y + 4z = 3 \qquad\qquad (20)$$

Solution: We attempt to reduce the system to triangular form. First, we eliminate x from Equations (19) and (20).

$$x - y + 2z = -1 \qquad\qquad\qquad\qquad\qquad\qquad (18)$$
$$y + 3z = 0 \qquad \text{[Eq. (18) plus Eq. (19)]} \qquad (21)$$
$$2y + 6z = 2 \qquad \text{[Eq. (18) plus Eq. (20)]} \qquad (22)$$

Next, we eliminate y from Equation (22).

$$x - y + 2z = -1 \qquad\qquad\qquad\qquad\qquad\qquad\qquad (18)$$
$$y + 3z = 0 \qquad\qquad\qquad\qquad\qquad\qquad\qquad (21)$$
$$0 = 2 \qquad \text{[-2 times Eq. (21) plus Eq. (22)]} \qquad (23)$$

Because Equation (23) is false, we conclude that the system is inconsistent and has no solution. The solution set is $\varnothing$, the empty set.

If one or more of the equations obtained when reducing a system of three first degree equations in three variables to triangular form turns out to be the identity $0 = 0$, we conclude that the system contains more than one solution. Such a system is said to be **dependent**. For a dependent system, either there are three planes that intersect in a line, or two planes coincide and the third plane is not parallel to the first two, or all three planes coincide. Thus, there are infinitely many solutions for a dependent system. A system that does not have more than one solution is said to be **independent**.

EXERCISES 5.4

For Exercises 1–6 use the Substitution Method and then Cramer's Rule, if desired, to find a solution for the system of equations.

1. $\begin{aligned} x + y + z &= 4 \\ 4x + y + 2z &= 11 \\ 2x + 3y + z &= 8 \end{aligned}$

2. $\begin{aligned} x + 2y - z &= 2 \\ 2x + y + z &= -2 \\ -x + 2y - z &= 4 \end{aligned}$

3. $\begin{aligned} x + 3y + z &= 5 \\ x + 2y + 2z &= 4 \\ x - y - z &= -5 \end{aligned}$

4. $\begin{aligned} x + 2y + z &= 3 \\ 3x + 2y + 4z &= 3 \\ 3x + y - z &= 12 \end{aligned}$

5. $\begin{aligned} x + y + 2z &= 1 \\ 2x - y - z &= 0 \\ 3x + y + 2z &= 2 \end{aligned}$

6. $\begin{aligned} 2x + y - z &= -1 \\ 3x + 2y + z &= -1 \\ x - 3y + 3z &= 3 \end{aligned}$

For Exercises 7–10 use the Elimination Method and then Cramer's Rule, if desired, to find a solution for the system of equations.

7. $\begin{aligned} 2x + 3y - 2z &= -1 \\ 3x - 2y + 2z &= 10 \\ -2x - 5y + 4z &= 5 \end{aligned}$

8. $\begin{aligned} 3x + 4y - 2z &= 7 \\ -3x + 2y + 4z &= 3 \\ 6x + 3y - 5z &= 5 \end{aligned}$

9. $\begin{aligned} 3x + 4y - 4z &= -2 \\ 2x + 4y + 3z &= -1 \\ 5x - 2y + 4z &= 4 \end{aligned}$

10. $\begin{aligned} 2x + 4y + 3z &= 5 \\ 5x + 3y + 2z &= 1 \\ 4x - 4y + 3z &= 1 \end{aligned}$

For Exercises 11–14 find a solution for the system by first reducing the system to triangular form, as illustrated in Example 3.

11. $\begin{aligned} x + y + z &= 3 \\ x + 2y - z &= 2 \\ 2x - y + z &= 2 \end{aligned}$

12. $\begin{aligned} x + y + z &= 2 \\ 2x + 3y + 4z &= 4 \\ -2x + y + z &= -1 \end{aligned}$

13. $\begin{aligned} x + 2y - z &= 1 \\ x + y + z &= 5 \\ -3x - y + 4z &= -1 \end{aligned}$

14. $\begin{aligned} x - y - z &= 0 \\ 3x + y - 2z &= -1 \\ -x + 2y + 3z &= 5 \end{aligned}$

For Exercises 15–20 use the method that you think is easiest to find a solution for the system of equations.

15. $3x - 2y + 3z = 10$
$\quad\; 2x + 2y - 2z = -4$
$\quad\; 5x - 2y - 4z = 5$

16. $2x - 3y + 2z = -1$
$\qquad 4x + 2y - 3z = -8$
$\qquad 2x + 5y - 4z = -5$

17. $x + 2y + z = 1$
$\quad\; x - y + z = 2$
$\quad\; x + y - 3z = -1$

18. $2x - y + 3z = 0$
$\qquad x + 2y + z = 4$
$\qquad -x + 3y + z = -1$

19. $x + 3y = 5$
$\quad\; y - 2z = 3$
$\quad\; 2x + z = 0$

20. $2x - 3z = -1$
$\qquad 2x - y = -5$
$\qquad y - z = 1$

For Exercises 21–24 determine whether the system has no solution, one solution, or many solutions.

21. $x - 2y + z = 3$
$\quad\;\; 3x - y + 2z = 3$
$\quad\;\; 2x + y + z = 0$

22. $x + y - z = 1$
$\qquad x - y + 2z = 1$
$\qquad 3x - y + 3z = 1$

23. $x - y + z = 1$
$\quad\;\; 2x + y + z = 2$
$\quad\;\; x - 4y + 2z = 2$

24. $x - 2y = 0$
$\qquad 3x + z = 2$
$\qquad x + 4y + z = 2$

For Exercises 25–26 use the solution of a system of three first degree equations to answer the stated question.

25. A total of \$12,000 is invested, partly at 5%, partly at 8%, and the rest at 10%. The total income from the three investments is \$1000 per year. Furthermore, the income from the 10% investment equals the sum of the incomes from the other two investments. How much is invested at each rate?

26. Every parabola with vertical axis has an equation of the form $y = ax^2 + bx + c$. Find an equation of the parabola that contains the three points $(1, 1)$, $(2, 1)$, and $(-1, -5)$. [*Hint:* Each point must satisfy an equation of the parabola.]

5.5   Solving by the Matrix Method (optional)

In Example 3 of Section 5.4, we solved the system of equations

$$x - y - 2z = 1$$
$$-2x + 3y + 6z = -1$$
$$3x + 2y - 3z = 1$$

Corresponding to this system is the matrix

$$A = \begin{bmatrix} 1 & -1 & -2 & 1 \\ -2 & 3 & 6 & -1 \\ 3 & 2 & -3 & 1 \end{bmatrix}$$

The elements in the first column of matrix A are the coefficients of x in the system of equations; the elements in the second column of A are the coefficients of y; the elements in the third column of A are the coefficients of z; and the elements in the last column of A are the constant terms in the system of equations.

By reducing the system of equations to triangular form, we obtained the system of equations

$$x - y - 2z = 1$$
$$y + 2z = 1$$
$$z = 1$$

which corresponds to the matrix

$$B = \begin{bmatrix} 1 & -1 & -2 & 1 \\ 0 & 1 & 2 & 1 \\ 0 & 0 & 1 & 1 \end{bmatrix}$$

Matrix B is said to be in **upper triangular form** because the first three columns of matrix B are

$$C = \begin{bmatrix} 1 & -1 & -2 \\ 0 & 1 & 2 \\ 0 & 0 & 1 \end{bmatrix}$$

and for matrix C each element on the first diagonal is 1 and each element below the first diagonal is 0. Thus, the nonzero elements of matrix C form a triangle.

If a system of three first degree equations in three variables has a unique solution, we can find the solution by reducing the matrix that corresponds to the system to an upper triangular form. We illustrate the method in the following example.

Example 1: Find the solution for the system.

$$-2x + y + 3z = 2$$
$$x + 2y - z = -5$$
$$x + y + 2z = 3$$

Solution: The given system corresponds to the matrix

$$\begin{bmatrix} -2 & 1 & 3 & 2 \\ 1 & 2 & -1 & -5 \\ 1 & 1 & 2 & 3 \end{bmatrix}$$

We reduce the matrix to a triangular form. First, we want the element in the first row and first column to be 1. Thus, we interchange the elements in the first two rows of the matrix.

$$\begin{bmatrix} 1 & 2 & -1 & -5 \\ -2 & 1 & 3 & 2 \\ 1 & 1 & 2 & 3 \end{bmatrix} \begin{matrix} (1) \\ (2) \\ (3) \end{matrix}$$

Next, we add a multiple of Row (1) to each of the other two rows in the matrix. The mulitipliers are chosen so that for the resulting matrix each element in the first column that is below the diagonal is 0. This results in the matrix

$$\begin{bmatrix} 1 & 2 & -1 & -5 \\ 0 & 5 & 1 & -8 \\ 0 & -1 & 3 & 8 \end{bmatrix} \begin{matrix} \text{[Row (1)]} & (1) \\ \text{[2 times Row (1) plus Row (2)]} & (4) \\ \text{[-1 times Row (1) plus Row (3)]} & (5) \end{matrix}$$

Next, we want the element in the second row and second column to be 1. Thus, we multiply the last row by -1 and then interchange the last two rows.

$$\begin{bmatrix} 1 & 2 & -1 & -5 \\ 0 & 1 & -3 & -8 \\ 0 & 5 & 1 & -8 \end{bmatrix} \begin{matrix} \text{[Row (1)]} & (1) \\ \text{[-1 times Row (5)]} & (6) \\ \text{[Row (4)]} & (4) \end{matrix}$$

Because we want the element in the second column that is below the diagonal to be 0, we add -5 times the middle row to the last row. The resulting matrix is

$$\begin{bmatrix} 1 & 2 & -1 & -5 \\ 0 & 1 & -3 & -8 \\ 0 & 0 & 16 & 32 \end{bmatrix} \begin{matrix} \text{[Row (1)]} & (1) \\ \text{[Row (6)]} & (6) \\ \text{[-5 times Row (6) plus Row (4)]} & (7) \end{matrix}$$

Because we want the element that is in the third row and third column to be 1, we divide each element in the third row by 16. Then we have the upper triangular matrix

$$\begin{bmatrix} 1 & 2 & -1 & -5 \\ 0 & 1 & -3 & -8 \\ 0 & 0 & 1 & 2 \end{bmatrix} \begin{matrix} \text{[Row (1)]} & (1) \\ \text{[Row (6)]} & (6) \\ \text{[$\frac{1}{16}$ times Row (7)]} & (8) \end{matrix}$$

The system of equations that corresponds to the upper triangular matrix is

$$x + 2y - z = -5 \tag{9}$$

$$y - 3z = -8 \tag{10}$$

$$z = 2 \tag{11}$$

We substitute from Equation (11) into Equation (10). Thus,

$$y - 3(2) = -8$$

$$y = -2 \tag{12}$$

We substitute from Equations (11) and (12) into Equation (9). Thus,

$$x + 2(-2) - 2 = -5$$
$$x \qquad\qquad = 1$$

Therefore, the solution for the system is $(1, -2, 2)$.

The following are called **elementary row operations** for matrices, and they can often be used to reduce a matrix to upper triangular form, as in Example 1.

5.5.1   Definition: *Elementary Row Operations*

(i)   Interchanging two rows
(ii) Multiplying each element in a row by the same nonzero constant
(iii) Replacing any row by the sum of that row and a multiple of some other row

If only elementary row operations are used on a matrix, the system of equations that corresponds to the resulting matrix is equivalent to the system of equations that corresponds to the original matrix.

A solution for a system of four equations with four variables x_1, x_2, x_3, and x_4 is an **ordered quadruple** of numbers (a, b, c, d) that satisfies all four equations in the system if $x_1 \leftarrow a, x_2 \leftarrow b, x_3 \leftarrow c$, and $x_4 \leftarrow d$. If the system has a unique solution, the solution can be found by using elementary row operations to reduce the matrix that corresponds to the system to a triangular form.

Example 2:   Find a solution for the system

$$x_1 - 2x_2 + x_3 - 3x_4 = 2$$
$$x_1 + x_2 + 2x_3 - x_4 = 3$$
$$-x_1 + x_2 + x_3 + 3x_4 = 3$$
$$2x_1 - x_2 - x_3 - x_4 = 0$$

Solution: The matrix that corresponds to the system is as follows.

$$
\begin{bmatrix}
① & -2 & 1 & -3 & 2 \\
1 & 1 & 2 & -1 & 3 \\
-1 & 1 & 1 & 3 & 3 \\
2 & -1 & -1 & -1 & 0
\end{bmatrix}
\begin{matrix}
(13) \\
(14) \\
(15) \\
(16)
\end{matrix}
$$

We use elementary row operations to reduce the matrix to a triangular form.

The element in the first row and first column is called the **pivot element**. We want each element in the first column below the pivot element to be 0. Because the pivot element is 1, we may obtain zeros in the first column by adding integer multiples of Row (13) to each of the other rows. The multiplier that we choose for each row is the opposite of the element that is in the first column of that row.

$$\begin{bmatrix} 1 & -2 & 1 & -3 & 2 \\ 0 & 3 & 1 & 2 & 1 \\ 0 & -1 & 2 & 0 & 5 \\ 0 & 3 & -3 & 5 & -4 \end{bmatrix}$$

[Row (13)]	(13)
[−1 times Row (13) plus Row (14)]	(17)
[1 times Row (13) plus Row (15)]	(18)
[−2 times Row (13) plus Row (16)]	(19)

We now regard the element in the second row and second column to be the pivot element. We want the pivot element to be 1. Thus, we multiply Row (18) by −1 and interchange Rows (18) and (17). This results in the following matrix.

$$\begin{bmatrix} 1 & -2 & 1 & -3 & 2 \\ 0 & ① & -2 & 0 & -5 \\ 0 & 3 & 1 & 2 & 1 \\ 0 & 3 & -3 & 5 & -4 \end{bmatrix}$$

[Row (13)]	(13)
[−1 times Row (18)]	(20)
[Row (17)]	(17)
[Row (19)]	(19)

We want each element in the second column below the pivot element to be 0. We add a multiple of the row that contains the pivot element to each row that is below the pivot row. This results in the following matrix.

$$\begin{bmatrix} 1 & -2 & 1 & -3 & 2 \\ 0 & 1 & -2 & 0 & -5 \\ 0 & 0 & 7 & 2 & 16 \\ 0 & 0 & 3 & 5 & 11 \end{bmatrix}$$

[Row (13)]	(13)
[Row (20)]	(20)
[−3 times Row (20) plus Row (17)]	(21)
[−3 times Row (20) plus Row (19)]	(22)

We now regard the element in the third row and third column to be the pivot element. To obtain 1 for the pivot element, we add −2 times Row (22) to Row (21).

$$\begin{bmatrix} 1 & -2 & 1 & -3 & 2 \\ 0 & 1 & -2 & 0 & -5 \\ 0 & 0 & ① & -8 & -6 \\ 0 & 0 & 3 & 5 & 11 \end{bmatrix}$$

[Row (13)]	(13)
[Row (20)]	(20)
[−2 times Row (22) plus Row (21)]	(23)
[Row (22)]	(22)

To obtain 0 in the third column below the pivot element, we add a multiple of the pivot row to the last row of the matrix

$$\begin{bmatrix} 1 & -2 & 1 & -3 & 2 \\ 0 & 1 & -2 & 0 & -5 \\ 0 & 0 & 1 & -8 & -6 \\ 0 & 0 & 0 & 29 & 29 \end{bmatrix}$$

[Row (13)]	(13)
[Row (20)]	(20)
[Row (23)]	(23)
[−3 times Row (23) plus Row (22)]	(24)

To obtain 1 in the fourth row and fourth column, we divide each element in the fourth row by 29.

$$
\begin{bmatrix}
1 & -2 & 1 & -3 & 2 \\
0 & 1 & -2 & 0 & -5 \\
0 & 0 & 1 & -8 & -6 \\
0 & 0 & 0 & 1 & 1
\end{bmatrix}
\qquad
\begin{array}{ll}
\text{[Row (13)]} & (13) \\
\text{[Row (20)]} & (20) \\
\text{[Row (23)]} & (23) \\
[\tfrac{1}{29} \text{ times Row (24)]} & (25)
\end{array}
$$

We have now reduced the matrix to an upper triangular form. The system of equations that corresponds to this upper triangular matrix is as follows.

$$x_1 - 2x_2 + x_3 - 3x_4 = 2 \tag{26}$$

$$x_2 - 2x_3 \quad\quad = -5 \tag{27}$$

$$x_3 - 8x_4 = -6 \tag{28}$$

$$x_4 = 1 \tag{29}$$

We substitute from Equation (29) into Equation (28).

$$x_3 - 8(1) = -6$$

$$x_3 \quad\quad = 2 \tag{30}$$

We substitute from Equation (30) into Equation (27).

$$x_2 - 2(2) = -5$$

$$x_2 \quad\quad = -1 \tag{31}$$

We substitute from Equations (31), (30), and (29) into Equation (26).

$$x_1 - 2(-1) + 2 - 3(1) = 2$$

$$x_1 \quad\quad\quad = 1 \tag{32}$$

From Equations (32), (31), (30), and (29), we conclude that the solution is $(1, -1, 2, 1)$.

EXERCISES 5.5

For Exercises 1–6 begin with the given matrix A, perform the elementary row operation that is described, and write the resulting matrix. (Do not consider the exercises as being sequential. For each operation begin with the original matrix A.)

$$
A = \begin{bmatrix}
1 & -1 & 2 & 0 \\
-1 & 2 & -3 & 2 \\
2 & 0 & -1 & -2
\end{bmatrix}
$$

1. Interchange Row (1) and Row (2).
2. Multiply each element in Row (3) by -1.

3. Replace Row (2) by Row (2) plus Row (1).

4. Replace Row (3) by Row (3) plus 2 times Row (2).

5. Replace Row (3) by Row (3) plus -2 times Row (1).

6. Replace Row (1) by Row (1) plus -1 times Row (2).

For Exercises 7–8 write a system of equations with variables x, y, and z that correspond to the given matrix. Do not find a solution for the system.

7. $\begin{bmatrix} 1 & 2 & -1 & 3 \\ 2 & -1 & 5 & 1 \\ -1 & 1 & 2 & 4 \end{bmatrix}$

8. $\begin{bmatrix} 0 & 0 & 3 & 1 \\ 0 & 2 & 0 & 5 \\ -2 & 0 & 0 & 3 \end{bmatrix}$

For Exercises 9–20 find a solution for the system of equations by reducing the corresponding matrix to upper triangular form.

9.
$$x - y - z = -2$$
$$-x + 2y + z = 4$$
$$x + y + z = 4$$

10.
$$x + 2y + z = 0$$
$$-x - y + z = 1$$
$$2x + y + z = 2$$

11.
$$x + y - z = -1$$
$$2x + y + z = -1$$
$$x - y - 2z = -6$$

12.
$$x - y - 2z = 2$$
$$-2x - y + z = -1$$
$$3x - 2y - 10z = -5$$

13.
$$2x - y + z = -2$$
$$x + y + z = 0$$
$$-3x - y - z = 0$$

14.
$$3x - y - z = 1$$
$$-2x + y + z = 0$$
$$x + 4y + z = 3$$

15.
$$x + y + z = -2$$
$$2x - y + z = 0$$
$$-x + y - z = -2$$

16.
$$x - y + 3z = 3$$
$$x + y + z = 3$$
$$2x + y = 3$$

17.
$$x_1 + x_2 + x_3 + x_4 = 2$$
$$x_1 + 2x_2 + x_3 - x_4 = -1$$
$$-x_1 - x_2 - x_3 + 2x_4 = 1$$
$$x_1 + 2x_2 + 2x_3 + x_4 = 2$$

18.
$$x_1 - x_2 + x_3 + x_4 = 2$$
$$x_1 - 2x_2 - x_3 - x_4 = 2$$
$$2x_1 + x_2 + x_3 - 2x_4 = 7$$
$$-x_1 + x_2 - x_3 + x_4 = -4$$

19.
$$x_1 - 2x_2 + x_3 + x_4 = -2$$
$$-x_1 + x_2 - x_3 + 2x_4 = 7$$
$$2x_1 - x_2 - x_3 + 3x_4 = 1$$
$$x_1 + 3x_2 + 2x_3 - x_4 = -1$$

20.
$$x_1 + x_2 + x_3 + x_4 = 4$$
$$2x_1 + x_2 - x_3 - x_4 = 0$$
$$-x_1 - x_2 + x_3 + x_4 = 2$$
$$x_1 + 2x_2 - 2x_3 - x_4 = -4$$

5.6 Determinants of a Square Matrix (optional)

If a matrix has the same number of rows and columns, it is called a **square matrix**. If the number a is an element of some square matrix A, then the **minor** of element a is the determinant of the **submatrix** obtained by deleting the row and column of matrix A in which the element a appears. For example, the minor of a_1 in the matrix

$$A = \begin{bmatrix} a_1 & b_1 & c_1 \\ a_2 & b_2 & c_2 \\ a_3 & b_3 & c_3 \end{bmatrix}$$

is given by

$$\begin{bmatrix} b_2 & c_2 \\ b_3 & c_3 \end{bmatrix}$$

and the minor of a_2 in matrix A is given by

$$\begin{bmatrix} b_1 & c_1 \\ b_3 & c_3 \end{bmatrix}$$

The determinant of a matrix with three rows and three columns is found by multiplying each element in the first column of the matrix by the minor of that element and then subtracting the second product from the sum of the other two products. That is, we define the determinant of a 3 by 3 matrix as follows.

5.6.1   Definition: Determinant

$$\begin{vmatrix} a_1 & b_1 & c_1 \\ a_2 & b_2 & c_2 \\ a_3 & b_3 & c_3 \end{vmatrix} = a_1 \begin{vmatrix} b_2 & c_2 \\ b_3 & c_3 \end{vmatrix} - a_2 \begin{vmatrix} b_1 & c_1 \\ b_3 & c_3 \end{vmatrix} + a_3 \begin{vmatrix} b_1 & c_1 \\ b_2 & c_2 \end{vmatrix}$$

Example 1:   Calculate the determinant.

$$\begin{vmatrix} 2 & -1 & 4 \\ 3 & 1 & 1 \\ -1 & 2 & -1 \end{vmatrix}$$

Solution: We apply Definition 5.6.1. Thus,

$$\begin{vmatrix} 2 & -1 & 4 \\ 3 & 1 & 1 \\ -1 & 2 & -1 \end{vmatrix} = (2)\begin{vmatrix} 1 & 1 \\ 2 & -1 \end{vmatrix} - (3)\begin{vmatrix} -1 & 4 \\ 2 & -1 \end{vmatrix} + (-1)\begin{vmatrix} -1 & 4 \\ 1 & 1 \end{vmatrix}$$

$$= 2(-3) - 3(-7) + (-1)(-5)$$

$$= 20$$

Cramer's Rule can be used to solve a system of three first degree equations in three variables. We state the rule for such systems.

5.6.2   Theorem: *Cramer's Rule*

For the system of three first degree equations

$$a_1 x + b_1 y + c_1 z = d_1$$
$$a_2 x + b_2 y + c_2 z = d_2$$
$$a_3 x + b_3 y + c_3 z = d_3$$

let

$$D = \begin{vmatrix} a_1 & b_1 & c_1 \\ a_2 & b_2 & c_2 \\ a_3 & b_3 & c_3 \end{vmatrix} \qquad D_x = \begin{vmatrix} d_1 & b_1 & c_1 \\ d_2 & b_2 & c_2 \\ d_3 & b_3 & c_3 \end{vmatrix}$$

$$D_y = \begin{vmatrix} a_1 & d_1 & c_1 \\ a_2 & d_2 & c_2 \\ a_3 & d_3 & c_3 \end{vmatrix} \qquad D_z = \begin{vmatrix} a_1 & b_1 & d_1 \\ a_2 & b_2 & d_2 \\ a_3 & b_3 & d_3 \end{vmatrix}$$

If $D \neq 0$, then the solution set of the system is $\{(x, y, z)\}$, where

$$x = \frac{D_x}{D} \qquad y = \frac{D_y}{D} \qquad z = \frac{D_z}{D}$$

Example 2:   Use Cramer's Rule to find the solution of the system.

$$x - 2y + z = 1$$
$$-3x + 2y + z = 5$$
$$2x - y + 3z = 0$$

Solution: First, we calculate the determinant of the coefficient matrix.

$$D = \begin{vmatrix} 1 & -2 & 1 \\ -3 & 2 & 1 \\ 2 & -1 & 3 \end{vmatrix} = (1)\begin{vmatrix} 2 & 1 \\ -1 & 3 \end{vmatrix} - (-3)\begin{vmatrix} -2 & 1 \\ -1 & 3 \end{vmatrix} + (2)\begin{vmatrix} -2 & 1 \\ 2 & 1 \end{vmatrix}$$

$$= (1)(7) + 3(-5) + 2(-4)$$
$$= -16$$

Next, we replace the first column of the coefficient matrix, which is the column that contains the coefficients of x, by the constant terms of the system.

$$D_x = \begin{vmatrix} 1 & -2 & 1 \\ 5 & 2 & 1 \\ 0 & -1 & 3 \end{vmatrix} = (1)\begin{vmatrix} 2 & 1 \\ -1 & 3 \end{vmatrix} - (5)\begin{vmatrix} -2 & 1 \\ -1 & 3 \end{vmatrix} + (0)\begin{vmatrix} -2 & 1 \\ 2 & 1 \end{vmatrix}$$

$$= (1)(7) - 5(-5)$$
$$= 32$$

Next, we replace the second column of the coefficient matrix, which is the column that contains the coefficients of y, by the constant terms of the system.

$$D_y = \begin{vmatrix} 1 & 1 & 1 \\ -3 & 5 & 1 \\ 2 & 0 & 3 \end{vmatrix} = (1)\begin{vmatrix} 5 & 1 \\ 0 & 3 \end{vmatrix} - (-3)\begin{vmatrix} 1 & 1 \\ 0 & 3 \end{vmatrix} + (2)\begin{vmatrix} 1 & 1 \\ 5 & 1 \end{vmatrix}$$

$$= (1)(15) + 3(3) + 2(-4)$$

$$= 16$$

Next, we replace the third column of the coefficient matrix, which is the column that contains the coefficients of z, by the constant terms of the system.

$$D_z = \begin{vmatrix} 1 & -2 & 1 \\ -3 & 2 & 5 \\ 2 & -1 & 0 \end{vmatrix} = (1)\begin{vmatrix} 2 & 5 \\ -1 & 0 \end{vmatrix} - (-3)\begin{vmatrix} -2 & 1 \\ -1 & 0 \end{vmatrix} + (2)\begin{vmatrix} -2 & 1 \\ 2 & 5 \end{vmatrix}$$

$$= (1)(5) + 3(1) + 2(-12)$$

$$= -16$$

Hence,

$$x = \frac{D_x}{D} = \frac{32}{-16} = -2$$

$$y = \frac{D_y}{D} = \frac{16}{-16} = -1$$

$$z = \frac{D_z}{D} = \frac{-16}{-16} = 1$$

The solution is $(-2, -1, 1)$.

———

The determinant of a 3 by 3 matrix can also be found by multiplying each element in the first row of the matrix by the minor of the element and then subtracting the second product from the sum of the other two products. In fact, if we multiply each element in any row or any column of the matrix by the minor of the element and then add or subtract the products according to the + or − signs in the following array, we obtain the determinant of the matrix.

$$\begin{vmatrix} + & - & + \\ - & + & - \\ + & - & + \end{vmatrix}$$

Example 3: Calculate the determinant of the matrix of Example 1 by using
(a) the minors of the elements in the third row.
(b) the minors of the elements in the second column.

Solution:
(a) We multiply each element in the third row by its minor and then alternately add and subtract the products.

$$\longrightarrow \begin{vmatrix} 2 & -1 & 4 \\ 3 & 1 & 1 \\ -1 & 2 & -1 \end{vmatrix} = (-1)\begin{vmatrix} -1 & 4 \\ 1 & 1 \end{vmatrix} - (2)\begin{vmatrix} 2 & 4 \\ 3 & 1 \end{vmatrix} + (-1)\begin{vmatrix} 2 & -1 \\ 3 & 1 \end{vmatrix}$$

$$= (-1)(-5) - 2(-10) + (-1)(5)$$

$$= 20$$

(b) We multiply each element in the second column by its minor and then alternately subtract and add the products.

$$\begin{vmatrix} 2 & -1 & 4 \\ 3 & 1 & 1 \\ -1 & 2 & -1 \end{vmatrix} = -(-1)\begin{vmatrix} 3 & 1 \\ -1 & -1 \end{vmatrix} + (1)\begin{vmatrix} 2 & 4 \\ -1 & -1 \end{vmatrix} - (2)\begin{vmatrix} 2 & 4 \\ 3 & 1 \end{vmatrix}$$

$$\uparrow$$

$$= (1)(-2) + (1)(2) - (2)(-10)$$

$$= 20$$

Note that the results in part (a) and part (b) both agree with the result
obtained in Example 1.

If we replace any row in a 3 by 3 matrix by the sum of that row and
some multiple of another row, the determinant of the resulting matrix is the
same as the determinant of the original matrix. And if we replace any column
in a 3 by 3 matrix by the sum of that column and some multiple of another
column, the determinant of the resulting matrix is the same as the determinant
of the original matrix. If the multiples are chosen so that the resulting matrix
contains a row or column with two zeros, then the determinant is easy to
calculate.

Example 4: Calculate the determinant by first obtaining two zeros in the
first row.

$$\begin{vmatrix} 1 & -2 & 1 \\ -3 & 2 & 1 \\ 2 & -1 & 3 \end{vmatrix}$$

Solution: Let the first column be the pivot column. We obtain two zeros in the first row by adding 2 times the first column to the second column and -1 times the first column to the third column. Thus,

$$
\begin{vmatrix}
① & -2 & 1 \\
-3 & 2 & 1 \\
2 & -1 & 3
\end{vmatrix}
=
\begin{vmatrix}
1 & 0 & 0 \\
-3 & -4 & 4 \\
2 & 3 & 1
\end{vmatrix}
$$

Now we calculate the determinant by using the minors of the elements in the first row of the matrix. Thus,

$$
\begin{vmatrix}
1 & 0 & 0 \\
-3 & -4 & 4 \\
2 & 3 & 1
\end{vmatrix}
= (1)\begin{vmatrix} -4 & 4 \\ 3 & 1 \end{vmatrix}
- (0)\begin{vmatrix} -3 & 4 \\ 2 & 1 \end{vmatrix}
+ (0)\begin{vmatrix} -3 & -4 \\ 2 & 3 \end{vmatrix}
$$

$$= (1)(-16)$$

$$= -16$$

Note that the matrix of this example is also the coefficient matrix of the system of equations of Example 2, and note that the result obtained here agrees with the result obtained in Example 2.

―――――――――――――――――――――――――――――――――――――――

We cannot apply the other two elementary row operations for matrices when calculating a determinant. That is, if we interchange two rows in a matrix or if we multiply each element in a row by the same nonzero constant, the determinant of the resulting matrix is not the same as the determinant of the original matrix.

If the number a is the element in the ith row and the jth column of a square matrix, then the **cofactor** of a is the product of $(-1)^{i+j}$ and the minor of a. For example, if a is in the third row and the fourth column of a square matrix, then the cofactor of a is the product of $(-1)^{3+4} = -1$ and the minor of a. Whereas if a is in the fifth row and the third column of a square matrix, then the cofactor of a is the product of $(-1)^{5+3} = 1$ and the minor of a. The determinant of any square matrix is found by multiplying each element in any row or column by the cofactor of the element and then adding the products. Note that this is the same as multiplying each element in any row or column by its minor and then alternately adding and subtracting the products.

Cramer's Rule can be extended to find the solution set for a system of n first degree equations in n variables, provided the determinant of the coefficient matrix is not zero. If $D = 0$, then the system is either inconsistent or dependent, and thus it does not have a unique solution.

Example 5: Show that the system does not have a unique solution.

$$
\begin{aligned}
x_1 + x_2 \qquad\qquad &= 1 \\
x_2 - x_3 \qquad &= -1 \\
-x_1 \qquad\qquad + x_4 &= 2 \\
2x_1 + 3x_2 - 2x_3 - x_4 &= 1
\end{aligned}
$$

Solution: We calculate the determinant of the coefficient matrix. We have

$$
D = \begin{vmatrix} 1 & 1 & 0 & 0 \\ 0 & 1 & -1 & 0 \\ -1 & 0 & 0 & ① \\ 2 & 3 & -2 & -1 \end{vmatrix} \longleftarrow
$$

We let the third row be the pivot row and obtain three zeros in the last column by replacing the last row by the sum of the third row and the last row. Thus,

$$
D = \begin{vmatrix} 1 & 1 & 0 & 0 \\ 0 & 1 & -1 & 0 \\ -1 & 0 & 0 & 1 \\ 1 & 3 & -2 & 0 \end{vmatrix}
$$

We use the minors of the elements in the last column to calculate the determinant. Because the pivot element is in the third row and the fourth column, the cofactor of the pivot element is found by multiplying the minor of the pivot element by $(-1)^{3+4} = -1$. Thus, we have

$$
D = (-1) \begin{vmatrix} ① & 1 & 0 \\ 0 & 1 & -1 \\ 1 & 3 & -2 \end{vmatrix}
$$

We let the first column be the pivot column and obtain two zeros in the first row by replacing the second column by the sum of the second column and -1 times the first column. Thus,

$$
D = (-1) \begin{vmatrix} 1 & 0 & 0 \\ 0 & 1 & -1 \\ 1 & 2 & -2 \end{vmatrix} \longleftarrow
$$

We use minors of the elements in the first row to calculate the determinant.

Because the pivot element is in the first row and the first column, the cofactor of the pivot element is the product of the minor of the pivot element and $(-1)^{1+1} = 1$. Thus,

$$D = (-1)(1)\begin{vmatrix} 1 & -1 \\ 2 & -2 \end{vmatrix}$$
$$= (-1)[(-2) - (-2)]$$
$$= 0$$

Because $D = 0$, we conclude that the system does not have a unique solution. If it turns out that $D_{x_1} \neq 0$, then the system is inconsistent and there is no solution. However, if $D_{x_1} = 0$, then the system is dependent and the solution set contains infinitely many members.

EXERCISES 5.6

For Exercises 1–4 use Definition 5.6.1 to calculate the simplest form of the indicated determinant.

1. $\begin{vmatrix} 2 & 1 & 1 \\ 3 & -1 & 2 \\ 1 & 2 & -2 \end{vmatrix}$

2. $\begin{vmatrix} 2 & 1 & 1 \\ 1 & 2 & 3 \\ -1 & 2 & -2 \end{vmatrix}$

3. $\begin{vmatrix} 3 & -2 & 1 \\ -1 & 1 & 3 \\ -2 & 2 & 1 \end{vmatrix}$

4. $\begin{vmatrix} -3 & 1 & 2 \\ 3 & 2 & 1 \\ 1 & 1 & -2 \end{vmatrix}$

For Exercises 5–8 use Cramer's Rule to find a solution for the system of equations.

5. $\begin{aligned} x + 2y - 2z &= 2 \\ 2x - y + 3z &= 1 \\ -x + 2y - 2z &= -1 \end{aligned}$

6. $\begin{aligned} 2x + y - z &= -1 \\ -x + 2y + z &= 2 \\ x - y + 2z &= 1 \end{aligned}$

7. $\begin{aligned} -2x + 3y - 2z &= 7 \\ 3x - 2y + 3z &= -3 \\ 4x + 5y - 5z &= 1 \end{aligned}$

8. $\begin{aligned} 3x + 2y - 2z &= 8 \\ 2x - 3y + 3z &= 1 \\ 5x + 4y + 5z &= -4 \end{aligned}$

For Exercises 9–12 calculate the simplest form of the indicated determinant by using the minors of the elements in whichever row or column contains the most zeros.

9. $\begin{vmatrix} -2 & -1 & 0 \\ 5 & 4 & 0 \\ -1 & 3 & 1 \end{vmatrix}$

10. $\begin{vmatrix} -1 & 3 & 1 \\ 0 & 2 & 0 \\ 2 & 1 & -5 \end{vmatrix}$

11. $\begin{vmatrix} 2 & -1 & 4 \\ -2 & -4 & -5 \\ 0 & 3 & 0 \end{vmatrix}$

12. $\begin{vmatrix} 0 & -3 & 0 \\ 2 & 4 & -3 \\ 1 & 3 & -4 \end{vmatrix}$

For Exercises 13–16 calculate the simplest form of the indicated determinant by first obtaining two zeros in a row or column.

13.
$$\begin{vmatrix} 2 & 1 & 3 \\ 3 & 2 & -3 \\ -4 & -3 & 2 \end{vmatrix}$$

14.
$$\begin{vmatrix} 4 & -3 & 2 \\ -2 & 1 & 3 \\ 3 & -2 & -2 \end{vmatrix}$$

15.
$$\begin{vmatrix} 3 & -2 & 4 \\ -2 & 3 & -2 \\ 1 & -2 & 4 \end{vmatrix}$$

16.
$$\begin{vmatrix} 3 & -4 & 3 \\ 2 & -2 & 1 \\ -5 & 3 & -2 \end{vmatrix}$$

For Exercises 17–20 calculate the simplest form of the indicated determinant by first obtaining three zeros in a row or column.

17.
$$\begin{vmatrix} 1 & 2 & -1 & 1 \\ -1 & -1 & 2 & 1 \\ 1 & 2 & 1 & -1 \\ 2 & 3 & -2 & 2 \end{vmatrix}$$

18.
$$\begin{vmatrix} 1 & 2 & -1 & 1 \\ 3 & -1 & -2 & 1 \\ -2 & 1 & 1 & -3 \\ 1 & 4 & -1 & -1 \end{vmatrix}$$

19.
$$\begin{vmatrix} 0 & 2 & -1 & 3 \\ 1 & 1 & -1 & 2 \\ -3 & 1 & 2 & -1 \\ 2 & 1 & -1 & 3 \end{vmatrix}$$

20.
$$\begin{vmatrix} 2 & 1 & -1 & 1 \\ 3 & 0 & 2 & -1 \\ 1 & -1 & 3 & 3 \\ -4 & 1 & 2 & 2 \end{vmatrix}$$

For Exercises 21–22 show that the system does not have a unique solution and determine whether there is no solution or many solutions.

21.
$$\begin{aligned}
x_1 \qquad + x_3 - 2x_4 &= 2 \\
x_2 - x_3 + x_4 &= -1 \\
2x_1 - x_2 \qquad + x_4 &= 1 \\
-x_1 + 2x_2 \qquad - 2x_4 &= 0
\end{aligned}$$

22.
$$\begin{aligned}
x_1 + x_2 - 2x_3 \qquad\qquad &= 1 \\
x_2 + x_3 - x_4 \qquad &= 2 \\
-x_1 \qquad x_3 \qquad - x_5 &= -1 \\
2x_2 \qquad + x_4 + x_5 &= 1 \\
- 2x_3 + x_4 - x_5 &= -1
\end{aligned}$$

REVIEW EXERCISES 5

For Exercises 1–2 use the Elimination Method to find the solution set for the system of equations.

1. $2x + 3y = 2$
$\ 5x + 6y = 2$

2. $4x = 8 - 3y$
$-5y = 6x - 10$

For Exercises 3–4 use Cramer's Rule to find the solution set for the system of equations.

3. $4x - 5y = 4$
$\ 3x - 3y = 2$

4. $2x + 3y + 2 = 0$
$\ 7x + 8y + 4 = 0$

For Exercises 5–6 use the Substitution Method to find the solution set for the system of equations.

5. $2x - y = 5$
$\ 3x - 2y = 7$

6. $5x + 6y = -4$
$\ x + 4y = 2$

For Exercises 7–20 use the method that you think is best to find the solution set for the system of equations.

7. $5x - 6y = 3$
      $-2x + 5y = 4$

8. $x - 3y = y - 2$
    $x + y = 2x + 5$

9. $5(x + y) = 1 + 3x$
   $3x + 4y = 6$

10. $7x + 3y + 1 = 0$
    $3x \quad\quad - 2 = y$

11. $x + \dfrac{y}{3} = \dfrac{x + 2}{6}$
    $2x + y = 2$

12. $\dfrac{x}{4} - \dfrac{x - 2y}{2} = 1$
    $2x - 3y = 2$

13. $\dfrac{x}{2} + \dfrac{y}{3} = 1$

   $\dfrac{x}{3} + \dfrac{y}{5} = 1$

14. $\dfrac{2}{x} + \dfrac{3}{y} = 1$

    $\dfrac{3}{x} + \dfrac{5}{y} = 1$

15. $4x + y = x^2$
    $3x - y = 10$

16. $x^2 + 2y^2 = 6$
    $2x^2 + y^2 = 9$

17. $x^2 + y^2 = 25$
    $x + 2y = 5$

18. $2x^2 - y^2 = 7$
    $x - y = 3$

19. $x^2 - y^2 = 9$
    $xy = 6$

20. $\quad\quad y = x\sqrt{x}$
    $6x^2 - y^2 = 8x$

For Exercises 21–22 use either the Substitution Method or the Elimination Method to find a solution for the system of equations.

21. $x + 2y - z = 5$
     $2x - y + 3z = 0$
     $2x + y + 2z = 3$

22. $2x + 5y + 3z = 5$
     $-2x + 3y - 4z = 5$
     $4x + 2y + 5z = 4$

For Exercises 23–24 reduce the given system of equations to a triangular form and indicate whether the system has one solution, no solution, or many solutions.

23. $x + 3y - z = 1$
     $2x + y + 4z = 1$
     $4x + 7y + 2z = 1$

24. $2x - 3y + z = 5$
     $x + y + 2z = 0$
     $5x - 5y + 4z = 10$

For Exercises 25–26 find a solution for the system of equations by reducing the corresponding matrix to a triangular form.

25. $x + 2y + z = 2$
      $2x + 3y + z = 1$
     $-3x + y - 4z = -1$

26. $x_1 + x_2 - x_3 - x_4 = 1$
    $x_1 - x_2 + 2x_3 + x_4 = 2$
    $2x_1 + x_2 \quad\quad + 2x_4 = 11$
    $2x_1 \quad\quad + x_3 - x_4 = 0$

For Exercises 27–28 calculate the simplest form of the indicated determinant.

27. $\begin{vmatrix} 5 & -3 & 2 \\ 2 & 1 & -1 \\ -1 & -1 & 2 \end{vmatrix}$

28. $\begin{vmatrix} 1 & 2 & -1 & 1 \\ -1 & -1 & 2 & 2 \\ 1 & 1 & -2 & 1 \\ 2 & 1 & 3 & 1 \end{vmatrix}$

For Exercises 29–32 use the solution of a system of equations to answer the stated question.

29. How much 10% acid solution and how much 30% acid solution must be mixed to make 80 milliliters of 16% acid solution?

30. What are the dimensions of a rectangle whose area is 6 square centimeters and whose diagonal is $\sqrt{15}$ centimeters long?

31. If an object is thrown upward from a height of s_0 feet with initial velocity v_0 feet per second, after t seconds the object is at a height of s feet, with $s = s_0 + v_0 t - 16t^2$. What is the initial height and initial velocity if the object is at a height of 156 feet after 3 seconds and the object strikes the ground after 5 seconds?

32. Find an equation of the parabola with horizontal axis that contains the points $(0, 1)$, $(1, 2)$, and $(4, -1)$. [*Hint:* Use Theorem 4.3.2.]

6
functions, sequences, and series

6.1 Relations, Functions, Domain, and Range

Every set of ordered pairs is called a **relation**. The set of all first components of the ordered pairs is called the **domain** of the relation, and the set of all second components of the ordered pairs is called the **range** of the relation. For example, if R is the relation given by

$$R = \{(1, -2), (-3, 1), (3, -2)\} \qquad (1)$$

then the domain and range of R are given by

$$\text{Domain} = \{1, -3, 3\}$$
$$\text{Range} = \{-2, 1\}$$

Figure 6.1.1 shows the graph of the relation R and the projection of that graph onto the x-axis. The projection consists of three points whose x-coordinates are -3, 1, and 3, the members of the domain of R. Figure 6.1.2 shows the graph of the relation R and the projection of that graph onto the y-axis. The projection consists of two points whose y-coordinates are -2 and 1, the members of the range of R.

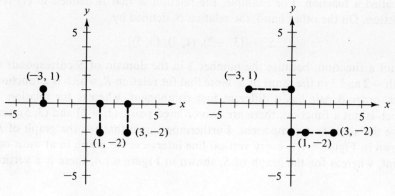

Figure 6.1.1   Figure 6.1.2

Example 1:   Find the domain and range of the relation

$$\{(x, y): x^2 + 4y^2 = 36\}$$

Solution: The graph of the relation is the ellipse shown in Figure 6.1.3. The domain of the relation is the projection of the graph onto the x-axis, and thus the domain is $\{x: -6 \leq x \leq 6\}$. The range of the relation is the projection of the graph onto the y-axis, and thus the range is $\{y: -3 \leq y \leq 3\}$.

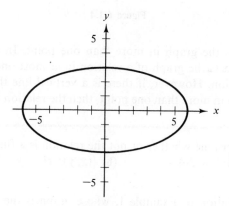

Figure 6.1.3

Every relation establishes a correspondence between the members of its domain and the members of its range. If for each member in the domain of the relation there corresponds only *one* member in the range, then the relation is called a **function**. For example, the relation R that is defined in (1) is a function. On the other hand, the relation S, defined by

$$S = \{(3, -2), (1, 2), (3, 5)\}$$

is not a function, because the number 3 in the domain of S corresponds to both -2 and 5 in the range of S. Note that for relation R, which is a function, each ordered pair has a different first component, whereas for relation S, which is not a function, there are two ordered pairs, $(3, -2)$ and $(3, 5)$, that have the same first component. Furthermore, note that for the graph of R, shown in Figure 6.1.1, every vertical line intersects the graph in at most one point, whereas for the graph of S, shown in Figure 6.1.4, there is a vertical

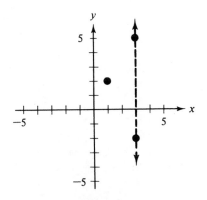

Figure 6.1.4

line that intersects the graph in more than one point. In general, if every vertical line intersects the graph of a relation in at most one point, then the relation is a function. However, if there is a vertical line that intersects the graph of a relation in more than one point, then the relation is not a function.

Example 2: Determine whether or not the relation is a function.
(a) $\{(x, y): x^2 + 4y^2 = 36\}$ (b) $\{(x, y): x^2 + y = 4\}$

Solution:
(a) This is the relation of Example 1, whose graph is the ellipse shown in Figure 6.1.3. Because there is a vertical line that intersects the graph in more than one point, the relation is not a function.
(b) The graph of this relation is the parabola shown in Figure 6.1.5. Because every vertical line intersects the graph in only one point, the relation is a function.

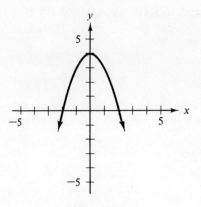

Figure 6.1.5

If x and y are the variables used to represent the members in the domain and range, respectively, of a relation that is a function, then we say that **y is a function of x**. Therefore, y is a function of x if and only if for each replacement of x from the domain there corresponds one and only one value of y. Note that for the relation of Example 2(b), which is a function, there is a unique y-form of the equation. We have

$$x^2 + y = 4$$
$$y = -x^2 + 4$$

However, for the relation of Example 2(a), which is not a function, there is not a unique y-form of the equation. We have

$$x^2 + 4y^2 = 36$$
$$4y^2 = -x^2 + 36$$
$$2y = \pm\sqrt{-x^2 + 36}$$
$$y = \frac{\pm\sqrt{-x^2 + 36}}{2}$$

If an equation in x and y can be solved uniquely for y, then y is a function of x. On the other hand, if there exist two or more equations when we solve for y, then y is not a function of x.

Example 3:   Show whether or not y is a function of x.
(a) $\{(x, y): x + y^3 = 2\}$ **(b)** $\{(x, y): x - y^2 = 4\}$

Solution: We attempt to solve the equation for y.

(a)
$$x + y^3 = 2$$
$$y^3 = 2 - x$$
$$y = \sqrt[3]{2 - x}$$

Because there is only one real cube root of a real number, there is a unique y-form for the equation. Thus, y is a function of x.

(b)
$$x - y^2 = 4$$
$$y^2 = x - 4$$
$$y = \pm\sqrt{x - 4}$$

Because there are two real square roots of a positive number, there is not a unique y-form for the equation. Thus, y is not a function of x.

Whenever y is a function of x and the function f is determined by an equation with variables x and y, it is possible to write the equation in the form

$$y = f(x)$$

where $f(x)$ is an expression whose only variable is x. For the function of Example 3(a) we found

$$y = \sqrt[3]{2 - x}$$

and thus

$$f(x) = \sqrt[3]{2 - x}$$

for this function.

Example 4: Let $f = \{(x, y): 2x - 3y = 6\}$, and find the expression $f(x)$ that defines the function f.

Solution: We want to find the expression $f(x)$ such that the equation which defines the function f can be written in the form $y = f(x)$. Thus, we solve the given equation for y.

$$2x - 3y = 6$$
$$3y = 2x - 6$$
$$y = \frac{2x - 6}{3}$$

We conclude that

$$f(x) = \frac{2x - 6}{3}$$

If a function f is defined by an expression $f(x)$, then the domain of f is the set of all real replacements for x that result in a real value for y, where $y = f(x)$. For example, if f is the function defined by

$$f(x) = x^2 - 3x + 2$$

then the domain of f is R because every real replacement of x results in a real value for y, where

$$y = x^2 - 3x + 2$$

In general, if $f(x)$ is any polynomial expression, then the domain of the function f is R.

Example 5:   Find the domain of the function

$$f = \{(x, y) \colon 4x^2 y = x + y\}$$

Solution: First, we find the expression $f(x)$ such that $y = f(x)$. We solve the given equation for y.

$$4x^2 y = x + y$$
$$4x^2 y - y = x$$
$$(4x^2 - 1)y = x$$

$$y = \frac{x}{4x^2 - 1}$$

Thus, we have

$$f(x) = \frac{x}{4x^2 - 1} \tag{2}$$

Because division by zero is not defined, from Equation (2) we conclude that

$$4x^2 - 1 \neq 0$$
$$x^2 \neq \tfrac{1}{4}$$
$$x \neq \pm\tfrac{1}{2}$$

Thus, the domain of f is $\{x \colon x \neq \tfrac{1}{2}, x \neq -\tfrac{1}{2}\}$

Example 6:   Let $f(x) = \sqrt{4 - x}$.
(a) Find the domain of the function f.
(b) Sketch the graph of the function f.

Solution:

(a) Because the square root of a negative number is not real, the expression under the radical sign must be nonnegative. Thus,

$$4 - x \geq 0$$
$$x \leq 4$$

Therefore, the domain of f is $\{x: x \leq 4\}$.

(b) Because $y = f(x)$, the graph of f is the graph of the equation

$$y = \sqrt{4 - x} \tag{3}$$

Squaring both sides of Equation (3), we obtain

$$y^2 = 4 - x \tag{4}$$

The graph of Equation (4) is the parabola shown in Figure 6.1.6. However, Figure 6.1.6 cannot be the graph of the function f because there are vertical lines that intersect the parabola in more than one point. Note that

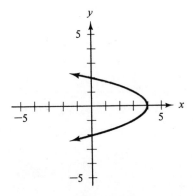

Figure 6.1.6

in Equation (3) we must have $y \geq 0$ because the principal square root of a number is not negative. Thus, the graph of Equation (3) is the part of the parabola for which $y \geq 0$. That is, the graph of Equation (3) is the upper half of the parabola, as illustrated in Figure 6.1.7. Because Equation (3) defines the function f, Figure 6.1.7 is also the graph of f.

The graph of the function defined by the equation

$$y = -\sqrt{4 - x} \tag{5}$$

is the curve shown in Figure 6.1.8, which is the lower half of the parabola of Figure 6.1.6. Note that the result of squaring both sides of Equation

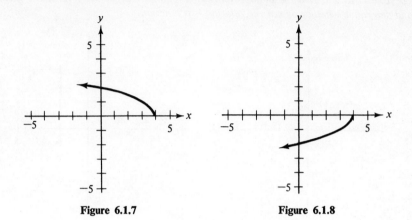

Figure 6.1.7 **Figure 6.1.8**

(5) is Equation (4). Thus, Equation (4) defines a relation that is the union of two functions; one function is defined by Equation (3), and the other function is defined by Equation (5).

As the examples have illustrated, the following steps are used to find the domain of a function that is defined by an equation in x and y. First, solve the equation for y.

---

1. If $y = f(x)$ and $f(x)$ is a polynomial expression, the domain of the function is R.
2. If $y = f(x)/g(x)$ and both $f(x)$ and $g(x)$ are polynomial expressions, the domain of the function is $\{x: g(x) \neq 0\}$.
3. If $y = \sqrt{f(x)}$ and $f(x)$ is a polynomial expression, the domain of the function is $\{x: f(x) \geq 0\}$.
4. If $y = f(x)$ and $f(x)$ is any expression not described above, then the domain of the function is the set of all real replacements for x that result in a real value for $f(x)$.

EXERCISES 6.1

For Exercises 1–8 find the domain and range of the relation whose graph is given, and determine whether or not the relation is a function.

1.

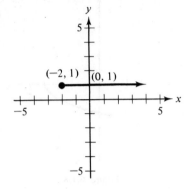

2.

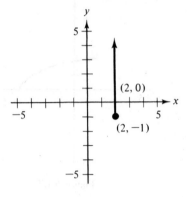

3.

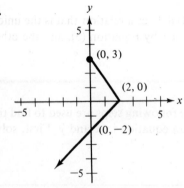

4.

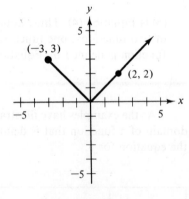

5.

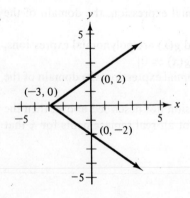

6.

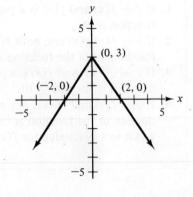

7.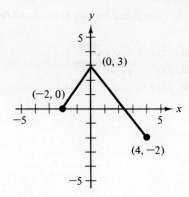

8.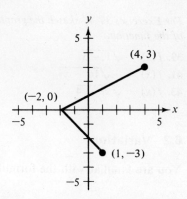

For Exercises 9–16 sketch the graph of the relation that is given. Use the graph to find the domain and range of the relation and to determine whether or not the relation is a function.

9. $\{(x, y): x + 3 = 0\}$

10. $\{(x, y): y - 2 = 0\}$

11. $\{(x, y): 2x - y = 4\}$

12. $\{(x, y): x + |y| = 0\}$

13. $\{(x, y): x + y^2 = 4\}$

14. $\{(x, y): 4x + y = x^2\}$

15. $\{(x, y): 2x^2 + y^2 = 16\}$

16. $\{(x, y): x^2 - y^2 = 3\}$

For Exercises 17–22 show whether or not y is a function of x without sketching the graph of the relation.

17. $\{(x, y): 3x - 2y = 6\}$

18. $\{(x, y): |x| + y = 2\}$

19. $\{(x, y): x + y^2 = 1\}$

20. $\{(x, y): y(y + 4) = x\}$

21. $\{(x, y): x^2 - y^3 = 1\}$

22. $\{(x, y): y\sqrt{y} = x\}$

For Exercises 23–28 find the expression f(x) that defines the function f.

23. $f = \{(x, y): x + 2y = 4\}$

24. $f = \{(x, y): 2x - 5y = 1\}$

25. $f = \{(x, y): xy + 2y = 3\}$

26. $f = \{(x, y): x^2y = 2y + x\}$

27. $f = \{(x, y): x - y^3 = 2\}$

28. $f = \{(x, y): xy^3 + y^3 = 1\}$

For Exercises 29–38 find the domain of the function f.

29. $f(x) = 2x - 3$

30. $f(x) = x^2 + 4x$

31. $f(x) = \dfrac{x}{x + 3}$

32. $f(x) = \dfrac{x + 2}{4x^2 + x}$

33. $f(x) = \sqrt{x + 2}$

34. $f(x) = \sqrt{3 - 2x}$

35. $f = \{(x, y): x^2y = 4 + y\}$

36. $f = \{(x, y): 2xy = x + y\}$

37. $f = \{(x, y): x^2y = 1 - y\}$

38. $f = \{(x, y): x - y^3 = 1\}$

For Exercises 39–44 sketch the graph of the function f, and find the domain and range of the function.

39. $f(x) = \sqrt{1 - x}$ **40.** $f(x) = -\sqrt{x + 4}$

41. $f(x) = -\sqrt{16 - x^2}$ **42.** $f(x) = \frac{1}{2}\sqrt{36 - x^2}$

43. $f(x) = \sqrt{x^2 - 4}$ **44.** $f(x) = -\sqrt{x^2 + 1}$

6.2 Variation

You are familiar with the formula

$$C = 2\pi r$$

which expresses C, the number of units in the circumference of a circle, as a function of r, the number of units in the radius of the circle, where 2π is a constant that is approximately 6.28. We say that C **varies directly as** r. In general, we have the following definition.

6.2.1   Definition

The variable y varies directly as the variable x if

$$y = kx$$

where k is a constant with $k \neq 0$.

Example 1:   The variable y varies directly as x, and $y = 5$ when $x = 2$.
(a) Find the equation that expresses y as a function of x.
(b) Find the value of y when $x = 3$.

Solution:
(a) We apply Definition 6.2.1. Because y varies directly as x, there is some constant k such that

$$y = kx \tag{1}$$

We let $y = 5$ and $x = 2$ in Equation (1) and solve for k.

$$5 = k \cdot 2$$

$$k = \tfrac{5}{2} \tag{2}$$

Substituting from Equation (2) into Equation (1), we have

$$y = \tfrac{5}{2}x \tag{3}$$

which is the equation that expresses y as a function of x.

(b) To find the value of y when $x = 3$, we let $x = 3$ in Equation (3). Thus,

$$y = \tfrac{5}{2}(3)$$
$$= \tfrac{15}{2}$$

Thus, $y = \tfrac{15}{2}$ when $x = 3$.

If a body is allowed to fall for t seconds, it will fall a distance of d feet, with

$$d = 16t^2$$

We say that d varies directly as the square of t. In general, we have the following definition.

6.2.2   Definition

The variable y varies directly as the nth power of x if

$$y = kx^n$$

where n and k are constants with $k \neq 0$ and $n > 0$.

Example 2:   If a ball is allowed to roll down an inclined plane, the distance that it rolls varies directly as the square of the time during which it has been rolling. Suppose that the ball rolls 60 centimeters in 3 seconds. How far will it roll in 5 seconds?

Solution: Let t seconds be the time required for the ball to roll s centimeters. Because s varies directly as the square of t, we have the formula

$$s = kt^2 \tag{4}$$

Because the ball rolls 60 centimeters in 3 seconds, we let $s = 60$ and $t = 3$ in Equation (4) and solve for k.

$$60 = k(3^2)$$
$$k = \tfrac{20}{3}$$

Substituting the value for k into Equation (4), we obtain

$$s = \tfrac{20}{3}t^2 \tag{5}$$

which is the equation that expresses s as a function of t. Because we want to find how far the ball rolls in 5 seconds, we now let $t = 5$ in Equation (5).

Thus,

$$s = \tfrac{20}{3} \cdot 5^2$$
$$= 166\tfrac{2}{3}$$

Therefore, the ball rolls $166\tfrac{2}{3}$ centimeters in 5 seconds.

If a force of 10 pounds is acting on a body whose mass is m slugs, then the body will accelerate at the rate of a feet per second per second, with

$$a = \frac{10}{m}$$

We say that a **varies inversely as** m. In general, we have the following definition.

6.2.3   Definition

The variable y varies inversely as the nth power of x if

$$y = \frac{k}{x^n}$$

where k and n are constants with $k \neq 0$ and $n > 0$.

Example 3:   The weight of a body varies inversely as the square of its distance from the center of the earth. If an astronaut weighs 160 pounds on the earth's surface, how much does he weigh at a distance of 500 miles above the earth's surface? Assume the radius of the earth is 4000 miles.

Solution: Let w pounds be the weight of the astronaut when he is x miles from the center of the earth. Because w varies inversely as the square of x, we have the formula

$$w = \frac{k}{x^2} \tag{6}$$

Because the astronaut weighs 160 pounds when he is 4000 miles from the center of the earth, we let $w = 160$ and $x = 4000$ in Equation (6) and solve for k.

$$160 = \frac{k}{(4000)^2}$$
$$k = (160)(4000)^2$$
$$= (2.56)10^9$$

Substituting the value for k into Equation (6), we have

$$w = \frac{(2.56)10^9}{x^2} \qquad (7)$$

which is the equation that expresses w as the function of x. When the astronaut is at a distance of 500 miles above the surface of the earth, he is 4500 miles from the center of the earth. Thus, we let $x = 4500$ in Equation (7).

$$w = \frac{(2.56)10^9}{(4500)^2}$$

$$\approx 126$$

Therefore, the astronaut weighs approximately 126 pounds when he is 500 miles above the surface of the earth.

If r units is the radius and h units is the altitude of a right circular cylinder, then V cubic units is its volume, where

$$V = \pi r^2 h$$

We say that V **varies jointly as h and the square of r.** In general, we have the following definition.

6.2.4   Definition

The variable z **varies jointly as the mth power of x and the nth power of y** if

$$z = kx^m y^n$$

where k, m, and n are constants with $k \neq 0$, $m > 0$, and $n > 0$.

Example 4: The safe load of a rectangular beam of fixed length varies jointly as the width of the beam and the square of the depth of the beam. If a beam that is 4 inches wide and 8 inches deep has a safe load of 1200 pounds, what is the safe load of the beam if it is turned so that the width is 8 inches and the depth is 4 inches?

Solution: Let x inches be the width of the beam, y inches be the depth of the beam, and S pounds be the safe load. Because S varies jointly as x and the square of y, we have the formula

$$S = kxy^2 \qquad (8)$$

Because the safe load of the beam is 1200 pounds when the width is 4 inches and the depth is 8 inches, we let $S = 1200$, $x = 4$, and $y = 8$ in Equation (8) and solve for k.

$$1200 = k(4)(8)^2$$

$$k = \tfrac{75}{16}$$

Substituting the value for k into Equation (8), we have

$$S = \tfrac{75}{16}xy^2 \tag{9}$$

which expresses S as a function of x and y. Because we want to find the safe load of the beam when the width is 8 inches and the depth is 4 inches, we let $x = 8$ and $y = 4$ in Equation (9). Thus,

$$S = \tfrac{75}{16}(8)(4^2)$$

$$= 600$$

We conclude that the safe load of the beam is 600 pounds.

Example 5:   The electrical resistance of a wire varies directly as its length and inversely as the square of its diameter. If a wire 10 meters long and 0.2 centimeters in diameter has a resistance of 0.5 ohms, what is the resistance of a wire of the same material that is 25 meters long and 0.3 centimeters in diameter?

Solution: Let L meters be the length of the wire, let D centimeters be the diameter of the wire, and let R ohms be the resistance of the wire. We are given that

$$R = \frac{kL}{D^2} \tag{10}$$

Because a wire 10 meters long and 0.2 centimeters in diameter has a resistance of 0.5 ohms, we let $L = 10$, $D = 0.2$, and $R = 0.5$ in Equation (10) and solve for k.

$$0.5 = \frac{k(10)}{(0.2)^2}$$

$$k = 0.002$$

Substituting the value for k into Equation (10), we have

$$R = \frac{0.002L}{D^2} \tag{11}$$

Because we want to find the resistance of a wire that is 25 meters long and 0.3 centimeters in diameter, we let $L = 25$ and $D = 0.3$ in Equation (11). Thus,

$$R = \frac{(0.002)(25)}{(0.3)^2}$$

$$\approx 0.556$$

Therefore, the resistance of the wire is approximately 0.556 ohms.

EXERCISES 6.2

For Exercises 1–6 find an equation that defines the indicated functional relationship.

1. If y varies directly as x and $y = 15$ when $x = 6$, find an equation that expresses y as a function of x.

2. If y varies directly as the square of x and $y = 36$ when $x = 4$, find an equation that expresses y as a function of x.

3. If p varies directly as the square root of q and $p = 6$ when $q = 4$, find an equation that expresses p as a function of q.

4. If p varies inversely as q and $p = 4$ when $q = 3$, find an equation that expresses p as a function of q.

5. If r varies jointly as s and t and $r = 9$ when $s = 3$ and $t = 4$, find an equation that expresses r as a function of s and t.

6. If r varies directly as the square root of s and inversely as the square of t and $r = 6$ when $s = 9$ and $t = 4$, find an equation that expresses r as a function of s and t.

For Exercises 7–12 use an equation that defines the functional relationship among the variables to find the indicated value.

7. If y varies inversely as x and $y = 4$ when $x = 12$, what is y when $x = 3$?

8. If y varies directly as x and $y = 6$ when $x = 4$, what is y when $x = 10$?

9. If p varies directly as the square of q and $p = 8$ when $q = 6$, what is p when $q = 4$?

10. If p varies inversely as the square root of q and $p = 6$ when $q = 3$, what is p when $q = 12$?

11. If r varies directly as s and inversely as t and $r = 15$ when $s = 6$ and $t = 2$, what is r when $s = 4$ and $t = 6$?

12. If r varies jointly as the square of s and the cube of t and $r = 16$ when $s = 4$ and $t = 2$, what is r when $s = 3$ and $t = 4$?

For Exercises 13–26 use a formula that expresses the functional relationship among the variables to answer the stated question.

13. The fluid pressure on an object that is immersed in a liquid varies directly as the depth of the object. If the pressure is 8 pounds per square inch at a depth of 18 feet, what is the pressure at a depth of 90 feet?

14. Hooke's Law states that the amount that a spring is stretched beyond its normal length varies directly as the force applied. If a weight of 6 pounds stretches an 8-inch spring to a length of 10 inches, what is the length of the spring when a weight of 15 pounds is applied?

15. The distance that an object falls varies directly as the square of the time during which it falls. If a skydiver falls 20 meters during the first 2 seconds, how far will he fall during the first 6 seconds?

16. The distance that a marble rolls down an inclined plane varies directly as the square of the time during which it rolls. If the marble rolls 8 feet during the first 2 seconds, how far will it roll during the next 3 seconds?

17. The time required for a pendulum to make one complete swing across and back is called the period of the pendulum, and the period varies directly as the square root of the length of the pendulum. If the period is one second for a pendulum that is 25 centimeters long, what is the period for a pendulum that is 64 centimeters long?

18. The speed with which an object strikes the ground varies directly as the square root of the height from which it is dropped. If the speed is 16 feet per second after a 4-foot fall, what is the speed after a 100-foot fall?

19. If the electromotive force in a circuit is held constant, then the current varies inversely as the resistance. If the current is 12 amperes when the resistance is 3 ohms, what is the current when the resistance is 4 ohms?

20. If the temperature of a confined ideal gas is held constant, then the volume of the gas varies inversely as the pressure. If the volume is 300 cubic inches when the pressure is 40 pounds per square inch, what is the volume when the pressure is 15 pounds per square inch?

21. The intensity of a light varies inversely as the square of the distance from the source of the light. If the intensity is 30 candle power at a distance of 6 feet, what is the intensity at a distance of 4 feet?

22. The attracting force of an electromagnet varies inversely as the square of the distance from the magnet. If the force is 12 pounds at a distance of 3 inches, what is the force at a distance of 4 inches?

23. The volume of a gas varies directly as its absolute temperature and inversely as its pressure. If the volume is 25 cubic feet when the temperature is 300° and the pressure is 20 pounds per square inch, what is the volume if the temperature is 360° and the pressure is 25 pounds per square inch?

24. The centrifugal force of a mass that travels at a constant speed in a circular path varies directly as the square of its speed and inversely as the radius of the circle. If the force is 20 pounds when the speed is 8 feet per second and the radius is 16 feet, what is the force when the speed is 12 feet per second and the radius is 9 feet?

25. The force of a wind blowing on a flat surface varies jointly as the area of the surface and the square of the wind velocity, provided the surface is perpendicular to the direction of the wind. If the force is 16 pounds on a plane surface whose area is 12 square feet when the wind's velocity is 20 miles per hour, what is the force on a plane surface of area 15 square feet when the velocity of the wind is 40 miles per hour?

26. The critical load of a cylindrical column varies directly as the fourth power of its diameter and inversely as the square of its height. If a 3-meter column whose diameter is 50 centimeters will support a load of 20,000 kilograms, what load will be supported by a 4-meter column whose diameter is 40 centimeters?

6.3   Arithmetic Progressions

A function whose domain is restricted to the set of natural numbers is called a **sequence function**. If the numbers in the range of such a function are listed in order, the listing is called a **sequence**, and the numbers are the **terms** of the sequence.

Example 1:   List the first four terms in the sequence $f(n) = n^2$.

Solution: We replace n by each of the first four natural numbers. Because $f(1) = 1^2 = 1$, $f(2) = 2^2 = 4$, $f(3) = 3^2 = 9$, and $f(4) = 4^2 = 16$, the first four terms are

$$1, 4, 9, 16 \tag{1}$$

Often we use the symbol a_n, read "a sub n," to represent the nth term in a sequence.

Example 2:   List the first four terms in the sequence

$$a_n = 3n + 2$$

Solution: We replace n by each of the first four natural numbers.

$$a_1 = 3 \cdot 1 + 2 = 5$$
$$a_2 = 3 \cdot 2 + 2 = 8$$
$$a_3 = 3 \cdot 3 + 2 = 11$$
$$a_4 = 3 \cdot 4 + 2 = 14$$

Hence, the listing is

$$5, 8, 11, 14 \tag{2}$$

We note that for Sequence (2) the difference between successive terms is always 3. That is, $8 - 5 = 3$; $11 - 8 = 3$; and so on. However, for Sequence (1) the difference between successive terms does not remain the same as we progress from term to term. That is, $4 - 1 \neq 9 - 4$. We call Sequence (2) an **arithmetic progression**. In general, any sequence in which the difference between successive terms remains constant is called an arithmetic progression. We show that any such sequence is determined by a first degree polynomial expression, such as $3n + 2$ in Example 2.

Let a and d be any two constants, and consider the sequence function determined by

$$a_n = a + d(n - 1)$$

By making natural number replacements for n, we obtain

$$a_1 = a + d(1 - 1) = a$$
$$a_2 = a + d(2 - 1) = a + d$$
$$a_3 = a + d(3 - 1) = a + 2d$$
$$a_4 = a + d(4 - 1) = a + 3d$$

and so on.

Because d is the difference between any two successive terms, the sequence is an arithmetic progression.

We have proved the following theorem.

6.3.1   Theorem: Arithmetic Progression

If a_n is the nth term of an arithmetic progression with first term a_1 and difference d, then

$$a_n = a_1 + d(n - 1)$$

Example 3:   Consider the arithmetic progression $3, 5, 7, 9, \ldots$.
(a) Find a_n.   **(b)** Find the 20th term.

Solution:
(a) We apply Theorem 6.3.1 with $a_1 = 3$ and $d = 2$ because the first term is 3 and the difference between terms is $5 - 3 = 2$.

$$a_n = a_1 + d(n - 1)$$
$$a_n = 3 + 2(n - 1)$$
$$a_n = 2n + 1 \tag{3}$$

(b) To find the 20th term in the sequence, we replace n by 20 in Formula (3).

$$a_{20} = 2 \cdot 20 + 1 = 41$$

The 20th term is 41.

If there is a first and last term in a sequence, it is called a **finite sequence**.

Example 4: How many terms are there in this finite arithmetic progression?

$$16, 12, 8, \ldots, -20$$

Solution: We use Theorem 6.3.1 with $a_1 = 16$ and $d = -4$ because the first term is 16 and the difference between terms is $12 - 16 = -4$. If n is the number of terms, then a_n is the last term, and thus $a_n = -20$.

$$a_n = a_1 + d(n - 1)$$
$$-20 = 16 + (-4)(n - 1)$$

Now we solve the equation for n.

$$-36 = -4(n - 1)$$
$$9 = n - 1$$
$$10 = n$$

There are 10 terms in the sequence.

If a_k is the kth term in any sequence function, we use the symbol

$$\sum_{k=1}^{n} a_k$$

to represent the sum of the first n terms in the sequence. Such a sum is called a **series**.

Example 5: Find

$$\sum_{k=1}^{5} k^2$$

Solution:

$$\sum_{k=1}^{5} k^2 = 1^2 + 2^2 + 3^2 + 4^2 + 5^2 = 55$$

We are particularly interested in a **finite arithmetic series**, which is the sum of the first n terms in an arithmetic progression. Suppose we wish to find the sum

$$\sum_{k=1}^{25} k = 1 + 2 + 3 + \cdots + 25$$

Because there are so many terms in this series, we use a "trick" to find the sum. Let

$$S = 1 + 2 + \cdots + 24 + 25 \tag{4}$$

Then we reverse the order of the terms to obtain

$$S = 25 + 24 + \cdots + 2 + 1 \qquad (5)$$

Now if we add Equation (4) and Equation (5), term by term, we have

$$2S = 26 + 26 + \cdots + 26 + 26$$

Because there are 25 terms in this sum and each term is 26, we have

$$2S = 25 \cdot 26$$

$$S = \frac{25 \cdot 26}{2} = 325$$

Thus, the sum we seek is 325.

The technique illustrated above may be used to derive a formula for any arithmetic series. Let S_n be the sum of the first n terms in an arithmetic progression with first term a_1, last term a_n, and difference d. Then

$$S_n = a_1 + (a_1 + d) + (a_1 + 2d) + \cdots + a_n \qquad (6)$$

Because a_n is the last term and the difference between terms is d, $a_n - d$ represents the term that precedes a_n. Similarly, $a_n - 2d$ represents the term that precedes $a_n - d$. And so on. Thus, if we reverse the order of the terms in Equation (6), we obtain

$$S_n = a_n + (a_n - d) + (a_n - 2d) + \cdots + a_1 \qquad (7)$$

If we add Equation (6) and Equation (7), term by term, for each d there is a corresponding $-d$, and so the sum reduces to

$$2 \cdot S_n = (a_1 + a_n) + (a_1 + a_n) + (a_1 + a_n) + \cdots + (a_1 + a_n) \qquad (8)$$

Because there are exactly n terms on the right side of Equation (8) and each term is $a_1 + a_n$, this equation reduces to

$$2 \cdot S_n = n \cdot (a_1 + a_n)$$

$$S_n = \frac{n(a_1 + a_n)}{2} \qquad (9)$$

Equation (9) is a formula for finding the sum of the first n terms in an arithmetic series. Note that in the formula, a_1 is the first term in the sum, a_n is the last term, and n is the number of terms. Because $(a_1 + a_n)/2$ is the average of a_1 and a_n, the formula may be expressed in words as follows.

The sum of the first n terms in an arithmetic progression is found by multiplying n by the average of the first and last terms in the progression.

If the symbol for sum is used, Formula (9) becomes the following theorem.

6.3.2   Theorem: Arithmetic Series

If a_k is the kth term of an arithmetic progression,

$$\sum_{k=1}^{n} a_k = \frac{n(a_1 + a_n)}{2}$$

Example 6:   Find

$$\sum_{k=1}^{20} (3k + 1)$$

Solution: Because $3k + 1$ is a first degree polynomial, we have an arithmetic series, and we may apply Theorem 6.3.2 with $n = 20$. Because

$$a_k = 3k + 1$$
$$a_1 = 3 \cdot 1 + 1 = 4$$
$$a_{20} = 3 \cdot 20 + 1 = 61$$

then $n = 20$, $a_1 = 4$, and $a_n = a_{20} = 61$. Thus, substituting into the equation of Theorem 6.3.2, we obtain

$$\sum_{k=1}^{20} (3k + 1) = \frac{20(4 + 61)}{2}$$
$$= 650$$

Example 7:   We wish to make a brick patio that is triangular in shape by arranging the bricks with 55 bricks in the first row, 53 bricks in the second row, 51 bricks in the next row, and so on, with only 1 brick in the last row. How many bricks are needed in all?

Solution: The number we seek is represented by the arithmetic series

$$55 + 53 + 51 + \cdots + 1$$

We note that $a_1 = 55$, $a_n = 1$, and $d = -2$ because $53 - 55 = -2$. First, we use Theorem 6.3.1 to find n, the number of rows.

$$a_n = a_1 + d(n - 1)$$
$$1 = 55 + (-2)(n - 1)$$

Solving for n, we obtain

$$n = 28$$

Next, we use Equation (9) to find the sum.

$$S_n = \frac{n(a_1 + a_n)}{2}$$

$$S_{28} = \frac{28(55 + 1)}{2}$$

$$= 784$$

Thus, we need 784 bricks in all.

EXERCISES 6.3

For Exercises 1–8 list the first four terms in the given sequence function, and indicate whether or not the sequence is an arithmetic progression.

1. $u_n = 5n - 1$ **2.** $u_n = 5 - 2n$ **3.** $u_n = \frac{1}{n}$

4. $u_n = \frac{1}{2n - 1}$ **5.** $u_n = n^3$ **6.** $u_n = n^4$

7. $u_n = 2^n$ **8.** $u_n = (-3)^n$

For Exercises 9–14 if the given numbers form an arithmetic progression, find an expression a_n that defines the sequence function.

9. $4, 7, 10, 13, \ldots$ **10.** $5, 7, 9, 11, \ldots$

11. $5, 3, 1, -1, \ldots$ **12.** $10, 6, 2, 0, \ldots$

13. $1, \frac{3}{2}, 2, \frac{5}{2}, \ldots$ **14.** $6, \frac{9}{2}, 3, \frac{3}{2}, \ldots$

For Exercises 15–20 find the indicated term in the given arithmetic progression.

15. $2, 5, 8, \ldots$; 25th term   **16.** $7, 11, 15, \ldots$; 30th term

17. $5, 2, -1, \ldots$; 21st term   **18.** $8, 2, -4, \ldots$; 15th term

19. $-10, -6, -2, \ldots$; 43rd term   **20.** $-8, -13, -18, \ldots$; 33rd term

For Exercises 21–26 find the number of terms in the given finite arithmetic progression.

21. $3, 5, 7, \ldots, 21$ **22.** $2, 5, 8, \ldots, 68$

23. $10, 6, 2, \ldots, -94$ **24.** $9, 7, 5, \ldots, -53$

25. $-3, -6, -9, \ldots, -78$ **26.** $-10, -6, -2, \ldots, 62$

For Exercises 27–32 write each term in the given series, and calculate the sum.

27. $\sum_{k=1}^{3} 2k^2$ **28.** $\sum_{k=1}^{3} k^3$ **29.** $\sum_{k=1}^{4} (k^3 + k)$

30. $\sum_{k=1}^{4} (k - k^4)$ **31.** $\sum_{k=1}^{5} 3^k$ **32.** $\sum_{k=1}^{5} 2^{-k}$

For Exercises 33–40 use Theorem 6.3.2 to calculate the indicated sum.

33. $\sum_{k=1}^{20} 3k$ **34.** $\sum_{k=1}^{20} 2k$ **35.** $\sum_{k=1}^{25} (2k + 3)$

36. $\sum_{k=1}^{30} (5k - 1)$ **37.** $\sum_{k=1}^{30} (3 - k)$ **38.** $\sum_{k=1}^{25} (1 - 4k)$

39. $\sum_{k=1}^{100} \frac{k - 1}{2}$ **40.** $\sum_{k=1}^{100} \frac{2k + 1}{3}$

For Exercises 41–46 use either an arithmetic progression or an arithmetic series to find the answer to the stated question.

41. If the population of a city is 120,000 in 1975 and increases by 8000 each year, what will the population be in 1990?

42. If the interest paid on a home mortgage is 260 dollars for the first month and the interest decreases by 75 cents each month thereafter, how much interest will be paid for the 10th month?

43. If an employee is paid a starting salary of $12,000 for the first year and is given a $400 raise each year, how much will be paid in all during the first 8 years?

44. If a merchant sells 300 items during the first day and increases the sales by 20 items each day thereafter, how many items does he sell in all during 30 days?

45. A merchant sells 400 items during the first day of a sale, and sales decrease by 15 items for each day thereafter. If the merchant sells only 40 items during the last day of the sale, how many items are sold in all during the sale?

46. What is the sum of all multiples of 3 that are between the numbers 10 and 200?

6.4 Geometric Progressions

In this section we continue the study of a sequence function.

Example 1: List the first four terms in the sequence $b_n = 3 \cdot 2^{n-1}$

Solution:

$$b_1 = 3 \cdot 2^{1-1} = 3 \cdot 2^0 = 3$$
$$b_2 = 3 \cdot 2^{2-1} = 3 \cdot 2^1 = 6$$
$$b_3 = 3 \cdot 2^{3-1} = 3 \cdot 2^2 = 12$$
$$b_4 = 3 \cdot 2^{4-1} = 3 \cdot 2^3 = 24$$

Hence, the listing is

$$3, 6, 12, 24, \ldots \tag{1}$$

We note that for Sequence (1) the ratio of successive terms is always 2. That is, $6 \div 3 = 2$, $12 \div 6 = 2$, $24 \div 12 = 2$, and so on. Sequence (1) is called a **geometric progression**. In general, any sequence in which the ratio of successive terms remains constant is called a geometric progression. The expression $3 \cdot 2^{n-1}$, used in Example 1 to define Sequence (1), is called an **exponential expression** because the variable n appears in the exponent. We show that any geometric progression is determined by an exponential expression.

Let b and r be any constants, and consider the sequence function defined by

$$b_n = b \cdot r^{n-1}$$

By making natural number replacements for n, we obtain

$$b_1 = b \cdot r^{1-1} = b$$
$$b_2 = b \cdot r^{2-1} = br$$
$$b_3 = b \cdot r^{3-1} = br^2$$
$$b_4 = b \cdot r^{4-1} = br^3$$

and so on.

We note that r is the ratio of any two successive terms in the above sequence, $b_1, b_2, b_3, b_4, \ldots$. That is, $b_2 \div b_1 = br \div b = r$, $b_3 \div b_2 = br^2 \div br = r$, and so on. Hence, the sequence is a geometric progression, and we have proved the following theorem.

6.4.1   *Theorem:* **Geometric Progression**

If b_n is the nth term of a geometric progression with first term b_1 and ratio r, then

$$b_n = b_1 \cdot r^{n-1}$$

Example 2:   Consider the geometric progression 2, 6, 18, 54, ...
(a) Find b_n.   (b) Find the 20th term.

Solution:
(a) We apply Theorem 6.4.1 with $b_1 = 2$ because the first term is 2. The ratio r is found by dividing. Because $6 \div 2 = 3$, $18 \div 6 = 3$, and so on, we take $r = 3$.

$$b_n = b_1 \cdot r^{n-1}$$
$$b_n = 2 \cdot 3^{n-1} \tag{2}$$

(b) We replace n by 20 in Formula (2). Thus,

$$b_{20} = 2 \cdot 3^{20-1}$$
$$= 2 \cdot 3^{19}$$

The 20th term is $2 \cdot 3^{19}$. We do not attempt to calculate the simplest form of this number without the aid of an electronic calculator. (Actually, $2 \cdot 3^{19} = 2{,}324{,}522{,}946$.)

Example 3:   Find the 16th term in the geometric progression 4, -8, 16, $-32, \ldots$.

Solution: We apply Theorem 6.4.1 to find an expression b_n that determines the sequence. Because the first term is 4, we let $b_1 = 4$. Because $-8 \div 4 = -2$, $16 \div (-8) = -2$, and so on, the ratio is $r = -2$. Thus, we have

$$b_n = 4(-2)^{n-1} \tag{3}$$

To find the 16th term, we let $n = 16$ in Formula (3). We have

$$b_{16} = 4(-2)^{15}$$

Because $4 = 2^2$, we apply the laws of exponents to simplify. Thus,

$$b_{16} = 2^2(-2)^{15}$$
$$= -2^{17}$$

If there is a last term in a geometric progression, the progression is said to be finite. The sum of the terms in a finite geometric progression is called a **finite geometric series**. Suppose we wish to calculate the finite geometric series

$$\sum_{k=1}^{15} 5^{k-1} = 5^{1-1} + 5^{2-1} + 5^{3-1} + \cdots + 5^{15-1}$$
$$= 1 + 5 + 5^2 + \cdots + 5^{14}$$

Because there are so many terms in this series, we use a "trick" to find the sum. Let

$$S = 1 + 5 + 5^2 + \cdots + 5^{14} \tag{4}$$

We multiply by 5 on each side of Equation (4) and simplify.

$$5S = 5 \cdot 1 + 5 \cdot 5 + 5 \cdot 5^2 + \cdots + 5 \cdot 5^{14}$$
$$5S = 5 + 5^2 + 5^3 + \cdots + 5^{15} \tag{5}$$

Next, we add Equation (5) and the opposite of Equation (4). That is, we subtract Equation (4) from Equation (5). Many terms on the right of the equal sign will cancel out, and we obtain

$$4S = 5^{15} - 1 \qquad \text{[Eq. (5) minus Eq. (4)]}$$
$$S = \frac{5^{15} - 1}{4}$$

Hence,

$$\sum_{k=1}^{15} 5^{k-1} = \frac{5^{15} - 1}{4}$$

The technique illustrated above may be used to derive a formula for any finite geometric series. Let S_n be the sum of the first n terms in a geometric progression with first term b_1 and ratio r. Then

$$S_n = b_1 + b_1 r + b_1 r^2 + \cdots + b_1 r^{n-1} \tag{6}$$

We multiply on both sides of Equation (6) by r and use the First Law of Exponents to simplify.

$$S_n \cdot r = b_1 \cdot r + b_1 r \cdot r + b_1 r^2 \cdot r + \cdots + b_1 r^{n-1} \cdot r$$

$$S_n \cdot r = b_1 r + b_1 r^2 + b_1 r^3 + \cdots + b_1 r^n \tag{7}$$

Now if we subtract Equation (6) from Equation (7), all terms on the right of the equal sign will cancel, except $b_1 r^n$ in Equation (7) and b_1 in Equation (6). Hence,

$$S_n \cdot r - S_n = b_1 r^n - b_1 \qquad \text{[Eq. (7) minus Eq. (6)]}$$

$$S_n(r - 1) = b_1(r^n - 1)$$

$$S_n = \frac{b_1(r^n - 1)}{r - 1} \tag{8}$$

Equation (8) is a formula for finding the sum of the first n terms in a geometric progression. Note that in the formula, b_1 is the first term in the sum, r is the ratio of successive terms, and n is the number of terms. If the symbol for sum is used, Formula (8) becomes the following theorem.

6.4.2   Theorem: *Finite Geometric Series*

If b_k is the kth term of a geometric progression with ratio r, with $r \neq 1$, then

$$\sum_{k=1}^{n} b_k = \frac{b_1(r^n - 1)}{r - 1}$$

Example 4: Find the sum $\sum_{k=1}^{10} 4^k$.

Solution:

$$\sum_{k=1}^{10} 4^k = 4^1 + 4^2 + 4^3 + \cdots + 4^{10}$$

We apply Theorem 6.4.2 with $n = 10$ to find the sum. Because the first term is 4, we let $b_1 = 4$. Because the ratio is 4, we let $r = 4$. Thus,

$$\sum_{k=1}^{10} 4^k = \frac{4(4^{10} - 1)}{4 - 1}$$

$$= \frac{4^{11} - 4}{3}$$

Example 5:   A merchant sells $200 worth of goods his first day in business, and sales increase by 25% on each successive day.
(a) How much does the merchant sell during the fifth day?
(b) What are the total sales for the first five days?

Solution:
(a) Because sales increase by 25% each day, then for each day after the first day, the sales will be 125% of what they were the previous day. Let b_k be the number of dollars in sales for the kth day. Then

$$b_1 = 200$$
$$b_2 = b_1 \cdot 125\% = 200 \cdot (1.25)$$
$$b_3 = b_2 \cdot 125\% = 200 \cdot (1.25)^2$$
$$b_4 = b_3 \cdot 125\% = 200 \cdot (1.25)^3$$
$$b_5 = b_4 \cdot 125\% = 200 \cdot (1.25)^4$$

Thus, during the fifth day the sales will be $200 \cdot (1.25)^4$ dollars, which is $488.28. We note that b_5 is the fifth term in a geometric progression with first term 200 and ratio 1.25.
(b) We want the sum of the sales for each of the first five days. That is, we want

$$\sum_{k=1}^{5} b_k = b_1 + b_2 + b_3 + b_4 + b_5$$

This is a finite geometric series with $b_1 = 200$, $r = 1.25$, and $n = 5$. Hence, by Theorem 6.4.2 the sum is

$$\frac{b_1(r^n - 1)}{r - 1} = \frac{200(1.25^5 - 1)}{1.25 - 1}$$
$$= 1641.41$$

The total sales for five days are $1641.41.

Example 6:   If $1000 is invested at the rate of 8% per year with interest compounded yearly, what is the value of the investment after 6 years?

Solution: Let b_k dollars be the value of the investment after k years. Because the value increases by 8% each year, at the end of each year the value is 108% of what it was at the beginning of the year. Thus, the sequence b_k is a geometric progression with ratio given by $r = 108\% = 1.08$. Furthermore, because the value at the end of the first year is 108% of 1000 dollars, then $b_1 = 1000(1.08)$. We make the substitutions for r and b_1 into Theorem 6.4.1. Thus,

$$b_k = b_1 \cdot r^{k-1}$$
$$= [1000(1.08)](1.08)^{k-1}$$
$$= 1000(1.08)^k \tag{9}$$

To find the value after 6 years, we replace k by 6 in Equation (9). Thus,

$$b_6 = 1000(1.08)^6$$
$$= 1586.87$$

The value of the investment after 6 years is \$1586.87.

EXERCISES 6.4

For Exercises 1–8 list the first four terms in the given sequence function, and indicate whether or not the sequence is a geometric progression.

1. $u_n = 3^n$
2. $u_n = -2^n$
3. $u_n = 2^{n-1}$
4. $u_n = (n-1)^2$
5. $u_n = 2(-3)^{n-1}$
6. $u_n = \frac{1}{2}(-2)^{n-1}$
7. $u_n = (\frac{1}{2})^n$
8. $u_n = 3^{-n}$

For Exercises 9–14 if the given numbers form a geometric progression, find an expression b_n that determines the sequence function.

9. $1, 3, 9, 27, \ldots$
10. $2, 4, 8, 16, \ldots$
11. $2, -8, 32, -128, \ldots$
12. $8, 12, 18, 27, \ldots$
13. $12, 6, 3, 1, \ldots$
14. $16, -8, 4, -2, \ldots$

For Exercises 15–22 find the indicated term in the given geometric progression, and use the laws of exponents to simplify your answer, if possible.

15. $3, 6, 12, \ldots$; 9th term
16. $5, 10, 20, \ldots$; 10th term
17. $3, 9, 27, \ldots$; 12th term
18. $4, 2, 1, \ldots$; 11th term
19. $1, -4, 16, \ldots$; 13th term
20. $3, -6, 12, \ldots$; 12th term
21. $8, -4, 2, \ldots$; 14th term
22. $-2, 6, -18, \ldots$; 16th term

For Exercises 23–30 use Theorem 6.4.2 to find the indicated sum, and simplify your answer, if possible.

23. $\sum_{k=1}^{10} 2^{k-1}$
24. $\sum_{k=1}^{7} 3^k$
25. $\sum_{k=1}^{8} 2 \cdot 5^k$
26. $\sum_{k=1}^{6} 3(4)^{k-1}$

27. $\sum_{k=1}^{6} (\frac{3}{2})^{k-1}$
28. $\sum_{k=1}^{8} (\frac{1}{2})^{k-1}$
29. $\sum_{k=1}^{6} 3(-2)^{k-1}$
30. $\sum_{k=1}^{5} (-3)^k$

For Exercises 31–38 use either a geometric progression or a geometric series to find the answer to the stated question.

31. A certain ball rebounds to a level that is $\frac{3}{4}$ the height from which it fell. If the ball is dropped from a height of 24 feet, how high does it rebound on the 6th bounce?

32. If there are 1000 bacteria in a certain culture and if the population doubles every 3 days, how many will be present after 30 days?

33. A certain automobile sells for $4000. If the price increases by 5% each year, what will be the price after 8 years?

34. There are 100 grams of a radioactive substance on hand. If $\frac{1}{4}$ of the substance decays each year, how much will be present after 12 years?

35. A merchant sells $600 worth of goods his first day in business. For each successive day the sales are $\frac{5}{6}$ of what they were the preceding day. What are the total sales for the first 8 days?

36. A worker is paid $12,000 for the first year and is given a 10% raise each year. How much is paid in all during the first 6 years?

37. What is the value after 10 years if $5000 is invested at the rate of 6% with interest compounded annually?

38. What is the value after 7 years if $1000 is invested at the rate of 8% per year with interest compounded every 6 months?

6.5 Infinite Geometric Series (optional)

Consider the geometric progression

$$b_n = (\tfrac{1}{2})^{n-1}$$

By making natural number replacements for n, we obtain the sequence

$$1, \tfrac{1}{2}, \tfrac{1}{4}, \tfrac{1}{8}, \ldots \tag{1}$$

The terms in Sequence (1) become closer and closer to zero as we progress from term to term. Moreover, the difference between the nth term and zero can be made as close to zero as we like by choosing n large enough. For example, the 25th term in sequence b_n is

$$b_{25} = (\tfrac{1}{2})^{24} = 0.00000006$$

We say that Sequence (1) has **limit** zero, and that the terms in the sequence **approach** zero. In symbols, we write

$$b_n \longrightarrow 0$$

Next, we consider the geometric progression

$$c_n = (1.2)^{n-1}$$

By making natural number replacements for n in c_n, we obtain the sequence

$$1, 1.2, (1.2)^2, (1.2)^3, \ldots$$

or

$$1, 1.2, 1.44, 1.73, \ldots \tag{2}$$

The terms in Sequence (2) become larger and larger as we progress from term to term. Moreover, the nth term can be made as large as we like by choosing n large enough. For example, the 100th term in sequence c_n is

$$c_{100} = (1.2)^{99} = 69{,}014{,}979$$

Thus, Sequence (2) does not have a limit. We say that it is a **divergent sequence**. In symbols, we write

$$c_n \longrightarrow \infty$$

Note that for Sequence (1), which has limit 0, the ratio is $\frac{1}{2}$, a number less than 1. On the other hand, for Sequence (2), which is divergent, the ratio is 1.2, a number greater than 1. It is possible to prove that the observations made about the above two geometric progressions are always true. The next theorem states this fact.

6.5.1   Theorem: Infinite Geometric Progression

If b_n is a geometric progression with ratio r, then
(i)   If $|r| < 1$, $b_n \rightarrow 0$.
(ii) If $|r| > 1$, $b_n \rightarrow \infty$.

Example 1: For each of the following geometric progressions, use Theorem 6.5.1 to show whether the limit is zero or whether the sequence is divergent.

(a) $2, 3, \frac{9}{2}, \frac{27}{4}, \ldots$ **(b)** $6, -3, \frac{3}{2}, -\frac{3}{4}, \ldots$

Solution:
(a) First, we find the ratio r.

$$r = 3 \div 2 = \frac{3}{2}$$

Because $|r| > 1$, by Theorem 6.5.1 the sequence is divergent.
(b) First, we find r.

$$r = -3 \div 6 = -\frac{1}{2}$$
$$|r| = |-\frac{1}{2}| = \frac{1}{2}$$

Because $|r| < 1$, then by Theorem 6.5.1 the sequence has limit zero.

Next, consider the sequence S_n determined by

$$S_n = \sum_{k=1}^{n} (\tfrac{1}{2})^k$$

We make natural number replacements for n and calculate the first four terms for sequence S_n.

$$S_1 = \sum_{k=1}^{1} (\tfrac{1}{2})^k = (\tfrac{1}{2})^1 = \tfrac{1}{2}$$

$$S_2 = \sum_{k=1}^{2} (\tfrac{1}{2})^k = (\tfrac{1}{2})^1 + (\tfrac{1}{2})^2 = \tfrac{3}{4}$$

$$S_3 = \sum_{k=1}^{3} (\tfrac{1}{2})^k = (\tfrac{1}{2})^1 + (\tfrac{1}{2})^2 + (\tfrac{1}{2})^3 = \tfrac{7}{8}$$

$$S_4 = \sum_{k=1}^{4} (\tfrac{1}{2})^k = (\tfrac{1}{2})^1 + (\tfrac{1}{2})^2 + (\tfrac{1}{2})^3 + (\tfrac{1}{2})^4 = \tfrac{15}{16}$$

Thus, the sequence S_n, which we call a sequence of partial sums, is

$$\tfrac{1}{2}, \tfrac{3}{4}, \tfrac{7}{8}, \tfrac{15}{16}, \cdots \tag{3}$$

The terms in Sequence (3) appear to approach 1. Let us prove that $S_n \longrightarrow 1$.

First, if $b_k = (\tfrac{1}{2})^k$, then b_k is a geometric progression with first term $\tfrac{1}{2}$ and ratio $\tfrac{1}{2}$. Thus, a formula for S_n is given by Theorem 6.4.2 with $b_1 = \tfrac{1}{2}$ and $r = \tfrac{1}{2}$. It is

$$S_n = \frac{\tfrac{1}{2}[(\tfrac{1}{2})^n - 1]}{\tfrac{1}{2} - 1} \tag{4}$$

Furthermore, by Theorem 6.5.1, $(\tfrac{1}{2})^n \longrightarrow 0$, and we may find the limit of S_n by replacing $(\tfrac{1}{2})^n$ by 0 in Equation (4). The result is

$$S_n \longrightarrow \frac{\tfrac{1}{2}(0 - 1)}{\tfrac{1}{2} - 1} = 1$$

We use the symbol

$$\sum_{k=1}^{+\infty} u_k$$

to represent the limit of a sequence of partial sums S_n given by

$$S_n = \sum_{k=1}^{n} u_k$$

provided that $u_k \longrightarrow 0$. Such a limit is called the sum of the **infinite series**. In the discussion above we proved that

$$\sum_{k=1}^{+\infty} (\tfrac{1}{2})^k = \tfrac{1}{2} + \tfrac{1}{4} + \tfrac{1}{8} + \tfrac{1}{16} + \cdots$$
$$= 1$$

We now prove the following theorem about an infinite geometric series.

6.5.2 Theorem: *Infinite Geometric Series*

If b_k is a geometric progression with ratio r and if $|r| < 1$, then

$$\sum_{k=1}^{+\infty} b_k = \frac{b_1}{1 - r}$$

PROOF: Let S_n be the sequence of partial sums for this series. Then by Theorem 6.4.2,

$$S_n = \frac{b_1(r^n - 1)}{r - 1} \tag{5}$$

Because $|r| < 1$, by Theorem 6.5.1, $r^n \to 0$. Thus, the limit of S_n may be found by replacing r^n by 0 in Equation (5). The result of this is

$$S_n \longrightarrow \frac{b_1(0 - 1)}{r - 1} = \frac{b_1}{1 - r}$$

We have proved the theorem.

Example 2: Find

$$\sum_{k=1}^{+\infty} (\tfrac{2}{3})^{k-1}$$

Solution: Let $b_k = (\tfrac{2}{3})^{k-1}$. Thus b_k is a geometric progression with first term $b_1 = (\tfrac{2}{3})^{1-1} = 1$ and ratio $r = \tfrac{2}{3}$. Because $|r| < 1$, we may use Theorem 6.5.2 to find the limit. Thus,

$$\sum_{k=1}^{+\infty} (\tfrac{2}{3})^{k-1} = \frac{1}{1 - \tfrac{2}{3}} = 3$$

Example 3: Find the limit of this infinite geometric series.

$$12 - 4 + \tfrac{4}{3} - \tfrac{4}{9} + \cdots$$

Solution: Because the first term is 12 and the ratio is $-4 \div 12 = -\tfrac{1}{3}$, let $b_1 = 12$ and $r = -\tfrac{1}{3}$. Because $|r| = |-\tfrac{1}{3}| = \tfrac{1}{3}$, then $|r| < 1$, and we apply Theorem 6.5.2. Thus,

$$12 - 4 + \tfrac{4}{3} - \tfrac{4}{9} + \cdots = \frac{12}{1 - (-\tfrac{1}{3})} = 9$$

We must be careful to use Theorem 6.5.2 only when $|r| < 1$. If $|r| > 1$, the sequence of partial sums is divergent and does not have a limit.

Example 4: Find a common fraction that is equivalent to the repeating decimal $0.\overline{36}$.

Solution:

$$0.\overline{36} = 0.36363636\cdots$$

$$= 0.36 + 0.0036 + 0.000036 + 0.00000036 + \cdots$$

This is an infinite geometric series with first term $b_1 = 0.36$ and ratio $r = 0.01$, because $0.0036 \div 0.36 = 0.01$. Because $|r| < 1$, we may use Theorem 6.5.2. Thus,

$$0.\overline{36} = \frac{0.36}{1 - 0.01} = \frac{0.36}{0.99} = \frac{4}{11}$$

The common fraction we seek is $\frac{4}{11}$. (Now use long division or a calculator to find a decimal form for $\frac{4}{11}$.)

Example 5: A variable force causes a particle to move a distance of 5 centimeters during the first second, and for each subsequent second a distance that is $\frac{7}{8}$ as far as during the preceding second. How far does the particle move in one minute?

Solution: Let b_k be the number of centimeters in the distance the particle moves during the kth second. We are given that

$$b_1 = 5$$
$$b_2 = 5 \cdot \left(\tfrac{7}{8}\right)$$
$$b_3 = 5 \cdot \left(\tfrac{7}{8}\right)^2$$

And so on.

Because there are 60 seconds in 1 minute, the number of centimeters in the total distance moved during 1 minute is represented by the finite geometric series

$$\sum_{k=1}^{60} b_k$$

whose value can be calculated by applying Theorem 6.4.2. However, because the series contains many terms and because $|r| = \frac{7}{8} < 1$ for the sequence b_k, the value of the finite series is approximately the same as the limit of the infinite series.

$$\sum_{k=1}^{+\infty} b_k$$

which is easier to calculate. We apply Theorem 6.5.2 with $b_1 = 5$ and $r = \frac{7}{8}$. Thus,

$$\sum_{k=1}^{+\infty} b_k = \frac{5}{1 - \tfrac{7}{8}}$$
$$= 40$$

We conclude that the particle moves approximately 40 centimeters. If we apply Theorem 6.4.2 and use a calculator, the result is

$$\sum_{k=1}^{60} b_k = \frac{5[\left(\tfrac{7}{8}\right)^{60} - 1]}{\tfrac{7}{8} - 1}$$
$$= 39.99$$

which agrees with the approximate value.

EXERCISES 6.5

For Exercises 1–8 use Theorem 6.5.1 to show whether the limit of the given geometric progression is zero or whether the sequence is divergent.

1. $27, 9, 3, \ldots$

2. $2, \frac{3}{2}, \frac{9}{8}, \ldots$

3. $\frac{3}{2}, \frac{9}{4}, \frac{27}{8}, \ldots$

4. $\frac{1}{4}, \frac{1}{3}, \frac{4}{9}, \ldots$

5. $\frac{1}{8}, -\frac{1}{4}, \frac{1}{2}, \ldots$

6. $\frac{1}{3}, -\frac{1}{6}, \frac{1}{12}, \ldots$

7. $\frac{2}{3}, -\frac{4}{9}, \frac{8}{27}, \ldots$

8. $\frac{1}{16}, -\frac{1}{12}, \frac{1}{9}, \ldots$

For Exercises 9–24 use Theorem 6.5.2, if possible, to find the limit of the indicated infinite geometric series.

9. $\displaystyle\sum_{k=1}^{+\infty} (\tfrac{1}{3})^{k-1}$

10. $\displaystyle\sum_{k=1}^{+\infty} (\tfrac{1}{3})^{k}$

11. $\displaystyle\sum_{k=1}^{+\infty} (\tfrac{3}{4})^{k}$

12. $\displaystyle\sum_{k=1}^{+\infty} (\tfrac{3}{4})^{k-1}$

13. $\displaystyle\sum_{k=1}^{+\infty} (-\tfrac{1}{2})^{k-1}$

14. $\displaystyle\sum_{k=1}^{+\infty} (-\tfrac{2}{3})^{k}$

15. $\displaystyle\sum_{k=1}^{+\infty} 4(-\tfrac{1}{3})^{k}$

16. $\displaystyle\sum_{k=1}^{+\infty} (\tfrac{3}{2})^{k-1}$

17. $1 + \frac{1}{2} + \frac{1}{4} + \cdots$

18. $1 + \frac{1}{4} + \frac{1}{16} + \cdots$

19. $12 + 8 + \frac{16}{3} + \cdots$

20. $15 + 6 + \frac{12}{5} + \cdots$

21. $27 - 9 + 3 - \cdots$

22. $\frac{1}{2} - \frac{1}{4} + \frac{1}{8} - \cdots$

23. $\frac{1}{6} - \frac{1}{4} + \frac{3}{8} - \cdots$

24. $\frac{1}{4} - \frac{1}{6} + \frac{1}{9} - \cdots$

For Exercises 25–30 find the simplest form of the common fraction that is equivalent to the given repeating decimal.

25. $0.\overline{7}$

26. $0.\overline{27}$

27. $0.\overline{405}$

28. $0.\overline{1683}$

29. $0.2\overline{3}$

30. $0.3\overline{45}$

[*Note:* $0.2\bar{3} = 0.2333\cdots.$]

For Exercises 31–34 use the limit of an infinite geometric series to answer the stated question.

31. A particle moves a distance of 60 centimeters during the first second, and for each subsequent second the distance that it moves is $\frac{5}{7}$ of the distance it moved during the preceding second. How far does the particle move in 1 hour?

32. During the first swing of a pendulum the bob moves 30 centimeters, and on each swing after the first the distance that it moves is 95% of the distance it moved during the preceding second. How far does the bob move before coming to rest?

33. An installment purchase is to be paid under the following payment schedule. The payment for the first month is $500, and for each month after the first the payment is to be 20% less than the amount paid for the preceding month. How much will be paid in all under this plan?

34. A ball is dropped from a point that is 10 feet above the floor and allowed to bounce until it comes to rest. After each bounce the ball rises to a level that is $\frac{2}{3}$ the height from which it fell. How far does the ball move altogether?

6.6   The Binomial Expansion (optional)

In Section 1.5 we proved the Binomial Square Theorem and the Binomial Cube Theorem, which we restate now.

$$(a + b)^2 = a^2 + 2ab + b^2 \tag{1}$$

$$(a + b)^3 = a^3 + 3a^2b + 3ab^2 + b^3 \tag{2}$$

Because $(a + b)^4 = (a + b)^3(a + b)$, we may find a standard form for $(a + b)^4$ as follows.

$$
\begin{array}{r}
a^3 + 3a^2b + 3ab^2 + b^3 \\
a + b \\
\hline
a^4 + 3a^3b + 3a^2b^2 + ab^3 \\
a^3b + 3a^2b^2 + 3ab^3 + b^4 \\
\hline
a^4 + 4a^3b + 6a^2b^2 + 4ab^3 + b^4
\end{array}
$$

Therefore,

$$(a + b)^4 = a^4 + 4a^3b + 6a^2b^2 + 4ab^3 + b^4 \tag{3}$$

The sums that appear on the right side of Equations (1), (2), and (3) are called **binomial expansions**. We want to make some general observations about these expansions that will allow us to write a general formula for the binomial expansion of $(a + b)^n$, where n is any natural number.

Note that the first term in the expansion of $(a + b)^4$ is a^4; the first term in the expansion of $(a + b)^3$ is a^3; and the first term in the expansion of $(a + b)^2$ is a^2. Furthermore, in each term of the expansion of $(a + b)^4$ the sum of the exponents of a and b is 4; in each term of the expansion of $(a + b)^3$ the sum of the exponents of a and b is 3; and in each term of the expansion of $(a + b)^2$ the sum of the exponents of a and b is 2. Moreover, as we progress from term to term in the expansion of $(a + b)^4$, the exponent of a decreases by 1 and the exponent of b increases by 1. There is a similar progression with the exponents of a and b in the expansions of $(a + b)^3$ and $(a + b)^2$.

It is more difficult to describe general facts about the numerical coefficients in the expansions. However, note that for the second term in the expansion of $(a + b)^4$ the numerical coefficient is 4; for the second term in the expansion of $(a + b)^3$ the numerical coefficient is 3; and for the second term in the expansion of $(a + b)^2$ the numerical coefficient is 2. Furthermore, note that for the third term in the expansion of $(a + b)^4$ the numerical coefficient is given by

$$\frac{4 \cdot 3}{1 \cdot 2} = 6$$

For the fourth term in the expansion of $(a + b)^4$ the numerical coefficient is given by

$$\frac{4 \cdot 3 \cdot 2}{1 \cdot 2 \cdot 3} = 4$$

For the fifth term in the expansion of $(a + b)^4$ the numerical coefficient is given by

$$\frac{4 \cdot 3 \cdot 2 \cdot 1}{1 \cdot 2 \cdot 3 \cdot 4} = 1$$

In general, we have the following facts about the terms in the expansion of $(a + b)^n$ if n is a natural number.

1. The first term is a^n.
2. The sum of the exponents of a and b in each term is n; the exponent of a decreases by 1 and the exponent of b increases by 1 as we progress from each term to the next term.
3. There are altogether $n + 1$ terms.
4. Provided there are a sufficient number of terms in the expansion, we have the following facts.

   (a) The numerical coefficient of the second term is

   $$\frac{n}{1}$$

   (b) The numerical coefficient of the third term is

   $$\frac{n(n - 1)}{1 \cdot 2}$$

   (c) The numerical coefficient of the fourth term is

   $$\frac{n(n - 1)(n - 2)}{1 \cdot 2 \cdot 3}$$

   (d) The numerical coefficients of the remaining terms follow the pattern established by the first four terms. For the $(r + 1)$th term the numerical coefficient is

   $$\frac{n(n - 1)(n - 2) \cdots [n - (r - 1)]}{1 \cdot 2 \cdot 3 \cdots r}$$

We summarize the above facts by stating the following theorem, called the **Binomial Theorem**. The proof of the theorem requires a concept called mathematical induction, which is studied in more advanced courses.

6.6.1 *Theorem:* **Binomial**

If n is a natural number, then

$$(a + b)^n = a^n + na^{n-1}b + \frac{n(n-1)}{1 \cdot 2} a^{n-2}b^2 + \frac{n(n-1)(n-2)}{1 \cdot 2 \cdot 3} a^{n-3}b^3$$

$$+ \cdots + \frac{n(n-1)(n-2) \cdots [n-(r-1)]}{1 \cdot 2 \cdot 3 \cdots r} a^{n-r}b^r$$

$$+ \cdots + b^n$$

Example 1: Find the binomial expansion of $(a + b)^5$.

Solution: We apply Theorem 6.6.1 with $n = 5$. Thus,

$$(a + b)^5 = a^5 + 5a^4b + \frac{5 \cdot 4}{1 \cdot 2} a^3b^2 + \frac{5 \cdot 4 \cdot 3}{1 \cdot 2 \cdot 3} a^2b^3 + \frac{5 \cdot 4 \cdot 3 \cdot 2}{1 \cdot 2 \cdot 3 \cdot 4} ab^4 + b^5$$

$$= a^5 + 5a^4b + 10a^3b^2 + 10a^2b^3 + 5ab^4 + b^5$$

We prove that the result obtained in Example 1 is correct. Because $(a + b)^5 = (a + b)^4(a + b)$, we may find the binomial expansion by using the result of Equation (3), as follows.

$$
\begin{array}{r}
a^4 + 4a^3b + \quad 6a^2b^2 + \quad 4ab^3 + b^4 \\
a + b \\
\hline
a^5 + 4a^4b + \quad 6a^3b^2 + \quad 4a^2b^3 + \quad ab^4 \\
a^4b + \quad 4a^3b^2 + \quad 6a^2b^3 + 4ab^4 + b^5 \\
\hline
a^5 + 5a^4b + 10a^3b^2 + 10a^2b^3 + 5ab^4 + b^5
\end{array}
$$

Note that this agrees with the result of Example 1.

Example 2: Find the binomial expansion of $(a - b)^6$.

Solution: Because

$$(a - b)^6 = [a + (-b)]^6$$

we apply the Binomial Theorem with $n = 6$ and with b replaced by $-b$. Thus,

$$(a - b)^6 = a^6 + 6a^5(-b) + \frac{6 \cdot 5}{1 \cdot 2} a^4(-b)^2 + \frac{6 \cdot 5 \cdot 4}{1 \cdot 2 \cdot 3} a^3(-b)^3$$

$$+ \frac{6 \cdot 5 \cdot 4 \cdot 3}{1 \cdot 2 \cdot 3 \cdot 4} a^2(-b)^4 + \frac{6 \cdot 5 \cdot 4 \cdot 3 \cdot 2}{1 \cdot 2 \cdot 3 \cdot 4 \cdot 5} a(-b)^5 + (-b)^6$$

$$= a^6 - 6a^5b + 15a^4b^2 - 20a^3b^3 + 15a^2b^4 - 6ab^5 + b^6$$

As in Example 2, if n is any natural number, the numerical coefficients in the binomial expansion of $(a - b)^n$ are alternately positive and negative.

Example 3:   Find the first four terms in the binomial expansion of $(x + 3)^7$.

Solution: We apply the Binomial Theorem with $n = 7$, $a = x$, and $b = 3$. Thus,

$$(x + 3)^7 = x^7 + 7x^6(3) + \frac{7 \cdot 6}{1 \cdot 2}x^5(3^2) + \frac{7 \cdot 6 \cdot 5}{1 \cdot 2 \cdot 3}x^4(3^3) + \cdots$$

$$= x^7 + 7x^6(3) + 21x^5(9) + 35x^4(27) + \cdots$$

$$= x^7 + 21x^6 + 189x^5 + 945x^4 + \cdots$$

Example 4:   Find the term in the expansion of $(a + b)^8$ that contains the factor a^3.

Solution: We apply the Binomial Theorem with $n = 8$. Because the required term contains the factor a^3 and because the sum of the exponents of a and b must be 8, we conclude that the term must also contain the factor b^5. Because the exponent of the factor b^5 is 5, the numerical coefficient of the term is found by taking $r = 5$ in the general term of the Binomial Theorem. Thus, the required term is given by

$$\frac{8 \cdot 7 \cdot 6 \cdot 5 \cdot 4}{1 \cdot 2 \cdot 3 \cdot 4 \cdot 5}a^3b^5$$

or, equivalently,

$$56a^3b^5$$

If an experiment has two possible outcomes with one of the outcomes regarded as being a success and if the probability of a success remains the same if the experiment is repeated, then the binomial expansion can be used to find the probability of any particular number of successes. Suppose that the probability of success for each experiment is p. Then the probability of failure is q, where $q = 1 - p$. For example, if the probability of success is $\frac{1}{4}$, then the probability of failure is $\frac{3}{4}$. That is, $p = \frac{1}{4}$ and $q = 1 - \frac{1}{4} = \frac{3}{4}$. If the experiment is repeated n times, then the probability of exactly r successes and $n - r$ failures is given by the term in the binomial expansion of $(p + q)^n$ that contains the factors $p^r q^{n-r}$.

Example 5:   If a perfectly balanced coin is tossed, the probability that it will land heads up is $\frac{1}{2}$. What is the probability that a coin will land heads up exactly 3 times if it is tossed 5 times?

Solution: We regard heads as a success in the experiment of tossing a coin. Let p be the probability of a success and q be the probability of a failure. Because the experiment is repeated 5 times, we consider the binomial expansion of $(p + q)^5$. Because we want to find the probability that there are exactly 3 successes, we take the term in the expansion of $(p + q)^5$ that contains the factor p^3. Thus, the required probability is given by

$$P = \frac{5 \cdot 4}{1 \cdot 2} p^3 q^2$$

$$= 10p^3 q^2 \tag{4}$$

Because the probability of success is $\frac{1}{2}$, we let $p = \frac{1}{2}$. Because $q = 1 - p$, we have $q = 1 - \frac{1}{2} = \frac{1}{2}$. Substituting these values for p and q into (4), we obtain

$$P = 10(\tfrac{1}{2})^3(\tfrac{1}{2})^2$$

$$= \tfrac{5}{16}$$

Therefore, the probability is $\frac{5}{16}$ that a coin will land heads up exactly 3 times if it is tossed 5 times.

EXERCISES 6.6

For Exercises 1–6 use the binomial expansion of $(a + b)^4$ given in Equation (3) to find a standard form for the given expression.

1. $(x + 2)^4$ **2.** $(x - 1)^4$ **3.** $(2x - 1)^4$

4. $(3x + 1)^4$ **5.** $(x^2 + y)^4$ **6.** $(x + y^3)^4$

For Exercises 7–20 use the Binomial Theorem to write the first four terms in the expansion of the given expression.

7. $(x + y)^6$ **8.** $(x + y)^7$ **9.** $(x - y)^8$

10. $(x - y)^9$ **11.** $(x + y)^{10}$ **12.** $(x + y)^{11}$

13. $(x + 2)^5$ **14.** $(x + 1)^6$ **15.** $(x - 1)^7$

16. $(x - 2)^8$ **17.** $(x^2 + y)^9$ **18.** $(x + y^2)^{10}$

19. $(2x + 3)^5$ **20.** $(2x - 5)^5$

For Exercises 21–26 find the single term that is described for the binomial expansion of the given expression.

21. $(x + y)^7$; the term that contains x^3

22. $(x - y)^8$; the term that contains x^3

23. $(x - y)^9$; the term that contains x^5

24. $(x + y)^{10}$; the term that contains x^5

25. $(x - 2)^5$; the term that contains x^2

26. $(x - 2)^6$; the term that contains x^2

For Exercises 27–30 use a term in the binomial expansion of $(p + q)^n$, *where p is the probability of success, q is the probability of failure, and n is the number of trials, to answer the stated question.*

27. What is the probability that a coin will land heads up exactly 4 times if it is tossed 5 times?

28. What is the probability that a coin will land heads up exactly 3 times if it is tossed 6 times?

29. If $\frac{1}{3}$ of all persons have blue eyes, what is the probability that exactly 2 persons will have blue eyes in a random sample of 4 persons?

30. If 60% of all voters favor a certain candidate, what is the probability that exactly 1 person in a random sample of 4 voters favors the candidate?

REVIEW EXERCISES 6

For Exercises 1–2 sketch the graph of the relation that is given. Find the domain and range of the relation, and determine whether or not the relation is a function.

1. $\{(x, y): x^2 + 4y = 4x\}$ **2.** $\{(x, y): x^2 + 2y^2 = 32\}$

For Exercises 3–4 show whether or not y is a function of x without sketching the graph of the relation.

3. $\{(x, y): x + |y| = 1\}$ **4.** $\{(x, y): x - y^3 = 1\}$

For Exercises 5–6 find the domain of the function f.

5. $f(x) = \sqrt{4x - 3}$ **6.** $f = \{(x, y): xy = 4 - x^2y\}$

For Exercises 7–8 sketch the graph of the function f, and find the domain and range of the function.

7. $f(x) = \sqrt{4 - x^2}$ **8.** $f(x) = 1 - \sqrt{x}$

For Exercises 9–10 find an equation that defines the functional relationship among the variables, and use the equation to find the indicated value.

9. If y varies inversely as the square of x and $y = 3$ when $x = 5$, what is y when $x = 4$?

10. If r varies jointly as the square root of s and the cube of t and $r = 12$ when $s = 9$ and $t = 2$, what is r when $s = 16$ and $t = 3$?

For Exercises 11–12 use a formula that expresses the functional relationship among the variables to answer the stated question.

11. The amount that a spring is compressed varies directly as the force applied. If a force of 40 pounds compresses a 12-inch spring to a length of 9 inches, what is the length of the spring if a force of 60 pounds is applied?

12. The electrical resistance of a wire varies directly as its length and inversely as the square of its diameter. If a wire 3 meters long with a diameter of 10 millimeters has a resistance of 0.5 ohms, what is the resistance in a wire of the same material that is 6 meters long with a diameter of 20 millimeters?

For Exercises 13–18 if the given numbers form either an arithmetic progression or a geometric progression, then determine which type of progression is given, find an expression u_n that defines the sequence function, and calculate the indicated term in the sequence.

13. $12, 9, 6, \ldots$; 20th term

14. $3, 6, 12, \ldots$; 16th term

15. $2, -6, 18, \ldots$; 18th term

16. $-6, -2, 2, \ldots$; 15th term

17. $\frac{1}{8}, \frac{1}{12}, \frac{1}{18}, \ldots$; 17th term

18. $\frac{1}{6}, \frac{5}{12}, \frac{2}{3}, \ldots$; 19th term

For Exercises 19–24 either an arithmetic series or a geometric series is given. Find the value of the indicated sum.

19. $\sum\limits_{k=1}^{20} 5^{k-1}$

20. $\sum\limits_{k=1}^{30} 3k$

21. $\sum\limits_{k=1}^{40} (7 - 2k)$

22. $\sum\limits_{k=1}^{10} 2^{-k}$

23. $6 + 9 + 12 + \cdots + 78$

24. $2 + 4 + 8 + \cdots + 2^{15}$

For Exercises 25–30 either an infinite geometric sequence or an infinite geometric series is given. Determine whether a sequence or a series is given, and find the limit, if possible.

25. $\sum\limits_{k=1}^{+\infty} (\frac{3}{2})^k$

26. $\sum\limits_{k=1}^{+\infty} (\frac{3}{5})^{k-1}$

27. $24, 12, 6, \ldots$

28. $18 + 6 + 2 + \cdots$

29. $\frac{3}{8} - \frac{1}{4} + \frac{1}{6} - \cdots$

30. $\frac{1}{12}, -\frac{1}{8}, \frac{3}{16}, \cdots$

For Exercises 31–34 use either a sequence or a series to find the answer to the stated question.

31. There are 1000 grams of a radioactive substance on hand. If $\frac{1}{5}$ of the substance decays each year, how much will be present after 10 years?

32. A particle moves 20 centimeters during the first second, and for each second after the first the distance that it moves is 2 centimeters more than during the preceding second. How far does the particle move during one minute?

33. A salesman sells 120 items during his first day, and for each day after the first he sells 4 items more than during the preceding day. If he sells 280 items on the last day, how many items in all does he sell?

34. The payment is $100 for the first month of an installment purchase, and for each month after the first the amount of the payment is reduced by 20%. What is the total amount paid during the first year?

For Exercises 35–36 use the limit of an infinite geometric series to answer the stated question.

35. What is the simplest form of the common fraction that is equivalent to the repeating decimal $0.04\overline{545}$?

36. A ball is dropped from a point that is 12 feet above the floor and allowed to continue bouncing until it comes to rest. After each bounce the ball rises to a level that is $\frac{3}{4}$ the height from which it fell. How far does the ball move altogether?

For Exercises 37–40 use the Binomial Theorem to write the first four terms in the expansion of the given expression.

37. $(x + y)^{12}$　　　　**38.** $(x - y)^{13}$　　　　**39.** $(x - 2)^{10}$　　　　**40.** $(x^2 + 3)^8$

For Exercises 41–42 use the Binomial Theorem to find the answer to the stated question.

41. What is the term in the expansion of $(x + y)^9$ that contains x^4?

42. What is the probability that a coin will land heads up exactly 4 times if it is tossed 6 times?

7

exponential and logarithmic functions

7.1 Exponential Functions

The expression b^x is defined by Definition 2.7.3 whenever $b > 0$ and x is a rational number. For example, we have

$$3^4 = 3 \cdot 3 \cdot 3 \cdot 3 = 81$$

$$2^{-3} = \frac{1}{2 \cdot 2 \cdot 2} = \frac{1}{8}$$

$$4^{2/3} = (\sqrt[3]{4})^2 = \sqrt[3]{16}$$

and so on. Although it is beyond the scope of this book to define precisely the expression b^x when x is an irrational number, we can give an intuitive understanding of irrational number powers of a positive base by showing how to interpret the expression $2^{\sqrt{2}}$.

Because $\sqrt{2}$ is approximately 1.4, we conclude that

$$2^{\sqrt{2}} \approx 2^{1.4} = 2^{14/10} = \sqrt[10]{2^{14}}$$

Because a closer approximation of $\sqrt{2}$ is 1.41, a closer approximation of $2^{\sqrt{2}}$ is given by

$$2^{\sqrt{2}} \approx 2^{1.41} = 2^{141/100} = \sqrt[100]{2^{141}}$$

A still closer approximation is given by

$$2^{\sqrt{2}} \approx 2^{1.414} = 2^{1414/1000} = \sqrt[1000]{2^{1414}}$$

Each time we use a closer rational number approximation for $\sqrt{2}$, we obtain a more precise estimate for $2^{\sqrt{2}}$. In this manner we find a sequence of numbers,

$$\sqrt[10]{2^{14}}, \ \sqrt[100]{2^{141}}, \ \sqrt[1000]{2^{1414}}, \dots$$

whose limit is $2^{\sqrt{2}}$.

Although the above discussion may suggest what we mean by a power whose exponent is an irrational number, it does not help us to find a decimal approximation for such a power. However, we can find decimal approximations for irrational number powers by using an electronic calculator. For example, by using a calculator, we obtain

$$2^{\sqrt{2}} \approx 2.67$$

It is possible to define the expression b^x whenever $b > 0$ and x is any real number, either rational or irrational. Thus, the expression b^x defines a function whose domain is the set of all real numbers.

Example 1: Sketch the graph of the function.
(a) $f(x) = 2^x$ (b) $g(x) = (\frac{1}{2})^x$
Solution:
(a) First, we make rational number replacements for x and calculate y, where $y = 2^x$. The results of the calculations are given in Table 7.1.1. Next, we plot the points from the table and draw a smooth curve that contains these points, as shown in Figure 7.1.1.

Table 7.1.1

x	3	2	1	0	-1	-2	-3
y	8	4	2	1	$\frac{1}{2}$	$\frac{1}{4}$	$\frac{1}{8}$

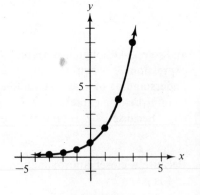

Figure 7.1.1

(b) We let $y = (\frac{1}{2})^x$, make rational number replacements for x, and calculate y. Table 7.1.2 gives the results of the calculations, and Figure 7.1.2 shows the graph, which is obtained by plotting points from the table and drawing a smooth curve through the points.

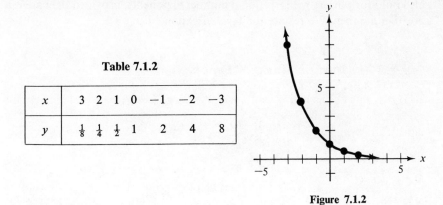

Table 7.1.2

x	3	2	1	0	−1	−2	−3
y	$\frac{1}{8}$	$\frac{1}{4}$	$\frac{1}{2}$	1	2	4	8

Figure 7.1.2

The functions f and g of Example 1 are both **exponential functions**. By projecting the graphs shown in Figure 7.1.1 and Figure 7.1.2 onto the y-axis, we see that the range of each of these functions is the set of all positive numbers. In general, we have the following definition.

7.1.1   Definition: *Exponential Function*

If $b > 0$ and $b \neq 1$, then the function defined by

$$f(x) = b^x$$

is an exponential function. The domain of f is R, and the range of f is $\{y : y > 0\}$.

If $b > 1$, then the graph of the exponential function defined by b^x slopes upward, as in Figure 7.1.1, and we say that the function is **increasing**. If $0 < b < 1$, then the graph of the exponential function defined by b^x slopes downward, as in Figure 7.1.2, and we say that the function is **decreasing**. If $b = 1$, then $b^x = 1^x = 1$ for all real x. Note that by Definition 7.1.1 the expression b^x does not define an exponential function when $b = 1$. However, for every exponential function the y-intercept point is $(0, 1)$, because $b^0 = 1$ if $b \neq 0$. Furthermore, for every exponential function the x-axis is a horizontal asymptote for the graph, as shown in Figure 7.1.1 and Figure 7.1.2.

It can be shown that the laws of exponents for rational number powers also hold for powers with irrational number exponents, provided the base is a positive number. We restate the laws of exponents.

7.1.2 *Theorem:* **Laws of Exponents**

If $a > 0, b > 0$, then

$$\text{(i)} \quad a^x \cdot a^y = a^{x+y}$$

$$\text{(ii)} \quad a^x \div a^y = a^{x-y}$$

$$\text{(iii)} \quad (a^x)^y = a^{xy}$$

$$\text{(iv)} \quad (ab)^x = a^x b^x$$

$$\text{(v)} \quad \left(\frac{a}{b}\right)^x = \frac{a^x}{b^x}$$

Example 2: Use the laws of exponents to calculate the simplest form.
(a) $(3^{\sqrt{2}})^{\sqrt{8}}$ **(b)** $2^{3+\sqrt{3}} \cdot 2^{3-\sqrt{3}}$

Solution:
(a) We apply the Third Law of Exponents.

$$(3^{\sqrt{2}})^{\sqrt{8}} = 3^{\sqrt{2} \cdot \sqrt{8}}$$

$$= 3^{\sqrt{16}}$$

$$= 3^4$$

$$= 81$$

(b) We apply the First Law of Exponents.

$$2^{3+\sqrt{3}} \cdot 2^{3-\sqrt{3}} = 2^{(3+\sqrt{3})+(3-\sqrt{3})}$$

$$= 2^6$$

$$= 64$$

Example 3: Use the laws of exponents to simplify the expression.
(a) $\sqrt[3]{2^{3x}}$ **(b)** $8^x \div 2^{x-1}$

Solution:
(a) First, we replace the radical by a power.

$$\sqrt[3]{2^{3x}} = (2^{3x})^{1/3}$$
$$= 2^{(3x)(1/3)}$$
$$= 2^x$$

(b) Because the bases are not the same, we cannot apply the laws of exponents with the expression in its present form. However, because $8 = 2^3$, we have

$$8^x \div 2^{x-1} = (2^3)^x \div 2^{x-1}$$
$$= 2^{3x} \div 2^{x-1}$$
$$= 2^{3x-(x-1)}$$
$$= 2^{2x+1}$$

An equation that contains the expression b^x is called an exponential equation. For the exponential equation

$$2^x = 32$$

it is obvious that the solution set is $\{5\}$. Because $32 = 2^5$, we have

$$2^x = 2^5$$

and thus

$$x = 5$$

In general, we have the following theorem that we state without proof.

7.1.3   Theorem: Exponential

If $b > 0$ and $b \neq 1$, then

$$b^{f(x)} = b^{g(x)}$$

if and only if

$$f(x) = g(x)$$

Example 4: Find the solution set.
(a) $3^{2x+3} = 9$ (b) $16^{x-1} = 8^x$

Solution:
(a) First, we express each side of the equation as a power with the same base. Thus,

$$3^{2x+3} = 9$$
$$3^{2x+3} = 3^2$$

Next, we apply Theorem 7.1.3. Thus,

$$2x + 3 = 2$$
$$2x = -1$$
$$x = -\tfrac{1}{2}$$

The solution set is $\{-\tfrac{1}{2}\}$.

(b) In order to express each side as a power with the same base, we take $16 = 2^4$ and $8 = 2^3$. Thus,

$$16^{x-1} = 8^x$$
$$(2^4)^{x-1} = (2^3)^x$$
$$2^{4(x-1)} = 2^{3x}$$
$$4(x - 1) = 3x$$
$$4x - 4 = 3x$$
$$x = 4$$

Thus, the solution set is $\{4\}$.

If it is not possible to express each side of an exponential equation as a power with the same rational number base, then we cannot at this time find the solution set. We consider such equations in Section 7.4.

EXERCISES 7.1

For Exercises 1–8 make a table of ordered pairs that satisfy the equation $y = f(x)$, with $x \in \{3, 2, 1, 0, -1, -2, -3\}$; plot the points that correspond to the pairs; and sketch the graph of the function f.

1. $f(x) = 3^x$ **2.** $f(x) = (\tfrac{2}{3})^x$ **3.** $f(x) = (1.5)^x$

4. $f(x) = (1.2)^x$ **5.** $f(x) = (0.8)^x$ **6.** $f(x) = (0.4)^x$

7. $f(x) = 2^{-x}$ **8.** $f(x) = -2^x$

For Exercises 9–16 use the laws of exponents to calculate the simplest form.

9. $(2^{\sqrt{2}})^{\sqrt{2}}$ **10.** $(\sqrt{3}^{\sqrt{2}})^{\sqrt{2}}$ **11.** $(\sqrt{3}^{\sqrt{2}})^{\sqrt{8}}$

12. $(\sqrt{2}^{\sqrt{3}})^{\sqrt{12}}$ **13.** $2^{2+\sqrt{5}} \cdot 2^{2-\sqrt{5}}$ **14.** $2^{1+\sqrt{2}} \cdot 2^{-4-\sqrt{2}}$

15. $3^{1+\sqrt{3}} \div 3^{2+\sqrt{3}}$ **16.** $3^{3-\sqrt{2}} \div 3^{1-\sqrt{2}}$

For Exercises 17–24 use the laws of exponents to simplify the given expression.

17. $\sqrt{3^{2x}}$ **18.** $\sqrt[3]{2^{6x}}$ **19.** $2^{2x} \cdot 2^{3x}$

20. $2^{2x-1} \cdot 2^{x+2}$ **21.** $3^{3x} \div 3^{x+1}$ **22.** $3^{2x-1} \div 3^{x-2}$

23. $8^x \div 4$ **24.** $(\tfrac{1}{3})^x \cdot 3^{2x}$

For Exercises 25–40 find the solution set.

25. $2^x = 16$ **26.** $2^x = \frac{1}{8}$ **27.** $3^x = 1$

28. $3^x = -3$ **29.** $8^x = 2$ **30.** $4^x = 8$

31. $9^x = \frac{1}{3}$ **32.** $8^x = \frac{1}{4}$ **33.** $2^{3x-1} = 8$

34. $2^{2x+1} = 4$ **35.** $4^{2x} = 2^{x+3}$ **36.** $9^{x+1} = 3^x$

37. $8^{x-1} = 4^x$ **38.** $8^{x+2} = 16^{x-1}$ **39.** $(\frac{2}{3})^x = \frac{27}{8}$

40. $(\frac{3}{2})^x = (\frac{2}{3})^{x+1}$

7.2 Logarithmic Functions

A function is a set of ordered pairs such that for each first component there corresponds only one second component. If for each second component of a function there corresponds only one first component, then the function is said to be **one-to-one**. For example, the function

$$F = \{(2, 4), (-1, 2), (0, 3)\}$$

is a one-to-one function, because no two ordered pairs in F have the same first component and no two ordered pairs in F have the same second component. On the other hand, the function

$$G = \{(2, 4), (-1, 1), (0, 4)\}$$

is not a one-to-one function, because the ordered pairs (2, 4) and (0, 4) have the same second component.

    If x and y are the variables used to represent the members of the domain and range, respectively, of a function, then we say that y is a function of x. If that function is a one-to-one function, then it is also true that x is a function of y. That is, in a one-to-one function, for each x there corresponds only one y and for each y there corresponds only one x. Thus, if an equation in x and y defines a one-to-one function, then it is possible to solve that equation uniquely for y in terms of x and it is also possible to solve the equation uniquely for x in terms of y. We have said that a vertical line intersects the graph of any function in at most one point. If the function is one-to-one, then a horizontal line also intersects the graph in at most one point.

Example 1: Determine whether or not the function is one-to-one.

(a) $f(x) = x^2$ (b) $g(x) = x^3$

Solution:

(a) First, we let $y = f(x)$. Thus,

$$y = x^2$$

Because this equation has two x-forms, namely

$$x = \sqrt{y} \quad \text{and} \quad x = -\sqrt{y}$$

we conclude that x is not a function of y. Hence, f is not a one-to-one function. Figure 7.2.1 shows the parabola that is the graph of f. Note that there are horizontal lines which intersect the graph in more than one point.

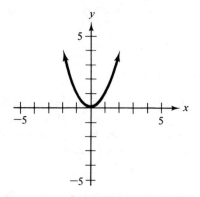

Figure 7.2.1

(b) First, we let $y = g(x)$. Thus,

$$y = x^3$$

Because this equation has a unique x-form, namely

$$x = \sqrt[3]{y}$$

we conclude that x is a function of y, and hence g is a one-to-one function. The graph of g is found by plotting points from Table 7.2.1, which contains some solutions of the equation $y = x^3$. See Figure 7.2.2. Note that every horizontal line intersects the graph in only one point.

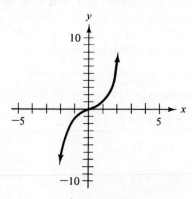

Figure 7.2.2

Table 7.2.1

x	2	1	0	-1	-2
y	8	1	0	-1	-8

If the components of each ordered pair of a one-to-one function f are interchanged, then the resulting set of ordered pairs is also a one-to-one function, called the **inverse** of function f. The inverse of f is represented by the symbol f^{-1}. For example, if

$$F = \{(2, 4), (-1, 2), (0, 3)\}$$

then F is a one-to-one function and the inverse of F is given by

$$F^{-1} = \{(4, 2), (2, -1), (3, 0)\}$$

Example 2: Let $f(x) = 2x - 4$, and find the expression $f^{-1}(x)$ that represents the inverse of function f.

Solution: First, we represent the function f by using set-builder notation. Because $y = f(x)$, we have

$$f = \{(x, y): y = 2x - 4\} \tag{1}$$

To find the inverse of f, we interchange x and y in Equation (1). Thus,

$$f^{-1} = \{(x, y): x = 2y - 4\} \tag{2}$$

To find the expression $f^{-1}(x)$ that represents the function f^{-1}, we solve Equation (2) for y. Thus,

$$x = 2y - 4$$
$$x + 4 = 2y$$
$$y = \frac{x + 4}{2}$$

Because $y = f^{-1}(x)$, we conclude that

$$f^{-1}(x) = \frac{x + 4}{2}$$

Figure 7.2.3 shows the graph of the union of functions f and f^{-1} of Example 2. The graph of f is the line that is the graph of Equation (1), and the graph of f^{-1} is the line that is the graph of Equation (2). Note that the union of these two lines is a figure that is symmetric with respect to the line $y = x$, which is shown as a dotted line in Figure 7.2.3. The graph of the union of any

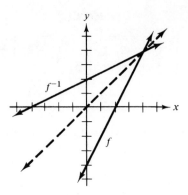

Figure 7.2.3

function and its inverse is a figure that is symmetric with respect to the line
$y = x$.

Consider the function

$$f = \{(x, y): y = 2^x\} \tag{3}$$

whose graph was found in Example 1 of Section 7.1 and is illustrated by
Figure 7.1.1. Because every horizontal line intersects the graph in at most one
point, f is a one-to-one function. By interchanging x and y in Equation (3), we
obtain the inverse of f, which is

$$f^{-1} = \{(x, y): x = 2^y\} \tag{4}$$

Because f^{-1} is a one-to-one function, it is possible to solve Equation (4)
uniquely for y in terms of x. However, none of the algebraic expressions that
we have so far considered can be used to write a y-form for Equation (4).
Therefore, we introduce some new notation. The y-form of Equation (4) is
given by

$$f^{-1} = \{(x, y): y = \log_2 x\} \tag{5}$$

Equation (5) is read "y equals log to the base 2 of x." Equations (4) and (5)
are equivalent equations. However, Equation (3) is not equivalent to either
Equation (4) or Equation (5). Because the domain of function f is the set of all
real numbers, the range of f^{-1} is the set of all real numbers. Because the
range of f is the set of all positive numbers, the domain of f^{-1} is the set of all
positive numbers. The graph of f^{-1} is the solid curve shown in Figure 7.2.4.
The figure also shows the graph of f as a broken curve and the graph of $y = x$
as a broken line. Note that the two curves are symmetric with respect to the
line.

Every exponential function is one-to-one and has an inverse that is
called a **logarithmic function**. In this book, however, we consider only those

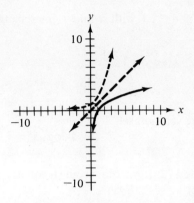

Figure 7.2.4

logarithmic functions for which the base is greater than 1. The numbers in the range of a logarithmic function are called **logarithms**.

7.2.1   *Definition:* **Logarithm**

If $b > 1$, then

$$y = \log_b x \qquad \text{if and only if} \qquad x = b^y$$

7.2.2   *Definition:* **Logarithmic Function**

If $b > 1$, then the function defined by

$$f(x) = \log_b x$$

is a logarithmic function. The domain of f is $\{x: x > 0\}$, and the range of f is R.

Example 3:   Solve for x.

(a) $y = \log_3 x$ 　　　　　　　　　　(b) $y = 5^x$

Solution:

(a) We apply Definition 7.2.1 with $b = 3$. Thus, if

$$y = \log_3 x$$

　　　then

$$x = 3^y$$

(b) We apply Definition 7.2.1 with x and y interchanged and with $b = 5$. Thus, if

$$y = 5^x$$

then

$$x = \log_5 y$$

Example 4:   Find the solution set.
(a) $\log_5 (x + 1) = 2$ **(b)** $2 \cdot \log_3 x = 1$

Solution:
(a) We apply Definition 7.2.1 to write the given equation in exponential form and then solve for x.

$$\log_5 (x + 1) = 2$$
$$(x + 1) = 5^2$$
$$x = 24$$

The solution set is $\{24\}$.

(b) First, we solve the given equation for $\log_3 x$ by dividing on both sides by 2.

$$2 \cdot \log_3 x = 1$$
$$\log_3 x = \tfrac{1}{2}$$

Next, we apply Definition 7.2.1. Thus,

$$x = 3^{1/2}$$

The solution set is $\{\sqrt{3}\}$.

Example 5:   Calculate the simplest form of the indicated logarithm.
(a) $\log_3 81$ **(b)** $\log_4 (\tfrac{1}{8})$

Solution:
(a) Let

$$\log_3 81 = x$$

From Definition 7.2.1 we have

$$81 = 3^x$$
$$3^4 = 3^x$$
$$4 = x$$

Thus,

$$\log_3 81 = 4$$

(b) Let

$$\log_4 (\tfrac{1}{8}) = x$$

Then

$$\tfrac{1}{8} = 4^x$$

We express each side as a power with the same base. Because $8 = 2^3$ and $4 = 2^2$, we have

$$\frac{1}{2^3} = (2^2)^x$$

$$2^{-3} = 2^{2x}$$

$$-3 = 2x$$

$$-\tfrac{3}{2} = x$$

The solution set is $\{-\tfrac{3}{2}\}$.

Example 6:   Let $f(x) = \log_2 (x - 3)$.
(a) Find the simplest form of $f(4)$.
(b) Find the domain of f.

Solution:
(a) We replace x by 4. Thus

$$f(x) = \log_2 (x - 3)$$

$$f(4) = \log_2 (4 - 3)$$

$$f(4) = \log_2 1$$

To find the simplest form of $f(4)$, we let $f(4) = z$. Thus,

$$z = \log_2 1$$

$$2^z = 1$$

$$2^z = 2^0$$

$$z = 0$$

Therefore,

$$f(4) = 0$$

(b) Because the domain of a logarithmic function is the set of all positive numbers, the expression $(x - 3)$ must be positive. That is,

$$x - 3 > 0$$

$$x > 3$$

Therefore, the domain of f is $\{x: x > 3\}$.

EXERCISES 7.2

For Exercises 1–8 determine whether or not the given function f is a one-to-one function. If f is one-to-one, find the expression $f^{-1}(x)$ that defines the inverse of f.

1. $f(x) = x + 3$ **2.** $f(x) = 2x$

3. $f(x) = 1 - 4x$ **4.** $f(x) = \tfrac{1}{2}(3x + 1)$

5. $f(x) = x^2 + 1$ **6.** $f(x) = x^3 + 1$

7. $f(x) = 2\sqrt[3]{x}$ **8.** $f(x) = |x|$

For Exercises 9–16 use Definition 7.2.1 to solve the given equation for x.

9. $y = \log_4 x$ **10.** $y = \log_{10} x$

11. $z = a^x$ **12.** $s = r^x$

13. $r = \log_e x$ **14.** $z = e^x$

15. $c = b^{ax}$ **16.** $c = \log_b (x + a)$

For Exercises 17–24 find the solution set.

17. $\log_2 x = 4$ **18.** $\log_3 x = 0$

19. $\log_3 (x - 1) = 1$ **20.** $\log_2 (1 - x) = 3$

21. $2 \cdot \log_4 x = 3$ **22.** $3 \cdot \log_8 x = 2$

23. $1 + \log_5 x = 0$ **24.** $1 + \frac{1}{2} \cdot \log_4 x = 0$

For Exercises 25–32 calculate the simplest form of the indicated logarithm.

25. $\log_2 8$ **26.** $\log_2 16$ **27.** $\log_3 3$ **28.** $\log_3 1$

29. $\log_4 8$ **30.** $\log_8 4$ **31.** $\log_8 \frac{1}{16}$ **32.** $\log_{16} \frac{1}{4}$

For Exercises 33–38 find the simplest form of the indicated function value, if it is defined.

33. If $f(x) = \log_4 (x - 2)$, find $f(3)$.

34. If $f(x) = \log_4 (x + 5)$, find $f(-1)$.

35. If $f(x) = \log_2 (x - 2)$, find $f(2)$.

36. If $f(x) = \log_2 (x + 1)$, find $f(-2)$.

37. If $f(x) = 2 \log_8 x$, find $f(4)$.

38. If $f(x) = 1 - \log_8 x$, find $f(\frac{1}{2})$.

For Exercises 39–42 find the domain of the function f.

39. $f(x) = \log_2 (x + 2)$ **40.** $f(x) = \log_2 (4 - x)$

41. $f(x) = \log_3 (1 - 2x)$ **42.** $f(x) = \log_3 (3x + 2)$

7.3   The Laws of Logarithms

From Definition 7.2.1 we see that $\log_b x$ is an exponent. This suggests that there are laws of logarithms which correspond to the laws of exponents. In this section we state and prove the **laws of logarithms**.

7.3.1   Theorem: *First Law of Logarithms*

If $b > 1$, $x > 0$, and $y > 0$, then

$$\log_b xy = \log_b x + \log_b y$$

PROOF: Let

$$\log_b x = r \quad \text{and} \quad \log_b y = s \qquad (1)$$

Thus, by Definition 7.2.1, we have

$$x = b^r \quad \text{and} \quad y = b^s$$

Next, we multiply corresponding sides of the latter two equations and apply the First Law of Exponents.

$$xy = b^r \cdot b^s$$
$$xy = b^{r+s}$$

Applying Definition 7.2.1 to this equation gives

$$\log_b xy = r + s$$

and by substituting from Equation (1) into the above, we obtain

$$\log_b xy = \log_b x + \log_b y$$

Example 1: If $\log_b x = 3$ and $\log_b y = 4$, find $\log_b xy$.

Solution: We apply Theorem 7.3.1. Thus,

$$\log_b xy = \log_b x + \log_b y$$
$$= 3 + 4$$
$$= 7$$

7.3.2 Theorem: Second Law of Logarithms

If $b > 1$, $x > 0$, and $y > 0$, then

$$\log_b \frac{x}{y} = \log_b x - \log_b y$$

PROOF: Because $\left(\dfrac{x}{y}\right) y = x$, then

$$\log_b \left(\frac{x}{y} \cdot y\right) = \log_b x$$

We apply the First Law of Logarithms to the left side of the above equation. Thus,

$$\log_b \frac{x}{y} + \log_b y = \log_b x$$

Next, we subtract $\log_b y$ from both sides. Hence,

$$\log_b \frac{x}{y} = \log_b x - \log_b y$$

Example 2: If $\log_b x = 2$, $\log_b y = 3$, and $\log_b z = 4$, find $\log_b \frac{x}{yz}$.

Solution: We apply the Second Law of Logarithms and then the First Law of Logarithms. Thus,

$$\begin{aligned}
\log_b \frac{x}{yz} &= \log_b x - \log_b yz \\
&= \log_b x - (\log_b y + \log_b z) \\
&= 2 - (3 + 4) \\
&= -5
\end{aligned}$$

By the First Law of Logarithms we have

$$\begin{aligned}
\log_b x^2 &= \log_b (x \cdot x) \\
&= \log_b x + \log_b x \\
&= 2 \cdot \log_b x \qquad\qquad (2)
\end{aligned}$$

Similarly, we have

$$\begin{aligned}
\log_b x^3 &= \log_b (x^2 \cdot x) \\
&= \log_b x^2 + \log_b x \qquad\qquad (3)
\end{aligned}$$

Substituting from Equation (2) into Equation (3), we obtain

$$\begin{aligned}
\log_b x^3 &= 2 \cdot \log_b x + \log_b x \\
&= 3 \cdot \log_b x \qquad\qquad (4)
\end{aligned}$$

The following theorem is a generalization of the results obtained in Equations (2) and (4).

7.3.3   Theorem: *Third Law of Logarithms*

If $b > 1$ and $x > 0$, then

$$\log_b x^r = r \cdot \log_b x$$

PROOF: Let

$$\log_b x = s \tag{5}$$

Thus,

$$x = b^s$$
$$x^r = (b^s)^r$$
$$x^r = b^{r \cdot s}$$

Applying Definition 7.2.1 to the latter equation, we have

$$\log_b x^r = r \cdot s$$

Substituting from Equation (5) into the above, we obtain

$$\log_b x^r = r \cdot \log_b x$$

Example 3:   If $\log_b x = 9$ and $\log_b y = 4$, find:

(a) $\log_b x^3 y^2$ **(b)** $\log_b \dfrac{\sqrt{x}}{y}$

Solution:
(a) We apply the First Law of Logarithms and then the Third Law of Logarithms. Thus,

$$\log_b x^3 y^2 = \log_b x^3 + \log_b y^2$$
$$= 3 \cdot \log_b x + 2 \cdot \log_b y$$
$$= 3 \cdot 9 + 2 \cdot 4$$
$$= 35$$

(b) Because $\sqrt{x} = x^{1/2}$, we may apply the laws of logarithms. Thus,

$$\log_b \frac{\sqrt{x}}{y} = \log_b \sqrt{x} - \log_b y$$
$$= \log_b x^{1/2} - \log_b y$$
$$= \tfrac{1}{2} \cdot \log_b x - \log_b y$$
$$= \tfrac{1}{2} \cdot 9 - 4$$
$$= \tfrac{1}{2}$$

Note that the expression $\log_b x^2$ means $\log_b (x^2)$ and is not the same as $(\log_b x)^2$. For example, if $\log_b x = 3$, then

$$\log_b x^2 = 2 \cdot \log_b x = 2 \cdot 3 = 6$$

and
$$(\log_b x)^2 = 3^2 = 9$$

Example 4:   Find the solution set.
(a) $\log_2 x = 3 + \log_2 5$
(b) $\log_3 x + \log_3 (2x + 1) = 0$

Solution:
(a) First, we separate the terms that contain logarithms from those that do not contain logarithms.
$$\log_2 x = 3 + \log_2 5$$
$$\log_2 x - \log_2 5 = 3$$

Next, we apply the Second Law of Logarithms to simplify the left side of the equation. Thus, we obtain

$$\log_2 \left(\frac{x}{5}\right) = 3$$

Thus,

$$\frac{x}{5} = 2^3$$

$$x = 40$$

The solution set is $\{40\}$.
(b) We apply the First Law of Logarithms to simplify the equation.
$$\log_3 x + \log_3 (2x + 1) = 0$$
$$\log_3 x(2x + 1) = 0$$

Thus,
$$x(2x + 1) = 3^0$$
$$2x^2 + x = 1$$
$$2x^2 + x - 1 = 0$$
$$(2x - 1)(x + 1) = 0$$
$$2x - 1 = 0 \quad \text{or} \quad x + 1 = 0$$
$$x = \tfrac{1}{2} \qquad\qquad x = -1$$

Because -1 is not in the domain of the function determined by $\log_b x$, we reject the extraneous solution $x = -1$. The solution set is $\{\tfrac{1}{2}\}$.

Example 5:   If $\log_b 2 = 0.3$ and $\log_b 3 = 0.5$, find $\log_b 24$.

Solution: First, we express 24 as a product whose factors are both powers of 2 and 3. Because $24 = 8 \cdot 3 = 2^3 \cdot 3$, then

$$\log_b 24 = \log_b 2^3 \cdot 3$$
$$= \log_b 2^3 + \log_b 3$$
$$= 3 \cdot \log_b 2 + \log_b 3$$
$$= 3(0.3) + 0.5$$
$$= 1.4$$

EXERCISES 7.3

For Exercises 1–6 use the laws of logarithms to write the given expression as a linear combination of $\log_b x$ and $\log_b y$.

1. $\log_b x^2 y$

2. $\log_b xy^3$

3. $\log_b \dfrac{x}{y^3}$

4. $\log_b \dfrac{x^2}{y}$

5. $\log_b \sqrt{xy}$

6. $\log_b \sqrt[3]{x^2 y}$

For Exercises 7–24 let $\log_b x = 2$, $\log_b y = 3$, and $\log_b z = 4$. Use the laws of logarithms, if possible, to calculate the indicated logarithm.

7. $\log_b xy$

8. $\log_b xz$

9. $\log_b \dfrac{x}{z}$

10. $\log_b \dfrac{z}{y}$

11. $\log_b x^3$

12. $\log_b y^4$

13. $\log_b xy^2$

14. $\log_b x^2 y^3$

15. $\log_b \dfrac{xy}{z}$

16. $\log_b \dfrac{y}{xz}$

17. $(\log_b z)^2$

18. $(\log_b x)(\log_b y)$

19. $\log_b \sqrt{y}$

20. $\log_b \sqrt{yz}$

21. $\log_b \sqrt[3]{y^2 z}$

22. $\log_b \sqrt[3]{\dfrac{x}{y^2}}$

23. $\log_b \dfrac{z^2}{\sqrt{xy}}$

24. $\log_b y^3 \sqrt{xz}$

For Exercises 25–34 apply the laws of logarithms to find the solution set of the equation.

25. $\log_2 x + \log_2 3 = 4$

26. $\log_2 x - \log_2 3 = 3$

27. $\log_3 x = 2 + \log_3 2$

28. $\log_3 x = 2 - \log_3 4$

29. $\log_3 (x + 1) - \log_3 x = 1$

30. $\log_2 x - \log_2 (x - 1) = 2$

31. $\log_4 x + \log_4 (3x + 2) = 0$

32. $\log_4 x + \log_4 (x - 3) = 1$

33. $2 \cdot \log_2 x = 1 + \log_2 (x + 4)$

34. $\frac{1}{2} \log_2 (x - 4) + 2 = \log_2 x$

For Exercises 35–40 let $\log_b 2 = 0.3$, $\log_b 3 = 0.5$, and $\log_b 5 = 0.7$. Use the laws of logarithms to calculate the indicated logarithm.

35. $\log_b 6$

36. $\log_b 15$

37. $\log_b 30$

38. $\log_b \frac{5}{6}$

39. $\log_b \frac{18}{5}$

40. $\log_b 54$

7.4 Common Logarithms and Natural Logarithms

The logarithmic function with base 10 is called the **common logarithmic function**, and it is represented by the expression log x. That is,

$$\log x = \log_{10} x$$

Unless x is a rational number power of 10, the expression log x represents an irrational number. Decimal approximations of log x can be found by using an electronic calculator or by using a table of common logarithms, such as Table 2 in the Appendix. In this section we use a calculator for such approximations. In Section 7.5 we show how to use Table 2 to find a decimal approximation for log x.

In Section 7.1 we found the solution set for those exponential equations in which it is possible to express each side of the equation as a power with the same base. We may use the common logarithmic function to solve exponential equations that contain powers with different bases.

Example 1:   Use common logarithms to solve for x.

(a) $3^x = 7$ **(b)** $5^{2x-1} = 4^x$

Solution:

(a) We take the common logarithm of both sides of the equation, apply the Third Law of Logarithms, and then solve for x.

$$3^x = 7$$
$$\log 3^x = \log 7$$
$$x \cdot \log 3 = \log 7$$
$$x = \frac{\log 7}{\log 3}$$

We have found the exact solution. To find a decimal approximation for x, we use an electronic calculator. Thus,

$$x = \frac{\log 7}{\log 3}$$
$$= \frac{0.8451}{0.4771}$$
$$= 1.77$$

(b) We take the common logarithm of both sides, apply the Third Law of Logarithms, and then solve for x.

$$5^{2x-1} = 4^x$$

$$\log 5^{2x-1} = \log 4^x$$

$$(2x - 1) \log 5 = x \cdot \log 4$$

We must separate the terms that contain x from the terms that do not contain x. Thus,

$$2x \cdot \log 5 - \log 5 = x \cdot \log 4$$

$$2x \cdot \log 5 - x \cdot \log 4 = \log 5$$

$$x(2 \cdot \log 5 - \log 4) = \log 5$$

$$x = \frac{\log 5}{2 \cdot \log 5 - \log 4}$$

We have found the exact solution. To find a decimal approximation, we first use the laws of logarithms to simplify the answer, and then we use an electronic calculator. Thus,

$$x = \frac{\log 5}{2 \cdot \log 5 - \log 4}$$

$$= \frac{\log 5}{\log 5^2 - \log 4}$$

$$= \frac{\log 5}{\log 25 - \log 4}$$

$$= \frac{\log 5}{\log \frac{25}{4}}$$

$$= \frac{\log 5}{\log 6.25}$$

$$= \frac{0.6990}{0.7959}$$

$$= 0.878$$

You are familiar with the irrational number represented by π that is used for many calculations in geometry. There is another irrational number, represented by e, that is very important in applications of mathematics in many fields. A decimal approximation for e is given by

$$e \approx 2.718$$

Decimal approximations for powers of e can be found by using an electronic calculator or by using a table of exponential functions, such as Table 3 in the Appendix.

Example 2: If P dollars is invested at the rate of k percent per annum with the interest compounded continuously, after t years the value of the investment is A dollars, where $A = Pe^{kt/100}$. Find the value after 10 years if $5000 is invested at the rate of 7% with interest compounded continuously.

Solution: Because the principal invested is $5000, we replace P by 5000 in the formula. Because the interest rate is 7%, we also let $k = 7$. Because the investment is held for 10 years, we let $t = 10$. Thus,

$$A = Pe^{kt/100}$$
$$= (5000)e^{(7)(10)/100}$$
$$= (5000)e^{0.7}$$

We have found the exact number of dollars in the value of the investment. To find a decimal approximation, we use an electronic calculator.

$$A = (5000)(2.014)$$
$$= 10,069$$

Therefore, the value of the investment is $10,069.

The logarithmic function with base e is called the **natural logarithmic function**, and it is represented by the expression $\ln x$. That is,

$$\ln x = \log_e x$$

Decimal approximations for $\ln x$ are found either by using an electronic calculator or by using a table of natural logarithms, such as Table 4 of the Appendix.

Example 3: Use natural logarithms to solve for x.

$$e^{2x-1} = 6e^x$$

Solution: Because $e^x \neq 0$, we may divide on both sides by e^x and apply the laws of exponents to simplify the equation.

$$e^{2x-1} = 6e^x$$
$$\frac{e^{2x-1}}{e^x} = \frac{6e^x}{e^x}$$
$$e^{(2x-1)-x} = 6$$
$$e^{x-1} = 6$$

Next, we apply Definition 7.2.1 to obtain

$$x - 1 = \log_e 6$$
$$x = 1 + \ln 6$$

We have found the exact solution. To find a decimal approximation for x, we use a calculator. Thus,

$$x = 1 + \ln 6$$
$$= 1 + 1.79$$
$$= 2.79$$

Example 4: Use the exponential function with base e to solve for x.

$$\ln (x + 2) - \ln x = 1$$

Solution: First, we apply the Second Law of Logarithms to simplify the equation.

$$\ln (x + 2) - \ln x = 1$$
$$\ln \frac{x + 2}{x} = 1$$

Next, we apply Definition 7.2.1 to write the equation in exponential form.

$$\log_e \frac{x + 2}{x} = 1$$
$$\frac{x + 2}{x} = e^1$$
$$x + 2 = ex$$
$$ex - x = 2$$
$$x(e - 1) = 2$$
$$x = \frac{2}{e - 1}$$

We have found the exact solution. Next, we use a calculator to find a decimal approximation for x. Thus,

$$x = \frac{2}{e - 1}$$
$$\cdot = \frac{2}{2.718 - 1}$$
$$= 1.16$$

Example 5: If 1000 bacteria of a certain culture are allowed to grow, after t days the number of bacteria is p, where $p = 1000 \cdot e^{t/10}$.
(a) How many bacteria are present after 12 days?
(b) How long does it take for the population to double?

Solution:
(a) We replace t by 12 and find p.

$$p = 1000 \cdot e^{t/10}$$
$$= 1000 \cdot e^{12/10}$$
$$= 1000 \cdot e^{1.2}$$
$$= (1000)(3.320)$$
$$= 3320$$

Therefore, after 12 days there are 3320 bacteria present.

(b) When the population doubles, there will be 2000 bacteria present. Therefore, we replace p by 2000 and then solve for t.

$$p = 1000 \cdot e^{t/10}$$
$$2000 = 1000 \cdot e^{t/10}$$
$$2 = e^{t/10}$$
$$\frac{t}{10} = \log_e 2$$
$$t = 10 \cdot \ln 2$$
$$= 10(0.693)$$
$$= 6.93$$

We conclude that it takes 6.93 days for the population to double.

EXERCISES 7.4

For Exercises 1–12 use common logarithms to solve for x, and then use an electronic calculator to find a decimal approximation for x.

1. $2^x = 3$ **2.** $5^x = 2$ **3.** $7^{x+1} = 4$

4. $3^{x-1} = 5$ **5.** $5^{1-2x} = 2$ **6.** $4^{3x+1} = 3$

7. $4^{x-1} = 3^x$ **8.** $2^{x+1} = 3^x$ **9.** $2^{x+2} = 6^{x-1}$

10. $7^{1-x} = 6^{x+1}$ **11.** $3^{1-2x} = 5^x$ **12.** $6^{2x-1} = 2^{x+2}$

For Exercises 13–20 use natural logarithms to solve for x, and then use an electronic calculator to find a decimal approximation for x.

13. $e^{3x} = 5$ **14.** $e^{x-1} = 2$ **15.** $e^{2x+1} = 3$

16. $e^{2-3x} = 4$ **17.** $-2 + e^{x+1} = 0$ **18.** $2e^x = 3$

19. $e^{2x+1} = 3e^x$ **20.** $\dfrac{2}{e^x} = e^x$

For Exercises 21–28 use the exponential function with base e to solve for x, and then use an electronic calculator to find a decimal approximation for x.

21. $\ln (x - 1) = 2$ **22.** $\ln 2x = 3$

23. $1 + \ln x = 0$ **24.** $2 \ln x = 5$

25. $\ln x + \ln 4 = 3$ **26.** $\ln (x + 1) + \ln 3 = 2$

27. $\ln (x + 1) = 1 + \ln x$ **28.** $\ln x = \ln (x - 1) + 1$

For Exercises 29–34 use either the exponential function with base e or the natural logarithmic function to find an expression that represents the exact answer to the stated question. Then use an electronic calculator to find a decimal approximation.

29. What is the value after 15 years if \$10,000 is invested at the rate of 6% with interest compounded continuously? Use the formula of Example 2.

30. What is the principal that must be invested at the rate of 8% with interest compounded continuously so that the value of the investment is \$10,000 after it is held for 5 years? Use the formula of Example 2.

31. How long will it take for \$10,000 to double in value if the principal is invested at the rate of 7% with interest compounded continuously? Use the formula of Example 2.

32. If 1000 bacteria are allowed to grow, after t weeks the number of bacteria present is p, where $p = 1000e^{t/5}$. How long will it take for the population to triple?

33. If 100 milligrams of radium are allowed to decompose for t years, there will be q milligrams remaining with $q = 100e^{-0.0003t}$. How much will remain after 1000 years?

34. The half-life of a radioactive substance is the time required for one-half of the substance to decompose. What is the half-life of radium? Use the formula of Exercise 33.

7.5   The Table of Common Logarithms (optional)

Table 2 in the Appendix can be used to find decimal approximations for common logarithms and for powers of 10 without the use of an electronic calculator. Part of this table is given in Table 7.5.1. If

$$y = \log_{10} x \tag{1}$$

then

$$x = 10^y \tag{2}$$

The numbers in the left-hand column and in the topmost row of the table are replacements for x in Equations (1) and (2). The numbers in the remaining rows and columns, the body of the table, are corresponding values of y in Equations (1) and (2).

Table 7.5.1

x	0	1	2	3	4	5	6	7	8	9
2.5	.3979	.3997	.4014	.4031	.4048	.4065	.4082	.4099	.4116	.4133
2.6	.4150	.4166	.4183	.4200	.4216	.4232	.4249	.4265	.4281	.4298
2.7	.4314	.4330	.4346	.4362	.4378	.4393	.4409	.4425	.4440	.4456
2.8	.4472	.4487	.4502	.4518	.4533	.4548	.4564	.4579	.4594	.4609
2.9	.4624	.4639	.4654	.4669	.4683	.4698	.4713	.4728	.4742	.4757
3.0	.4771	.4786	.4800	.4814	.4829	.4843	.4857	.4871	.4886	.4900
3.1	.4914	.4928	.4942	.4955	.4969	.4983	.4997	.5011	.5024	.5038

Example 1: Use Table 7.5.1 to find a decimal approximation for the indicated number.

(a) $\log_{10} 2.84$ (b) $10^{.4265}$

Solution:

(a) Let

$$y = \log_{10} 2.84$$

By comparing the equation with Equation (1), we conclude that $x = 2.84$, and we must use the table to find y. The required value of y is found in the intersection of the row that begins with 2.8 and the column that is headed by 4. (Note that 2.8 contains the first two digits of $x = 2.84$ and that 4 is the third digit.) Thus, from the table we have

$$\log_{10} 2.84 = .4533$$

(b) Let

$$x = 10^{.4265}$$

By comparing this equation with Equation (2), we conclude that $y = .4265$, and we must use the table to find x. Because .4265 is found in the row of the table that begins with 2.6 and in the column of the table that is headed by 7, we conclude that

$$10^{.4265} = 2.67$$

Note that in Table 2 the replacements for x are numbers between 1.00 and 9.99. However, the table can also be used to find an approximation for the common logarithm of a positive number that is not between 1.00 and 9.99 if we first write the number in scientific form. The scientific form of a number is $a \cdot 10^k$, where a is a number between 1.00 and 9.99 and k is an integer. (See Section 2.4.) By Definition 7.2.1 we have the following fact

$$\log_{10} 10^k = k \tag{3}$$

which can be used with Table 2 to find the common logarithm of a positive number that is written in scientific form.

Example 2:   Use Table 2 to find a decimal approximation for the indicated logarithm.

(a) $\log_{10} 277$ (b) $\log_{10} 0.378$

Solution:

(a) First, we write the given number in scientific form

$$277 = (2.77) \cdot 10^2$$

Thus,

$$\log_{10} 277 = \log_{10}[(2.77) \cdot 10^2] \qquad (4)$$

Next, we apply the First Law of Logarithms and Equation (3) to the right side of Equation (4). Thus,

$$\log_{10} 277 = \log_{10} 2.77 + \log_{10} 10^2$$
$$= \log_{10} 2.77 + 2 \qquad (5)$$

Substituting from Table 2 into Equation (5), we obtain

$$\log_{10} 277 = .4425 + 2$$
$$= 2.4425$$

(b) We write the given number in scientific form, apply the laws of logarithms, and then apply Table 2.

$$\log_{10} 0.378 = \log_{10} [(3.78) \cdot 10^{-1}]$$
$$= \log_{10} 3.78 + \log_{10} 10^{-1}$$
$$= .5775 + (-1)$$

Each of the logarithms found in Example 2 is the sum of a decimal fraction, called the **mantissa** of the logarithm, and an integer, called the **characteristic** of the logarithm. That is, in Example 2(a), we have

$$\log_{10} 277 = .4425 + 2$$

We call .4425 the mantissa and 2 the characteristic. And in Example 2(b) we have

$$\log_{10} 0.378 = .5775 + (-1)$$

Thus, .5775 is the mantissa and -1 is the characteristic. Note that the characteristic is also the exponent k when the given number is written in scientific form, $a \cdot 10^k$, while the mantissa is $\log a$, which is found by using the table. When the characteristic is a negative number, we represent the logarithm as a sum (or difference) as in Example 2(b). Note that

$$.5775 + (-1) \neq -1.5775$$

Rather

$$.5775 + (-1) = -0.4225$$

Because the mantissas given in Table 2 are numbers between .0000 and .9996, the table can be used to approximate 10^x if $0 \leq x \leq 1$, as illustrated in Example 1(b). The following example illustrates how to calculate 10^x if x is not between 0 and 1.

Example 3:   Use Table 2 to find a decimal approximation for the indicated power of 10.

(a) $10^{1.775}$ (b) $10^{-1.4}$.

Solution:

(a) Because $1.775 = .775 + 1$, we may apply the First Law of Exponents to write

$$10^{1.775} = 10^{.775+1}$$

$$= 10^{.775} \cdot 10^1 \qquad (6)$$

Because the exponent .775 is between 0 and 1, we may use Table 2 to find a decimal approximation for $10^{.775}$. However, we cannot find .775 exactly among the mantissas in the body of Table 2. Because .7752 is the closest approximation for .775 that is in the body of the Table, we approximate $10^{.775}$ as follows.

$$10^{.775} = 10^{.7752}$$

$$= 5.96 \qquad (7)$$

Substituting from Equation (7) into Equation (6), we obtain

$$10^{1.775} = (5.96)10^1$$

$$= 59.6$$

(b) First, we express the exponent -1.4 as the sum of an integer and a decimal fraction between 0 and 1. Because

$$-1.4 = -2.0 + 0.6$$

we have

$$10^{-1.4} = 10^{.6+(-2)}$$

$$= 10^{.6} \cdot 10^{-2} \qquad (8)$$

Next, we use Table 2 to approximate $10^{.6}$. The mantissa closest to .6 in the Table is .5999. Thus, we approximate

$$10^{.6} = 10^{.5999}$$

$$= 3.98 \qquad (9)$$

Substituting from Equation (9) into Equation (8), we obtain
$$10^{-1.4} = (3.98)10^{-2}$$
$$= 0.0398$$

Example 4:   Use Table 2 to find a decimal approximation for z if $\log z = 3.45$.

Solution: Because $\log z = \log_{10} z$, we are given that
$$\log_{10} z = 3.45$$
Thus,
$$z = 10^{3.45}$$
$$= 10^{3+.45}$$
$$= 10^3 \cdot 10^{.45}$$
$$= 10^3(2.82)$$
$$= 2820$$
Note that we use Table 2 to approximate
$$10^{.45} = 10^{.4502} = 2.82$$

EXERCISES 7.5

For Exercises 1–8 use Table 2 to find a decimal approximation for the indicated number.

1. $\log_{10} 6.27$	**2.** $\log_{10} 9.35$	**3.** $\log_{10} 1.03$
4. $\log_{10} 6.99$	**5.** $10^{.8774}$	**6.** $10^{.4969}$
7. $10^{.9613}$	**8.** $10^{.2155}$	

For Exercises 9–20 write the given number in scientific form, and then use the laws of logarithms and Table 2 to find a decimal approximation for the indicated logarithm.

9. $\log_{10} 536$	**10.** $\log_{10} 18.9$	**11.** $\log_{10} 0.782$
12. $\log_{10} 0.00577$	**13.** $\log_{10} 93.7$	**14.** $\log_{10} 8440$
15. $\log_{10} 0.0225$	**16.** $\log_{10} 0.584$	**17.** $\log_{10} 7000$
18. $\log_{10} 0.0003$	**19.** $\log_{10} (35 \cdot 10^{-6})$	**20.** $\log_{10} (73 \cdot 10^7)$

For Exercises 21–32 use the laws of exponents and Table 2 to find a decimal approximation for the indicated power of 10.

21. $10^{1.3505}$	**22.** $10^{2.8176}$	**23.** $10^{3.0855}$	**24.** $10^{4.9177}$
25. $10^{.6181-2}$	**26.** $10^{.9917-1}$	**27.** $10^{.5435-4}$	**28.** $10^{.2011-3}$
29. $10^{-0.3}$	**30.** $10^{-1.8}$	**31.** $10^{-2.9}$	**32.** $10^{-3.4}$

For Exercises 33–44 use Table 2 to find a decimal approximation for z.

33. $\log z = 0.715$ **34.** $z = \log 2.15$

35. $z = \log 0.49$ **36.** $\log z = 1.57$

37. $\log z = 3.4$ **38.** $z = \log 53.2$

39. $z = \log 0.072$ **40.** $\log z = .35$

41. $\log z = 2.7143 - 4$ **42.** $\log z = 1.3147 - 2$

43. $\log z = 9.8163 - 10$ **44.** $\log z = 7.1216 - 10$

7.6 Computations with Common Logarithms (optional)

Common logarithms can be used to find decimal approximations for products, quotients, and powers of positive numbers. Although the use of logarithms in performing such calculations is not necessary if an electronic calculator is available, we can nevertheless increase our understanding of the logarithmic function by applying logarithms for such calculations. Because we need to make use of the laws of logarithms, we restate those laws now for the common logarithmic function.

> **1.** $\log xy = \log x + \log y$
>
> **2.** $\log \dfrac{x}{y} = \log x - \log y$
>
> **3.** $\log x^a = a \cdot \log x$

Example 1: Use common logarithms to find a decimal approximation for $(3.74)(81.6)$.

Solution: Let

$$x = (3.74)(81.6)$$

We take the common logarithm of both sides and then apply the First Law of Logarithms.

$$\log x = \log (3.74)(81.6)$$
$$= \log 3.74 + \log 81.6 \qquad (1)$$

Next, we use Table 2 to find each of the logarithms in Equation (1) and then add the results.

$$\log 3.74 = .5729$$
$$\log 81.6 = \underline{1.9117}$$
$$\log 3.74 + \log 81.6 = 2.4846 \qquad (2)$$

Substituting from Equation (2) into Equation (1), we have

$$\log x = 2.4846$$

Thus,

$$x = 10^{2.4846}$$
$$= 10^2 \cdot 10^{.4846}$$
$$= 10^2(3.05) \qquad \text{[Table 2]}$$
$$= 305$$

Example 2:   Use common logarithms to find a decimal approximation for $\sqrt{837}$.

Solution: Let

$$x = \sqrt{837}$$
$$= 837^{1/2}$$

We take the common logarithm of both sides and then apply the Third Law of Logarithms.

$$\log x = \log 837^{1/2}$$
$$= \tfrac{1}{2} \log 837$$
$$= \tfrac{1}{2}(2.9227) \qquad \text{[Table 2]}$$
$$= 1.4614$$

Therefore,

$$x = 10^{1.4614}$$
$$= 10^1 \cdot 10^{.4614}$$
$$= 10(2.89) \qquad \text{[Table 2]}$$
$$= 28.9$$

Example 3:   Use common logarithms to find a decimal approximation for $(4.31)^3/153$.

Solution: Let

$$x = \frac{(4.31)^3}{153}$$

We apply the Second Law of Logarithms and then the Third Law of Logarithms.

$$\log x = \log \frac{(4.31)^3}{153}$$
$$= \log (4.31)^3 - \log 153$$
$$= 3 \cdot \log 4.31 - \log 153 \qquad\qquad (3)$$

We use Table 2 to find the logarithms in Equation (3). We have

$$\log 4.31 = .6345$$

$$3 \cdot \log 4.31 = 1.9035 \qquad (4)$$

$$\log 153 = 2.1847 \qquad (5)$$

By Equation (3) we see that we want to subtract Equation (5) from Equation (4). We wish to avoid obtaining a negative mantissa when subtracting. Thus, we apply a "trick" to write the logarithm in Equation (4) in a different form. By adding and then subtracting 1 to the right side of Equation (4), we obtain

$$3 \cdot \log 4.31 = 2.9035 - 1 \qquad \text{[Eq. (4)]}$$

$$\log 153 = \underline{2.1847} \qquad \text{[Eq. (5)]}$$

$$3 \cdot \log 4.31 - \log 153 = .7188 - 1 \qquad \text{[Difference]} \qquad (6)$$

Substituting from Equation (6) into Equation (3), we have

$$\log x = .7188 - 1$$

Thus,

$$x = 10^{.7188-1}$$

$$= 10^{.7188} \cdot 10^{-1}$$

$$= (5.23) \cdot 10^{-1} \qquad \text{[Table 2]}$$

$$= 0.523$$

Example 4:   Use common logarithms to find a decimal approximation for $\sqrt[3]{0.916}$.

Solution: Let

$$x = \sqrt[3]{0.916} = (0.916)^{1/3}$$

Then

$$\log x = \log (0.916)^{1/3}$$

$$= \tfrac{1}{3} \log 0.916 \qquad (7)$$

From Table 2 we have

$$\log 0.916 = .9619 - 1 \qquad (8)$$

From Equation (7) we see that we want to multiply both sides of Equation (8) by $\tfrac{1}{3}$. Furthermore, we want the characteristic, after multiplying, to be an integer. Because the characteristic of the logarithm in Equation (8) is not divisible by 3, we must write the logarithm in a different form before multiplying. Adding and subtracting 2 from the right side of Equation (8), we obtain

$$\log 0.916 = 2.9619 - 3 \qquad \text{[Eq. (8)]}$$

$$\tfrac{1}{3} \log 0.916 = \tfrac{1}{3}(2.9619 - 3)$$

$$= .9873 - 1 \qquad (9)$$

Substituting from Equation (9) into Equation (7), we have

$$\log x = .9873 - 1$$

Thus,

$$x = 10^{.9873-1}$$
$$= 10^{.9873} \cdot 10^{-1}$$
$$= (9.71) \cdot 10^{-1} \qquad [\text{Table 2}]$$
$$= 0.971$$

Example 5:   If the radius and altitude of a right circular cylinder are r units and h units, respectively, then the volume is V units, with $V = \pi r^2 h$. Use common logarithms to find the approximate volume of a steel drum whose length is 2.45 meters and whose diameter is 85 centimeters.

Solution: We let the unit of measure be meters. Because 1 meter equals 100 centimeters, the diameter of the drum is 0.85 meters. Because the radius is one-half the diameter, we let $r = \frac{1}{2}(0.85) = 0.425$. Because the length of the drum is 2.45 meters, we let $h = 2.45$. Thus,

$$V = \pi r^2 h$$
$$= (3.14)(0.425)^2(2.45)$$

Thus,

$$\log V = \log (3.14)(0.425)^2(2.45)$$
$$= \log 3.14 + \log (0.425)^2 + \log 2.45$$
$$= \log 3.14 + 2 \cdot \log 0.425 + \log 2.45$$
$$= 2 \cdot \log 0.425 + \log 3.14 + \log 2.45 \qquad (10)$$

We use Table 2 to approximate the sum in Equation (10). We have

$$\log 0.425 = .6284 - 1$$

Multiplying on both sides by 2, we have

$$2 \cdot \log 0.425 = 1.2568 - 2$$
$$\log 3.14 = .4969$$
$$\log 2.45 = \underline{.3892}$$
$$[\text{Sum}] = 2.1429 - 2$$
$$= .1429 \qquad (11)$$

Substituting from Equation (11) into Equation (10), we have

$$\log V = .1429$$

Thus,

$$V = 10^{.1429}$$
$$= 1.39$$

Therefore, the volume of the drum is approximately 1.39 cubic meters.

EXERCISES 7.6

For Exercises 1–18 use common logarithms and Table 2 to calculate a decimal approximation for the given expression.

1. $(3.75)(82.9)$

2. $(954)(0.216)$

3. $\dfrac{52.6}{8.19}$

4. $\dfrac{622}{19.4}$

5. $(3.49)^3$

6. $(29.3)^4$

7. $\sqrt{27.1}$

8. $\sqrt[3]{8950}$

9. $\dfrac{(52.3)(125)}{755}$

10. $(0.0084)\sqrt{54.2}$

11. $(0.416)^4$

12. $(0.021)^3$

13. $\sqrt[3]{0.685}$

14. $\sqrt{0.0059}$

15. $\dfrac{7.18}{(53.2)(91.6)}$

16. $\dfrac{121}{(6.52)^5}$

17. $\sqrt{\dfrac{98.4}{0.542}}$

18. $\dfrac{\sqrt[4]{899}}{\sqrt[3]{27.5}}$

For Exercises 19–24 use common logarithms and Table 2 to find the answer to the stated question.

19. If P dollars is invested at k percent per year and held for t years with interest compounded yearly, the investment has value A dollars, with $A = P(1 + k/100)^t$. What is the value after 30 years if $1000 is invested at 6% with interest compounded yearly?

20. What principal must be invested at 8% with interest compounded yearly to have a value of $1000 after 12 years? Use the formula in Exercise 19.

21. If r centimeters is the radius of a sphere, then V cubic centimeters is the volume of the sphere, with $V = 1.33\pi r^3$. What is the volume of a sphere whose radius is 16.3 centimeters?

22. A cylindrical drum is 6.13 feet long and has a diameter of 2.50 feet. The drum is filled with oil that weighs 57.1 pounds per cubic foot. What is the weight of the oil? Use the formula in Example 5 to find the volume.

23. The period of a pendulum that is L feet long is T seconds, with $T = 2\pi\sqrt{L/32}$. What is the period of a pendulum that is 3.86 feet long?

24. What is the length of a pendulum whose period is 1.8 seconds? Use the formula in Exercise 23.

7.7   Linear Interpolation (optional)

The number of significant digits in a numeral is the number of digits in the numeral when all zeros used only as placeholders either on the left or on the right are not counted. For example, the numeral 3.20 has three significant digits, whereas both 320 and 0.032 have only two significant digits, because we do not count the zeros used only as placeholders. We have used Table 2 to find a decimal approximation for $\log x$ when x has three significant digits.

By using a process called **linear interpolation**, we can find a decimal approximation for log x when x has four significant digits, such as in log 3.254.

Suppose that $A(1, 2)$ and $B(3, 5)$ are two given points and we wish to find the y-coordinate of the point P on line segment AB, if it is given that the x-coordinate of P is 2.6. See Figure 7.7.1. We let $P = (2.6, \bar{y})$, and thus we want to find $\bar{y}$. First, we let d be the vertical distance between points P and A. Because the y-coordinate of points P and A are $\bar{y}$ and 2, respectively, we have

$$d = \bar{y} - 2 \tag{1}$$

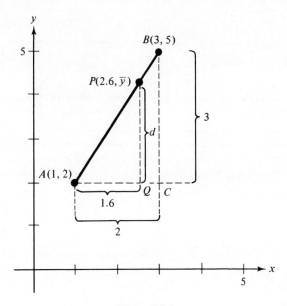

Figure 7.7.1

Because the difference of the x-coordinates of points P and A is $2.6 - 1.0 = 1.6$, the horizontal distance between P and A is 1.6. Similarly, the vertical distance between points B and A is the difference of their y-coordinates, $5 - 2 = 3$; and the horizontal distance between the points B and A is the difference of their x-coordinates, $3 - 1 = 2$. In Figure 7.7.1, triangles ACB and AQP are similar. Thus, the sides of the triangles are proportional, and we have

$$\frac{d}{1.6} = \frac{3}{2}$$

Thus,

$$d = (1.6)(\tfrac{3}{2})$$

$$= 2.4 \tag{2}$$

Solving Equation (1) for y and then substituting the value given in Equation (2) for d, we have

$$\bar{y} = 2 + d$$
$$= 2 + 2.4$$
$$= 4.4$$

Therefore, the y-coordinate of point P is 4.4.

The above discussion about the similar triangles in Figure 7.7.1 is summarized by the following table. The process used to find $\bar{y}$ is called linear interpolation.

			x	y		
Point A			1.0	2.0		
Point P	2.0	$1.6\begin{cases}1.0\\2.6\\3.0\end{cases}$	2.6	$\bar{y}$ $\Big\}d$	3.0
Point B			3.0	5.0		

Example 1:   Use Table 2 with linear interpolation to find a decimal approximation for log 2.856.

Solution: Let

$$\bar{y} = \log 2.856$$

Because 2.856 is between 2.850 and 2.860, we first use Table 2 to find log 2.85 and log 2.86. Next, we calculate the differences that are indicated in the following table.

			x	$\log x$		
			2.850	.4548		
0.010	0.006	$\begin{cases}2.850\\2.856\\2.860\end{cases}$	2.856	$\bar{y}$ $\Big\}d$	.0016
			2.860	.4564		

We have

$$d = \bar{y} - .4548 \tag{3}$$

Furthermore,

$$\frac{d}{0.006} = \frac{0.0016}{0.010}$$

or, equivalently,

$$\frac{d}{0.0016} = \frac{0.006}{0.010}$$

$$\frac{d}{0.0016} = 0.6$$

Hence,

$$d = (0.6)(0.0016)$$
$$= 0.00096$$

Because the mantissas in Table 2 are rounded off to the fourth decimal place, we round off d to the fourth decimal place. Thus, we take

$$d = 0.0010$$

Next, we solve Equation (3) for $\bar{y}$ and substitute in the value for d. Thus,

$$\bar{y} = .4548 + d$$
$$= .4548 + .0010$$
$$= .4558$$

Hence, log 2.856 = 0.4558.

Because the graph of the function defined by log x is not a straight line, the result obtained in Example 1 is not exact. However, the error is less than 0.0001, and thus the result is accurate to the fourth decimal place.

Example 2:   Use Table 2 with linear interpolation to find a decimal approximation for $10^{.7948}$.

Solution: Let

$$\bar{x} = 10^{.7948}$$

Then

$$\log \bar{x} = .7948$$

We find the two mantissas in Table 2 that are closest to .7948. They are .7945 and .7952. In the following table we show the results found in Table 2 and the differences required to find $\bar{x}$.

		x	$\log x$		
0.01	d	6.23	.7945	.0003	.0007
		$\bar{x}$	.7948		
		6.24	.7952		

Therefore,

$$\frac{d}{0.01} = \frac{.0003}{.0007}$$

$$\frac{d}{0.01} = \frac{3}{7}$$

$$d = \frac{3}{7}(.01)$$

$$= .004$$

Because

$$d = \bar{x} - 6.23$$

then

$$\bar{x} = 6.23 + d$$
$$= 6.23 + .004$$
$$= 6.234$$

Hence,

$$10^{.7948} = 6.234$$

Example 3: If 100 grams of a certain substance are allowed to decompose, after t years its mass will be w grams, with $w = 100 \cdot e^{-0.2t}$. Use Table 2 with linear interpolation to find the mass after 3 years.

Solution: We let $t = 3$ in the formula. Thus,

$$w = 100 \cdot e^{-0.6}$$
$$\log w = \log 100 \cdot e^{-0.6}$$
$$= \log 100 + \log e^{-0.6}$$
$$= \log 10^2 + (-0.6) \log e$$
$$= 2 - 0.6 \log e \qquad (4)$$

Because $e = 2.718$, we use linear interpolation to find $\log 2.718$. Let

$$\bar{y} = \log e = \log 2.718$$

From Table 2 we have

	x	$log\ x$
0.0010 $\left\{ \begin{array}{l} \\ \\ \\ \end{array} \right.$ 0.008 $\left\{ \begin{array}{l} 2.710 \\ 2.718 \\ 2.720 \end{array} \right.$		$\left. \begin{array}{l} .4330 \\ \bar{y} \\ .4346 \end{array} \right\} d \right\}$ .0016

Therefore,

$$\frac{d}{.0016} = \frac{.008}{.010}$$

$$d = (.0016)(.8)$$
$$= .0013$$

Because

$$d = \bar{y} - .4330$$

then

$$\bar{y} = .4330 + d$$
$$= .4330 + .0013$$
$$= .4343$$

Hence,

$$\log e = .4343$$

Substituting the value for $\log e$ into Equation (4), we have

$$\log w = 2 - (0.6)(.4343)$$
$$= 2.0000 - .2606$$
$$= 1.7394$$

Therefore,

$$w = 10^{1.7394}$$
$$= 10^1 \cdot 10^{.7394} \tag{5}$$

We use linear interpolation to find

$$\bar{x} = 10^{.7394}$$

	x	$\log x$	
$0.01 \left\{ d \begin{cases} 5.48 \\ \bar{x} \\ 5.49 \end{cases} \right.$		$\left. \begin{matrix} .7388 \\ .7394 \\ .7396 \end{matrix} \right\} .0006 \\ \left. \begin{matrix} \end{matrix} \right\} .0008$	

Thus,

$$\frac{d}{.01} = \frac{.0006}{.0008}$$
$$d = (0.1)(.75)$$
$$= .0075$$
$$= .008$$

and

$$\bar{x} = 5.48 + d$$
$$= 5.48 + .008$$
$$= 5.488$$

Therefore,
$$10^{.7394} = 5.488$$
and substituting into Equation (5), we have
$$w = 10(5.488)$$
$$= 54.88$$
We conclude that after 3 years the mass of the substance will be 54.88 grams.

EXERCISES 7.7

For Exercises 1–8 use Table 2 with linear interpolation to find a decimal approximation for the indicated logarithm that is accurate to the fourth decimal place.

1. log 7.205   **2.** log 8.944   **3.** log 2.823   **4.** log 5.346

5. log 52.33   **6.** log 437.5   **7.** log .8107   **8.** log .03325

For Exercises 9–16 use Table 2 with linear interpolation to find a decimal approximation for the indicated power of 10 that is accurate to four significant digits.

9. $10^{.6163}$ **10.** $10^{.9306}$ **11.** $10^{.5745}$ **12.** $10^{.8832}$

13. $10^{3.7149}$ **14.** $10^{1.7877}$ **15.** $10^{-1.350}$ **16.** $10^{-0.5900}$

For Exercises 17–20 use Table 2 with linear interpolation to find a decimal approximation that is accurate to four significant digits, and answer the stated question. Use the approximation log e = 0.4343, if needed.

17. If \$1000 is invested at the rate of 6% per year with interest compounded continuously, after t years the investment will have value A dollars, with $A = 1000e^{0.06t}$. What is the value after 12 years?

18. If 5000 bacteria are allowed to grow, after t weeks the number present is P, with $P = 5000e^{0.3t}$. How many are present after 20 weeks?

19. If 300 grams of a substance are allowed to decompose, after t years the mass is q grams, with $q = 300e^{-0.5t}$. How much remains after 15 years?

20. If 100 milligrams of radium are allowed to decompose, after t years the amount remaining is r milligrams, with $r = 100e^{-0.0003t}$. How much will remain after 100 years?

REVIEW EXERCISES 7

For Exercises 1–2 sketch the graph of the function.

1. $f(x) = 3^{x/2}$ **2.** $g(x) = -2^{-x}$

For Exercises 3–4 use the laws of exponents to simplify the given expression.

3. $(\sqrt{2}^{\sqrt{2}})^{\sqrt{8}}$ **4.** $4^{3x} \cdot 2^x$

For Exercises 5–6 use the laws of exponents to find the solution set.

5. $3^{2x+1} = 9$ **6.** $8^x = 4^{x+1}$

For Exercises 7–8 find the expression $f^{-1}(x)$ that defines the inverse of the function f.

7. $f(x) = 4x + 3$ **8.** $f(x) = x^3 - 1$

For Exercises 9–10 use Definition 7.2.1 to solve the equation for r.

9. $s = \log_a rt$ **10.** $t = s + a^r$

For Exercises 11–12 use Definition 7.2.1 to find the solution set.

11. $\log_3 (x + 1) = 2$ **12.** $1 + \log_4 3x = 0$

For Exercises 13–14 find the simplest form of the indicated logarithm without using a calculator or a table of logarithms.

13. $\log_9 27$ **14.** $\log_8 \frac{1}{4}$

For ·Exercises 15–16 find the simplest form of the indicated function value, if it is defined.

15. If $f(x) = \log_8 (x + 1)$, find $f(-\frac{1}{2})$.
16. If $f(x) = \log_2 (x - 4)$, find $f(4)$.

For Exercises 17–18 use the laws of logarithms to write the given expression as a linear combination of $\log_b x$ and $\log_b y$.

17. $\log_b x^3 y^2$ **18.** $\log_b \dfrac{\sqrt{x}}{\sqrt[3]{y^2}}$

For Exercises 19–20 let $\log_b x = 2$, $\log_b y = 3$, and $\log_b z = 4$. Use the laws of logarithms to calculate the simplest form of the indicated logarithm.

19. $\log_b \sqrt{xyz}$ **20.** $\log_b \dfrac{z\sqrt[3]{y}}{x^3}$

For Exercises 21–22 use the laws of logarithms to find the solution set.

21. $\log_2 (5x + 1) - \log_2 (x - 1) = 3$
22. $\log_3 (2x + 5) = 1 - \log_3 x$

For Exercises 23–24 use common logarithms to solve the equation for x, and then use an electronic calculator to find a decimal approximation for x.

23. $2^{x+3} = 5$ **24.** $3^{x+1} = 4^x$

For Exercises 25–26 use natural logarithms to solve the equation for x, and then use an electronic calculator to find a decimal approximation for x.

25. $e^{3x-1} = 2$ **26.** $2e^{2x+1} = 3e^x$

For Exercises 27–28 use the exponential function with base e to solve the equation for x, and then use an electronic calculator to find a decimal approximation for x.

27. $2 + \ln x = 0$ **28.** $\ln x = 1 + \ln (x - 2)$

For Exercises 29–30 use either the exponential function with base e or the natural logarithmic function to find an expression that represents the exact answer to the stated question. Then use an electronic calculator to find a decimal approximation.

29. It is estimated that the population of the world is 4 billion, and the growth rate is 2% per year. After t years the population will be given by the formula $P = 4 \cdot 10^9 e^{0.02t}$. What will the population be after 40 years?

30. If P dollars is invested at the rate of k percent per year with the interest compounded continuously, after t years the value of the investment is A dollars, with $A = Pe^{kt/100}$. At what interest rate must the principal be invested if the investment doubles in value every 5 years?

For Exercises 31–32 find the domain and range of the indicated function.

31. $f(x) = e^x$ **32.** $f(x) = \ln (x - 1)$

For Exercises 33–36 use Table 2 without interpolation to find a decimal approximation for the indicated logarithm or power of 10.

33. $\log_{10} 0.416$ **34.** $\log_{10} 745$ **35.** $10^{1.3416}$ **36.** $10^{-2.45}$

For Exercises 37–38 use Table 2 without interpolation to find a decimal approximation for z.

37. $\log z = 3.18$ **38.** $z = \log 0.8160$

For Exercises 39–42 use common logarithms and Table 2 without interpolation to calculate a decimal approximation for the given expression.

39. $\sqrt[3]{83.5}$ **40.** $(0.216)^5$ **41.** $\dfrac{63.4}{(752)(0.419)}$ **42.** $4.68\sqrt{\dfrac{291}{564}}$

For Exercises 43–46 use Table 2 with linear interpolation to find a decimal approximation for the given expression that is accurate to four significant digits.

43. $\log_{10} 872.4$ **44.** $10^{1.376}$ **45.** $\sqrt{7.436}$ **46.** $(731.5)e^{-2.610}$

an introduction to complex numbers

8.1 Numbers That Are Not Real

The square of every real number is greater than or equal to zero. If the square of a number is negative, the number is said to be **imaginary**. Let i represent an imaginary number whose square is -1. Then

$$i = \sqrt{-1}$$
$$i^2 = -1$$

The product of the real number b and the imaginary number i is represented by bi. The sum of the real number a and the imaginary number bi is represented by $a + bi$ and is called a **complex number**.

8.1.1 Definition: *Complex Number*

If a and b are real numbers and if $i^2 = -1$, then a number of the form $a + bi$ is called a complex number.

The set of all complex numbers is represented by C. The axioms for real numbers given in Section 1.2, except for the axioms of order, also hold for set C. In particular, the commutative, associative, and distributive axioms are valid for complex numbers. A complex number is neither positive nor negative. Therefore, the axioms of order do not apply to the set C, and the relations "less than" and "greater than" are not defined for complex numbers. However, all of the theorems about real numbers that can be proved without using the axioms of order also hold for complex numbers.

The complex number $a + bi$ is imaginary if and only if $b \neq 0$. A number of the form bi with $b \neq 0$ is called a **pure imaginary number**. Because

$$a = a + 0i$$
$$bi = 0 + bi$$

the real number a and the pure imaginary number bi are both members of set C. The simplest form of a complex number that is neither a real number nor a pure imaginary number is $a + bi$. The simplest form for the sum or product of two complex numbers is found by applying the axioms and theorems for real numbers to write the sum or product in the form $a + bi$.

Example 1:   Find the simplest form.

(a) $(-2 + 3i) + (1 + i)$ (b) $(5 - 3i) - (3 - 2i)$

Solution:

(a) We apply the axioms as in finding a standard form for the sum of two binomials. Thus,

$$(-2 + 3i) + (1 + i) = (-2 + 1) + (3i + 1 \cdot i)$$
$$= -1 + (3 + 1)i$$
$$= -1 + 4i$$

(b) The difference of two complex numbers is found by adding the first plus the opposite of the second, as in real numbers. Thus,

$$(5 - 3i) - (3 - 2i) = 5 - 3i - 3 + 2i$$
$$= (5 - 3) + (-3 + 2)i$$
$$= 2 + (-1)i$$
$$= 2 - i$$

Example 2:   Find the simplest form.

(a) $i(4 + 3i)$ (b) $(2 - 3i)(5 + 2i)$

Solution:

(a) First, we apply the distributive axiom to multiply out, and then we replace i^2 by -1.

$$i(4 + 3i) = 4i + 3i^2$$
$$= 4i + 3(-1)$$
$$= -3 + 4i$$

(b) We multiply out, as in the product of two binomials, and then let $i^2 = -1$.

$$(2 - 3i)(5 + 2i) = 10 + 4i - 15i - 6i^2$$
$$= 10 + 4i - 15i + 6$$
$$= 16 - 11i$$

Example 3:   Find the simplest form.

(a) $(3 + 4i)^2$ **(b)** $(2 + 3i)(2 - 3i)$

Solution:

(a) We apply the Binomial Square Theorem, $(a + b)^2 = a^2 + 2ab + b^2$.
Thus,

$$(3 + 4i)^2 = 3^2 + 2(3)(4i) + (4i)^2$$
$$= 9 + 24i + 16i^2$$
$$= 9 + 24i - 16$$
$$= -7 + 24i$$

(b) We apply the Sum-Difference Theorem, $(a + b)(a - b) = a^2 - b^2$.
Thus,

$$(2 + 3i)(2 - 3i) = 2^2 - (3i)^2$$
$$= 4 - 9i^2$$
$$= 4 + 9$$
$$= 13$$

The complex number $2 - 3i$ is said to be the **conjugate** of $2 + 3i$. In general, the conjugate of $a + bi$ is $a - bi$, and the conjugate of $a - bi$ is $a + bi$. As we illustrated in Example 3(b), the product of any complex number and its conjugate is always a real number.

The quotient of two complex numbers is represented by a fraction whose numerator is the dividend and whose denominator is the divisor. That is,

$$(a + bi) \div (c + di) = \frac{a + bi}{c + di}$$

If we multiply both the numerator and denominator of the fraction by the conjugate of the denominator, the result is an equivalent fraction whose denominator is real. In this manner we can find the simplest form for the quotient of two complex numbers.

Example 4: Find the simplest form.

(a) $\dfrac{i}{1 + 3i}$ **(b)** $(2 + i) \div (1 - 2i)$

Solution:

(a) We multiply both the numerator and denominator by $1 - 3i$, which is the conjugate of the denominator. Thus,

$$\frac{i}{1 + 3i} = \frac{i(1 - 3i)}{(1 + 3i)(1 - 3i)}$$

$$= \frac{i - 3i^2}{1 - 9i^2}$$

$$= \frac{i + 3}{10}$$

$$= \frac{3}{10} + \frac{1}{10}i$$

(b) We replace the quotient by a fraction and then multiply both the numerator and denominator by the conjugate of the denominator.

$$(2 + i) \div (1 - 2i) = \frac{2 + i}{1 - 2i}$$

$$= \frac{(2 + i)(1 + 2i)}{(1 - 2i)(1 + 2i)}$$

$$= \frac{2 + 4i + i + 2i^2}{1 - 4i^2}$$

$$= \frac{2 + 4i + i - 2}{1 + 4}$$

$$= \frac{5i}{5}$$

$$= i$$

Example 5: Find the simplest form.

(a) i^3 **(b)** i^{-6}

Solution:

(a) Because $i^2 \cdot i = i^3$, we have

$$i^3 = i^2 \cdot i$$

$$= (-1)i$$

$$= -i$$

(b) We apply the laws of exponents. Thus,

$$i^{-6} = \frac{1}{i^6}$$

$$= \frac{1}{(i^2)^3}$$

$$= \frac{1}{(-1)^3}$$

$$= -1$$

EXERCISES 8.1

For Exercises 1–44 find the simplest form of the complex number.

1. $(2 + i) + (3 - 4i)$ **2.** $(1 - 3i) + (-1 + 5i)$

3. $(6 + 4i) + (6 - 4i)$ **4.** $(-2 + 3i) + (-1 - 8i)$

5. $(1 + i) - (2 + 3i)$ **6.** $(3 - 5i) - (1 + 2i)$

7. $(-4 + i) - (-4 + 3i)$ **8.** $(1 + 2i) - (-1 + 2i)$

9. $(1 + i) + (\sqrt{2} + i)$ **10.** $(\sqrt{3} + i) + (1 - 2i)$

11. $(-2 + i) - (1 + \sqrt{3}\,i)$ **12.** $(1 + i) - (1 + \sqrt{2}\,i)$

13. $3(2 + i)$ **14.** $-2(1 - 3i)$

15. $i(2 + i)$ **16.** $-3i(2 + 4i)$

17. $(1 + i)(2 + i)$ **18.** $(3 - i)(2 + i)$

19. $(2 + 3i)(1 - i)$ **20.** $(4 - i)(1 - 2i)$

21. $(2 + i)^2$ **22.** $(1 + i)^2$

23. $(1 - 3i)^2$ **24.** $(2 - i)^2$

25. $(5 + 4i)(5 - 4i)$ **26.** $(3 + 2i)(3 - 2i)$

27. $(\sqrt{2} + i)(\sqrt{2} - i)$ **28.** $(2 - \sqrt{3}\,i)(2 + \sqrt{3}\,i)$

29. $(1 + \sqrt{2}\,i)^2$ **30.** $(\sqrt{3} + i)^2$

31. $\dfrac{2}{1 + 2i}$ **32.** $\dfrac{3}{1 + i}$

33. $\dfrac{i}{2 + 3i}$ **34.** $\dfrac{1 + i}{2 - i}$

35. $5i \div (2 + i)$ **36.** $(2 + 3i) \div i$

37. $(1 + i) \div (1 - i)$ **38.** $-10i \div (1 + 2i)$

39. i^4 **40.** i^7

41. i^{-3} **42.** i^{-10}

43. $(1 + i)^3$ **44.** $(1 - i)^4$

8.2 Imaginary Square Roots and Cube Roots

Because $(3i)^2 = 9i^2 = -9$, we conclude that $3i$ is a square root of -9. Because $(-3i)^2 = 9i^2 = -9$, then $-3i$ is also a square root of -9. Every negative number has two square roots that are imaginary, and each square root is the opposite of the other. The radical sign is used to represent the **principal square root** of a negative number. In general, we have the following definition for the principal square root of a negative number.

> ### 8.2.1　Definition
> If b is a positive number, then the principal square root of the negative number $-b$ is given by
> $$\sqrt{-b} = \sqrt{b}\,i$$

Example 1:　Find the simplest form.

(a) $\sqrt{-25}$　　　　　　　　　　　(b) $-\sqrt{-16}$

Solution:

(a) We apply Definition 8.2.1. Thus,
$$\sqrt{-25} = \sqrt{25}\,i$$
$$= 5i$$

(b) We want the opposite of the principal square root. Thus,
$$-\sqrt{-16} = -\sqrt{16}\,i$$
$$= -4i$$

Example 2:　Find the simplest form.

(a) $\sqrt{-3}\sqrt{-12}$.　　　　　　　(b) $\sqrt{-2}(\sqrt{2} + \sqrt{-8})$

Solution:

(a) Theorem 2.5.3, $\sqrt{a} \cdot \sqrt{b} = \sqrt{ab}$, does not apply because -3 and -12 are negative numbers. Therefore, we first apply Definition 8.2.1 and then apply the theorem.
$$\sqrt{-3} \cdot \sqrt{-12} = (\sqrt{3}\,i)(\sqrt{12}\,i)$$
$$= (\sqrt{3} \cdot \sqrt{12})i^2$$
$$= \sqrt{36}\,i^2$$
$$= 6(-1)$$
$$= -6$$

(b) First, we apply Definition 8.2.1. Thus,

$$\sqrt{-2}(\sqrt{2} + \sqrt{-8}) = \sqrt{2}\,i(\sqrt{2} + \sqrt{8}\,i)$$
$$= \sqrt{2}\cdot\sqrt{2}\,i + \sqrt{2}\cdot\sqrt{8}\,i^2$$
$$= 2i + 4i^2$$
$$= -4 + 2i$$

The set that contains all the solutions, both real and imaginary, of an equation is called the **complete solution set**. To find the complete solution set, we apply the same techniques that we use when finding the real solutions. The Square Root Theorem and the Quadratic Formula hold even when the number under the radical sign is negative, provided we apply Definition 8.2.1.

Example 3: Find the complete solution set.
(a) $x^2 - 4x + 5 = 0$ (b) $3x^2 + 2x + 1 = 0$

Solution:
(a) We complete the square.

$$x^2 - 4x + 5 = 0$$
$$x^2 - 4x = -5$$
$$x^2 - 4x + 4 = -5 + 4$$
$$(x - 2)^2 = -1$$
$$x - 2 = \pm\sqrt{-1}$$
$$x - 2 = \pm i$$
$$x = 2 \pm i$$

The complete solution set is $\{2 + i, 2 - i\}$.

(b) We apply the Quadratic Formula.

$$3x^2 + 2x + 1 = 0$$

$$x = \frac{-b \pm \sqrt{b^2 - 4ac}}{2a}$$

$$= \frac{-2 \pm \sqrt{2^2 - 4(3)(1)}}{2(3)}$$

$$= \frac{-2 \pm \sqrt{-8}}{6}$$

$$= \frac{-2 \pm \sqrt{8}\,i}{6}$$

$$= \frac{-2 \pm 2\sqrt{2}\,i}{6}$$

$$= \frac{2(-1 \pm \sqrt{2}\,i)}{2(3)}$$

$$= \frac{-1 \pm \sqrt{2}\,i}{3}$$

The complete solution set is $\left\{ \dfrac{-1 + \sqrt{2}\,i}{3}, \dfrac{-1 - \sqrt{2}\,i}{3} \right\}$.

As Example 3 illustrates, if the numerical coefficients in a quadratic equation are real numbers and if the equation has an imaginary solution, then the conjugate of that imaginary solution is also a solution. Thus, the imaginary solutions of such a quadratic equation always occur in conjugate pairs.

Example 4:   Find the complete solution set.
(a) $x^4 + 3x^2 - 4 = 0$ (b) $x^3 = 8$

Solution:
(a) We solve by factoring. Thus,

$$x^4 + 3x^2 - 4 = 0$$
$$(x^2 - 1)(x^2 + 4) = 0$$

$x^2 - 1 = 0$	or	$x^2 + 4 = 0$
$x^2 = 1$		$x^2 = -4$
$x = \pm\sqrt{1}$		$x = \pm\sqrt{-4}$
$x = \pm 1$		$x = \pm 2i$

The complete solution set is $\{1, -1, 2i, -2i\}$.

(b) First we write the equation in zero form and then we apply the Sum of Cubes Theorem to factor.

$$x^3 = 8$$
$$x^3 - 8 = 0$$
$$x^3 - 2^3 = 0$$
$$(x - 2)(x^2 + 2x + 4) = 0$$

$x - 2 = 0$	or	$x^2 + 2x + 4 = 0$
$x = 2$		$x^2 + 2x + 1 = -3$
		$(x + 1)^2 = -3$
		$x + 1 = \pm\sqrt{-3}$
		$x + 1 = \pm\sqrt{3}\,i$
		$x = -1 \pm \sqrt{3}\,i$

The complete solution set is $\{2, -1 + \sqrt{3}\,i, -1 - \sqrt{3}\,i\}$.

Because each of the numbers in the complete solution set of Example 4(b) satisfies the equation $x^3 = 8$, each of these numbers is a cube root of 8. We show that $-1 + \sqrt{3}\,i$ is a cube root of 8.

$$
\begin{aligned}
(-1 + \sqrt{3}\,i)^3 &= (-1 + \sqrt{3}\,i)(-1 + \sqrt{3}\,i)^2 \\
&= (-1 + \sqrt{3}\,i)(1 - 2\sqrt{3}\,i + 3i^2) \\
&= (-1 + \sqrt{3}\,i)(-2 - 2\sqrt{3}\,i) \\
&= (-1 + \sqrt{3}\,i)(-1 - \sqrt{3}\,i)(2) \\
&= [(-1)^2 - (\sqrt{3}\,i)^2](2) \\
&= (1 - 3i^2)(2) \\
&= (1 + 3)(2) \\
&= 8
\end{aligned}
$$

Every real number except zero has three cube roots. One of the cube roots is real, and the other two cube roots are imaginary. Furthermore, each of the imaginary roots is the conjugate of the other.

Example 5: Find three cube roots of -1.

Solution: Let x be a cube root of -1. Then

$$x^3 = -1$$
$$x^3 + 1 = 0$$
$$(x + 1)(x^2 - x + 1) = 0$$

$$x + 1 = 0 \qquad \text{or} \qquad x^2 - x + 1 = 0$$

$$x = -1 \qquad\qquad x = \frac{-(-1) \pm \sqrt{(-1)^2 - 4(1)(1)}}{2(1)}$$

$$= \frac{1 \pm \sqrt{-3}}{2}$$

$$= \frac{1 \pm \sqrt{3}\,i}{2}$$

Therefore, -1, $\dfrac{1 + \sqrt{3}\,i}{2}$, and $\dfrac{1 - \sqrt{3}\,i}{2}$ are the three cube roots of -1.

EXERCISES 8.2

For Exercises 1–16 find the simplest form.

1. $\sqrt{-49}$ 2. $-\sqrt{-36}$
3. $1 - \sqrt{-8}$ 4. $-1 + \sqrt{-12}$
5. $\sqrt{-4} \cdot \sqrt{-9}$ 6. $\sqrt{-16} \cdot \sqrt{-25}$

7. $\sqrt{-2} \cdot \sqrt{-8}$

8. $\sqrt{-3} \cdot \sqrt{-27}$

9. $\sqrt{-16}(\sqrt{9} + \sqrt{-36})$

10. $-\sqrt{-4}(\sqrt{-49} - \sqrt{9})$

11. $\sqrt{-3}(\sqrt{-3} - \sqrt{12})$

12. $-\sqrt{-2}(\sqrt{8} + \sqrt{-32})$

13. $\dfrac{3 + \sqrt{-9}}{3}$

14. $\dfrac{-2 + \sqrt{-12}}{2}$

15. $\dfrac{4 - \sqrt{-20}}{6}$

16. $\dfrac{-5 - \sqrt{-50}}{20}$

For Exercises 17–32 find the complete solution set.

17. $3x^2 + 4 = 2x^2 - 5$

18. $x^2 + 2 = 5x^2 + 3$

19. $x^2 + 2x + 5 = 0$

20. $x^2 - 6x + 12 = 0$

21. $2x^2 - 3x + 2 = 0$

22. $3x^2 + 5x + 4 = 0$

23. $5x^2 + 2x + 1 = 0$

24. $4x^2 - 6x + 5 = 0$

25. $x^3 + 4x = 0$

26. $x^3 + 2x^2 + 2x = 0$

27. $x^4 + 8x^2 - 9 = 0$

28. $x^4 + 6x^2 + 8 = 0$

29. $x^3 + 8 = 0$

30. $x^3 = 27$

31. $x^4 = 16$

32. $16x^4 - 81 = 0$

For Exercises 33–36 find three cube roots of the indicated number.

33. 64   **34.** 1   **35.** -27 **36.** $-\frac{1}{8}$

appendix tables

Table 1
Powers and Roots

n	n^2	$\sqrt{n}$	n^3	$\sqrt[3]{n}$	n	n^2	$\sqrt{n}$	n^3	$\sqrt[3]{n}$
1	1	1.000	1	1.000	51	2,601	7.141	132,651	3.708
2	4	1.414	8	1.260	52	2,704	7.211	140,608	3.732
3	9	1.732	27	1.442	53	2,809	7.280	148,877	3.756
4	16	2.000	64	1.587	54	2,916	7.348	157,464	3.780
5	25	2.236	125	1.710	55	3,025	7.416	166,375	3.803
6	36	2.449	216	1.817	56	3,136	7.483	175,616	3.826
7	49	2.646	343	1.913	57	3,249	7.550	185,193	3.848
8	64	2.828	512	2.000	58	3,364	7.616	195,112	3.871
9	81	3.000	729	2.080	59	3,481	7.681	205,379	3.893
10	100	3.162	1,000	2.154	60	3,600	7.746	216,000	3.915
11	121	3.317	1,331	2.224	61	3,721	7.810	226,981	3.936
12	144	3.464	1,728	3.289	62	3,844	7.874	238,328	3.958
13	169	3.606	2,197	2.351	63	3,969	7.937	250,047	3.979
14	196	3.742	2,744	2.410	64	4,096	8.000	262,144	4.000
15	225	3,873	3,375	2.466	65	4,225	8.062	274,625	4.021
16	256	4.000	4,096	2.520	66	4,356	8.124	287,496	4.041
17	289	4.123	4,913	2.571	67	4,489	8.185	300,763	4.062
18	324	4.243	5,832	2.621	68	4,624	8.246	314,432	4.082
19	361	4.359	6,859	2.668	69	4,761	8.307	328,509	4.102
20	400	4.472	8,000	2.714	70	4,900	8.367	343,000	4.121
21	441	4.583	9,261	2.759	71	5,041	8.426	357,911	4.141
22	484	4.690	10,648	2.802	72	5,184	8.485	373,248	4.160
23	529	4.796	12,167	2.844	73	5,329	8.544	389,017	4.179
24	576	4.899	13,824	2.884	74	5,476	8.602	405,224	4.198
25	625	5.000	15,625	2.924	75	5,625	8.660	421,875	4.217
26	676	5.099	17,576	2.962	76	5,776	8.718	438,976	4.236
27	729	5.196	19,683	3.000	77	5,929	8.775	456,533	4.254
28	784	5.291	21,952	3.037	78	6,084	8.832	474,552	4.273
29	841	5.385	24,389	3.072	79	6,241	8.888	493,039	4.291
30	900	5.477	27,000	3.107	80	6,400	8.944	512,000	4.309
31	961	5.568	29,791	3.141	81	6,561	9.000	531,441	4.327
32	1,024	5.657	32,768	3.175	82	6,724	9.055	551,368	4.344
33	1,089	5.745	35,937	3.208	83	6,889	9.110	571,787	4.362
34	1,156	5.831	39,304	3.240	84	7,056	9.165	592,704	4.380
35	1,225	5.916	42,875	3.271	85	7,225	9.220	614,125	4.397
36	1,296	6.000	46,656	3.302	86	7,396	9.274	636,056	4.414
37	1,369	6.083	50,653	3.332	87	7,569	9.327	658,503	4.431
38	1,444	6.164	54,872	3.362	88	7,744	9.381	681,472	4.448
39	1,521	6.245	59,319	3.391	89	7,921	9.434	704,969	4.465
40	1,600	6.325	64,000	3.420	90	8,100	9.487	729,000	4.481
41	1,681	6.403	68,921	3.448	91	8,281	9.539	753,571	4.498
42	1,764	6.481	74,088	3.476	92	8,464	9.592	778,688	4.514
43	1,849	6.557	79,507	3.503	93	8,649	9.643	804,357	4.531
44	1,936	6.633	85,184	3.530	94	8,836	9.695	830,584	4.547
45	2,025	6.708	91,125	3.557	95	9,025	9.747	857,375	4.563
46	2,116	6.782	97,336	3.583	96	9,216	9.798	884,736	4.579
47	2,209	6.856	103,823	3.609	97	9,409	9.849	912,673	4.595
48	2,304	6.928	110,592	3.634	98	9,604	9.899	941,192	4.610
49	2,401	7.000	117,649	3.659	99	9,801	9.950	970,299	4.626
50	2,500	7.071	125,000	3.684	100	10,000	10.000	1,000,000	4.642

Table 2
Common Logarithms

x	0	1	2	3	4	5	6	7	8	9
1.0	.0000	.0043	.0086	.0128	.0170	.0212	.0253	.0294	.0334	.0374
1.1	.0414	.0453	.0492	.0531	.0569	.0607	.0645	.0682	.0719	.0755
1.2	.0792	.0828	.0864	.0899	.0934	.0969	.1004	.1038	.1072	.1106
1.3	.1139	.1173	.1206	.1239	.1271	.1303	.1335	.1367	.1399	.1430
1.4	.1461	.1492	.1523	.1553	.1584	.1614	.1644	.1673	.1703	.1732
1.5	.1761	.1790	.1818	.1847	.1875	.1903	.1931	.1959	.1987	.2014
1.6	.2041	.2068	.2095	.2122	.2148	.2175	.2201	.2227	.2253	.2279
1.7	.2304	.2330	.2355	.2380	.2405	.2430	.2455	.2480	.2504	.2529
1.8	.2553	.2577	.2601	.2625	.2648	.2672	.2695	.2718	.2742	.2765
1.9	.2788	.2810	.2833	.2856	.2878	.2900	.2923	.2945	.2967	.2989
2.0	.3010	.3032	.3054	.3075	.3096	.3118	.3139	.3160	.3181	.3201
2.1	.3222	.3243	.3263	.3284	.3304	.3324	.3345	.3365	.3385	.3404
2.2	.3424	.3444	.3464	.3483	.3502	.3522	.3541	.3560	.3579	.3598
2.3	.3617	.3636	.3655	.3674	.3692	.3711	.3729	.3747	.3766	.3784
2.4	.3802	.3820	.3838	.3856	.3874	.3892	.3909	.3927	.3945	.3962
2.5	.3979	.3997	.4014	.4031	.4048	.4065	.4082	.4099	.4116	.4133
2.6	.4150	.4166	.4183	.4200	.4216	.4232	.4249	.4265	.4281	.4298
2.7	.4314	.4330	.4346	.4362	.4378	.4393	.4409	.4425	.4440	.4456
2.8	.4472	.4487	.4502	.4518	.4533	.4548	.4564	.4579	.4594	.4609
2.9	.4624	.4639	.4654	.4669	.4683	.4698	.4713	.4728	.4742	.4757
3.0	.4771	.4786	.4800	.4814	.4829	.4843	.4857	.4871	.4886	.4900
3.1	.4914	.4928	.4942	.4955	.4969	.4983	.4997	.5011	.5024	.5038
3.2	.5051	.5065	.5079	.5092	.5105	.5119	.5132	.5145	.5159	.5172
3.3	.5185	.5198	.5211	.5224	.5237	.5250	.5263	.5276	.5289	.5302
3.4	.5315	.5328	.5340	.5353	.5366	.5378	.5391	.5403	.5416	.5428
3.5	.5441	.5453	.5465	.5478	.5490	.5502	.5514	.5527	.5539	.5551
3.6	.5563	.5575	.5587	.5599	.5611	.5623	.5635	.5647	.5658	.5670
3.7	.5682	.5694	.5705	.5717	.5729	.5740	.5752	.5763	.5775	.5786
3.8	.5798	.5809	.5821	.5832	.5843	.5855	.5866	.5877	.5888	.5899
3.9	.5911	.5922	.5933	.5944	.5955	.5966	.5977	.5988	.5999	.6010
4.0	.6021	.6031	.6042	.6053	.6064	.6075	.6085	.6096	.6107	.6117
4.1	.6128	.6138	.6149	.6160	.6170	.6180	.6191	.6201	.6212	.6222
4.2	.6232	.6243	.6253	.6263	.6274	.6284	.6294	.6304	.6314	.6325
4.3	.6335	.6345	.6355	.6365	.6375	.6385	.6395	.6405	.6415	.6425
4.4	.6435	.6444	.6454	.6464	.6474	.6484	.6493	.6503	.6513	.6522
4.5	.6532	.6542	.6551	.6561	.6571	.6580	.6590	.6599	.6609	.6618
4.6	.6628	.6637	.6646	.6656	.6665	.6675	.6684	.6693	.6702	.6712
4.7	.6721	.6730	.6739	.6749	.6758	.6767	.6776	.6785	.6794	.6803
4.8	.6812	.6821	.6830	.6839	.6848	.6857	.6866	.6875	.6884	.6893
4.9	.6902	.6911	.6920	.6928	.6937	.6946	.6955	.6964	.6972	.6981
5.0	.6990	.6998	.7007	.7016	.7024	.7033	.7042	.7050	.7059	.7067
5.1	.7076	.7084	.7093	.7101	.7110	.7118	.7126	.7135	.7143	.7152
5.2	.7160	.7168	.7177	.7185	.7193	.7202	.7210	.7218	.7226	.7235
5.3	.7243	.7251	.7259	.7267	.7275	.7284	.7292	.7300	.7308	.7316
5.4	.7324	.7332	.7340	.7348	.7356	.7364	.7372	.7380	.7388	.7396

x	0	1	2	3	4	5	6	7	8	9

x	0	1	2	3	4	5	6	7	8	9
5.5	.7404	.7412	.7419	.7427	.7435	.7443	.7451	.7459	.7466	.7474
5.6	.7482	.7490	.7497	.7505	.7513	.7520	.7528	.7536	.7543	.7551
5.7	.7559	.7566	.7574	.7582	.7589	.7597	.7604	.7612	.7619	.7627
5.8	.7634	.7642	.7649	.7657	.7664	.7672	.7679	.7686	.7694	.7701
5.9	.7709	.7716	.7723	.7731	.7738	.7745	.7752	.7760	.7767	.7774
6.0	.7782	.7789	.7796	.7803	.7810	.7818	.7825	.7832	.7839	.7846
6.1	.7853	.7860	.7868	.7875	.7882	.7889	.7896	.7903	.7910	.7917
6.2	.7924	.7931	.7938	.7945	.7952	.7959	.7966	.7973	.7980	.7987
6.3	.7993	.8000	.8007	.8014	.8021	.8028	.8035	.8041	.8048	.8055
6.4	.8062	.8069	.8075	.8082	.8089	.8096	.8102	.8109	.8116	.8122
6.5	.8129	.8136	.8142	.8149	.8156	.8162	.8169	.8176	.8182	.8189
6.6	.8195	.8202	.8209	.8215	.8222	.8228	.8235	.8241	.8248	.8254
6.7	.8261	.8267	.8274	.8280	.8287	.8293	.8299	.8306	.8312	.8319
6.8	.8325	.8331	.8338	.8344	.8351	.8357	.8363	.8370	.8376	.8382
6.9	.8388	.8395	.8401	.8407	.8414	.8420	.8426	.8432	.8439	.8445
7.0	.8451	.8457	.8463	.8470	.8476	.8482	.8488	.8494	.8500	.8506
7.1	.8513	.8519	.8525	.8531	.8537	.8543	.8549	.8555	.8561	.8567
7.2	.8573	.8579	.8585	.8591	.8597	.8603	.8609	.8615	.8621	.8627
7.3	.8633	.8639	.8645	.8651	.8657	.8663	.8669	.8675	.8681	.8686
7.4	.8692	.8698	.8704	.8710	.8716	.8722	.8727	.8733	.8739	.8745
7.5	.8751	.8756	.8762	.8768	.8774	.8779	.8785	.8791	.8797	.8802
7.6	.8808	.8814	.8820	.8825	.8831	.8837	.8842	.8848	.8854	.8859
7.7	.8865	.8871	.8876	.8882	.8887	.8893	.8899	.8904	.8910	.8915
7.8	.8921	.8927	.8932	.8938	.8943	.8949	.8954	.8960	.8965	.8971
7.9	.8976	.8982	.8987	.8993	.8998	.9004	.9009	.9015	.9020	.9025
8.0	.9031	.9036	.9042	.9047	.9053	.9058	.9063	.9069	.9074	.9079
8.1	.9085	.9090	.9096	.9101	.9106	.9112	.9117	.9122	.9128	.9133
8.2	.9138	.9143	.9149	.9154	.9159	.9165	.9170	.9175	.9180	.9186
8.3	.9191	.9196	.9201	.9206	.9212	.9217	.9222	.9227	.9232	.9238
8.4	.9243	.9248	.9253	.9258	.9263	.9269	.9274	.9279	.9284	.9289
8.5	.9294	.9299	.9304	.9309	.9315	.9320	.9325	.9330	.9335	.9340
8.6	.9345	.9350	.9355	.9360	.9365	.9370	.9375	.9380	.9385	.9390
8.7	.9395	.9400	.9405	.9410	.9415	.9420	.9425	.9430	.9435	.9440
8.8	.9445	.9450	.9455	.9460	.9465	.9469	.9474	.9479	.9484	.9489
8.9	.9494	.9499	.9504	.9509	.9513	.9518	.9523	.9528	.9533	.9538
9.0	.9542	.9547	.9552	.9557	.9562	.9566	.9571	.9576	.9581	.9586
9.1	.9590	.9595	.9600	.9605	.9609	.9614	.9619	.9624	.9628	.9633
9.2	.9638	.9643	.9647	.9652	.9657	.9661	.9666	.9671	.9675	.9680
9.3	.9685	.9689	.9694	.9699	.9703	.9708	.9713	.9717	.9722	.9727
9.4	.9731	.9736	.9741	.9745	.9750	.9754	.9759	.9763	.9768	.9773
9.5	.9777	.9782	.9786	.9791	.9795	.9800	.9805	.9809	.9814	.9818
9.6	.9823	.9827	.9832	.9836	.9841	.9845	.9850	.9854	.9859	.9863
9.7	.9868	.9872	.9877	.9881	.9886	.9890	.9894	.9899	.9903	.9908
9.8	.9912	.9917	.9921	.9926	.9930	.9934	.9939	.9943	.9948	.9952
9.9	.9956	.9961	.9965	.9969	.9974	.9978	.9983	.9987	.9991	.9996
x	0	1	2	3	4	5	6	7	8	9

Table 3
Exponential Functions

x	e^x	e^{-x}
0	1.0000	1.0000
0.1	1.1052	0.90484
0.2	1.2214	0.81873
0.3	1.3499	0.74082
0.4	1.4918	0.67032
0.5	1.6487	0.60653
0.6	1.8221	0.54881
0.7	2.0138	0.49659
0.8	2.2255	0.44933
0.9	2.4596	0.40657
1.0	2.7183	0.36788
1.1	3.0042	0.33287
1.2	3.3201	0.30119
1.3	3.6693	0.27253
1.4	4.0552	0.24660
1.5	4.4817	0.22313
1.6	4.9530	0.20190
1.7	5.4739	0.18268
1.8	6.0496	0.16530
1.9	6.6859	0.14957
2.0	7.3891	0.13534
2.1	8.1662	0.12246
2.2	9.0250	0.11080
2.3	9.9742	0.10026
2.4	11.023	0.09072
2.5	12.182	0.08208
2.6	13.464	0.07427
2.7	14.880	0.06721
2.8	16.445	0.06081
2.9	18.174	0.05502
3.0	20.086	0.04979
3.1	22.198	0.04505
3.2	24.533	0.04076
3.3	27.113	0.03688
3.4	29.964	0.03337
3.5	33.115	0.03020
3.6	36.598	0.02732
3.7	40.447	0.02472
3.8	44.701	0.02237
3.9	49.402	0.02024
4.0	54.598	0.01832
4.1	60.340	0.01657
4.2	66.686	0.01500
4.3	73.700	0.01357
4.4	81.451	0.01228
4.5	90.017	0.01111
4.6	99.484	0.01005
4.7	109.95	0.00910
4.8	121.51	0.00823
4.9	134.29	0.00745
5.0	148.41	0.00674

Table 4
Natural Logarithms

n	$\ln n$	n	$\ln n$	n	$\ln n$
	*	4.5	1.5041	9.0	2.1972
0.1	7.6974	4.6	1.5261	9.1	2.2083
0.2	8.3906	4.7	1.5476	9.2	2.2192
0.3	8.7960	4.8	1.5686	9.3	2.2300
0.4	9.0837	4.9	1.5892	9.4	2.2407
0.5	9.3069	5.0	1.6094	9.5	2.2513
0.6	9.4892	5.1	1.6292	9.6	2.2618
0.7	9.6433	5.2	1.6487	9.7	2.2721
0.8	9.7769	5.3	1.6677	9.8	2.2824
0.9	9.8946	5.4	1.6864	9.9	2.2925
1.0	0.0000	5.5	1.7047	10	2.3026
1.1	0.0953	5.6	1.7228	11	2.3979
1.2	0.1823	5.7	1.7405	12	2.4849
1.3	0.2624	5.8	1.7579	13	2.5649
1.4	0.3365	5.9	1.7750	14	2.6391
1.5	0.4055	6.0	1.7918	15	2.7081
1.6	0.4700	6.1	1.8083	16	2.7726
1.7	0.5306	6.2	1.8245	17	2.8332
1.8	0.5878	6.3	1.8405	18	2.8904
1.9	0.6419	6.4	1.8563	19	2.9444
2.0	0.6931	6.5	1.8718	20	2.9957
2.1	0.7419	6.6	1.8871	25	3.2189
2.2	0.7885	6.7	1.9021	30	3.4012
2.3	0.8329	6.8	1.9169	35	3.5553
2.4	0.8755	6.9	1.9315	40	3.6889
2.5	0.9163	7.0	1.9459	45	3.8067
2.6	0.9555	7.1	1.9601	50	3.9120
2.7	0.9933	7.2	1.9741	55	4.0073
2.8	1.0296	7.3	1.9879	60	4.0943
2.9	1.0647	7.4	2.0015	65	4.1744
3.0	1.0986	7.5	2.0149	70	4.2485
3.1	1,1314	7.6	2.0281	75	4.3175
3.2	1.1632	7.7	2.0412	80	4.3820
3.3	1.1939	7.8	2.0541	85	4.4427
3.4	1.2238	7.9	2.0669	90	4.4998
3.5	1.2528	8.0	2.0794	100	4.6052
3.6	1.2809	8.1	2.0919	110	4.7005
3.7	1.3083	8.2	2.1041	120	4.7875
3.8	1.3350	8.3	2.1163	130	4.8676
3.9	1.3610	8.4	2.1282	140	4.9416
4.0	1.3863	8.5	2.1401	150	5.0106
4.1	1.4110	8.6	2.1518	160	5.0752
4.2	1.4351	8.7	2.1633	170	5.1358
4.3	1.4586	8.8	2.1748	180	5.1930
4.4	1.4816	8.9	2.1861	190	5.2470

* Subtract 10 for $n < 1$. Thus $\ln 0.1 = 7.6974 - 10 \doteq -2.3026$.

answers to selected exercises

EXERCISES 1.1 (*page 6*)

1. False	**2.** True
3. True	**5.** True
6. False	**7.** True
9. False	**10.** False
11. False	**13.** $\{1, 2, 3, 4\}$
14. $\{1, 2\}$	**15.** $\{4\}$
17. $\{4\}$	**18.** $\{1, 2, 4\}$
19. $\{2, 3, 4\}$	**21.** $\{\ \ \}$
22. $\{1, 2, 3, 4\}$	**23.** $\{1, 2\}$
25. $\{5, 0, -2\}$	**26.** $\{3, 0, -5, \frac{3}{5}, -1.3\}$
27. $\{\sqrt{3}\}$	**29.** $\{3\}$
30. $\{5, 0, -2, -\frac{1}{2}, 0.7, \sqrt{3}\}$	**31.** $\{3, 0, -5, \frac{3}{5}, -1.3, \sqrt{5}\}$

33.

-3

34.

1

35.

37.

38.

39.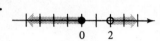

41.

42.

43. I **45.** F

46. F **47.** $\varnothing$

EXERCISES 1.2 (*page 13*)

1. $s = r$ **2.** $p < q$

3. Reflexive   **5.** rq

6. $ps + t$ **7.** $z + xy$

9. $x(z + y)$ **10.** $(y + x)z$

11. $yx + z$ **13.** $(y + z)x$

14. $z(x + y)$ **15.** $20x$

17. $2x + 9$ **18.** $30x$

19. $4x + 12$ **21.** $x(y + z)$

22. $(x + z)y$ **23.** $7x$

25. Associative   **26.** Commutative

27. Commutative   **29.** Distributive

30. Distributive   **31.** Commutative

33. Associative   **34.** Associative

35. Associative   **37.** Distributive

38. Distributive   **39.** Distributive

41. Commutative, associative   **42.** Commutative, associative

43. Distributive, associative   **45.** Distributive, identity

46. Distributive, identity   **47.** Inverse, identity

49. Commutative, closure   **50.** Commutative, closure

51.   (i) Inverse axiom   (ii) Multiplication Theorem
     (iii) Distributive axiom   (iv) Identity axiom
       (v) Zero-factor Theorem   (vi) Addition Theorem
     (vii) Associative axiom   (viii) Inverse axiom
       (ix) Identity axiom

EXERCISES 1.3 (page 20)

1. -6	**2.** -20
3. 21	**5.** -11
6. -7	**7.** -3
9. 3	**10.** 1
11. -7	**13.** -3
14. 1	**15.** 4
17. -13	**18.** -25
19. -1	**21.** 3
22. 21	**23.** -18
25. -7	**26.** -9
27. 30	**29.** -18
30. -40	**31.** -16
33. 81	**34.** -32
35. 17	**37.** -39
38. 30	**39.** 48
41. 24 inches	**42.** -14 feet per second
43. \$1875	**45.** 880 meters
46. 42 watts	

EXERCISES 1.4 (page 26)

1. $6x^5$	**2.** $-x^6y^4$
3. $-2x^3y^4$	**5.** $-3x^4$
6. $-4y$	**7.** x^3y
9. $16x^4$	**10.** $-27y^3$
11. $-x^3y^3$	**13.** x^8y^4
14. $-x^6y^3$	**15.** x^4y^6
17. $3x^5 + 6x^4$	**18.** $2x^3y + x^2y^2$
19. $2x^2y^3 - 2xy^4$	**21.** $8x^4 + 8x^3y$
22. $-x^4y^3 - x^3y^4$	**23.** $x^7y^3 - x^6y^5$
25. $3x^2 + 1$	**26.** $x^3 + x^2 + 2x + 1$
27. $5x^2 - x$	**29.** $-x^2 - 4x + 3$
30. $-4x^2$	**31.** $-x^2 - 3x$
33. $5x$	**34.** $4x^2y - 3x$
35. $5x^2y$	**37.** $-4xy^2$
38. $x^2y - 3xy^2$	**39.** $-3x + 24$

41. $3x - 3$ **42.** $-6x^2y + 2xy - 6x$
43. $2xy$ **45.** $2x + 7$
46. $3x + 2$ **47.** $10x - 6$
49. $9x^2 + 15x + 1$ **50.** $12x^2 + 8x + 2$

EXERCISES 1.5 *(page 31)*

1. $2x^2 + 5x - 12$ **2.** $2xy + x + 6y + 3$
3. $2x^2 + 5xy - 3y^2$ **5.** $2x^3 - 2x^2y - xy + y^2$
6. $x^3 + 2x^2y + xy + 2y^2$ **7.** $2x^2y^4 + 7xy^2 + 3$
9. $25x^2 - 9$ **10.** $x^2 - 16y^2$
11. $4x^2 - y^4$ **13.** $x^6y^2 - 16$
14. $x^6 - y^4$ **15.** $9x^2 + 30x + 25$
17. $x^4 - 2x^2y + y^2$ **18.** $16x^2y^2 + 40xy + 25$
19. $x^2y^4 + 4xy^2 + 4$ **21.** $x^3 + 3x^2 + 3x + 1$
22. $x^3 - 3x^2y + 3xy^2 - y^3$ **23.** $8x^3 + 12x^2y + 6xy^2 + y^3$
25. $64x^3 - 144x^2 + 108x - 27$ **26.** $8x^3 - 60x^2 + 150x - 125$
27. $2x^3 - 5x^2 - 10x + 3$ **29.** $x^3 - x^2y - 5xy^2 + 2y^3$
30. $x^4 - x^3 - 7x^2 + 9x - 18$ **31.** $x^3 + 2x^2y - 5xy^2 - 6y^3$
33. $x^4 + 4x^3 + 2x^2 - 5x - 2$ **34.** $4x^2 - 4xy + y^2 + 12x - 6y + 9$
35. $x^4 - 2x^3y - 3x^2y^2 + 4xy^3 + 4y^4$ **37.** $x^2 + x + 1$
38. $7x + 2$ **39.** $-3x^2 - 2xy - 4y^2$
41. $x^2 + 3x + 2$ **42.** $x^2 - 1$
43. $3x^3 + 6x^2 + 4x$ **45.** $2x + 2$
46. $4x + 4$

EXERCISES 1.6 *(page 35)*— 36

1. $3(2x - 3y)$ **2.** $x(x + 4)$
3. $y(x + 1)$ **5.** $2x(x + 3)$
6. $xy(x - 2)$ **7.** $x^2(x - y)$
9. $xy^2(x - y^2)$ **10.** $x^2y^3(x + 1)$
11. $6x^2y(3 + 2xy^3)$ **13.** $(x + 5y)(x - 5y)$
14. $(3x + 4y)(3x - 4y)$ **15.** $(6x + y^2)(6x - y^2)$
17. $(xy^3 + 1)(xy^3 - 1)$ **18.** $(x^3 + 5y^2)(x^3 - 5y^2)$
19. $(x + 2)(x^2 - 2x + 4)$ **21.** $(4x - y)(16x^2 + 4xy + y^2)$
22. $(2x - y)(4x^2 + 2xy + y^2)$ **23.** $(2x + 3y)(4x^2 - 6xy + 9y^2)$
25. $x^2y(x + y^2)$ **26.** $2xy^2(3x^2 - 4y)$
27. $4xy^3(3x - 1)$ **29.** $(4xy + 5)(4xy - 5)$

30. $(1 + 3x^3y)(1 - 3x^3y)$
31. $(x^2 + 2y^3)(x^2 - 2y^3)$
33. $(x + 1)(x^2 - x + 1)$
34. $(xy - 2)(x^2y^2 + 2xy + 4)$
35. $x(x + 2)(x - 2)$
37. $xy(3x + y)(3x - y)$
38. $y^2(2x + y)(2x - y)$
39. $(x^2 + 1)(x + 1)(x - 1)$
41. $x(x - y)(x^2 + xy + y^2)$
42. $y(y + 4)(y^2 - 4y + 16)$
43. $(x^2 + y^2)(x^4 - x^2y^2 + y^4)$

EXERCISES 1.7 (page 41)

1. $x(x + y - 1)$
2. $xy(2x - y + 3)$
3. $x^2(x^2 + x - y)$
5. $2y(x + 3y - z + 2)$
6. $yz(x - 2y + z)$
7. $(x + 6)(x + 2)$
9. $(x - 8)(x - 8)$
10. $(x - 8)(x - 5)$
11. $(y - 8)(y + 6)$
13. $(x^2 - 3)(x^2 - 2)$
14. $(x^3 + 4)(x^3 + 4)$
15. $(3x + 1)(x + 1)$
17. $(2x - 1)(x + 2)$
18. $(3x - 1)(x - 2)$
19. $(4x + 3y)(4x + 3y)$
21. $(2x - 5y)(3x + 2y)$
22. $(4x - 5y)(x + 6y)$
23. $(4xy + 1)(xy - 2)$
25. $x(x + 2)(x + 1)$
26. $y(x + y)(x + y)$
27. $xy(2x - y)(x + y)$
29. $(x + 4)(x - 3)$
30. $(x - 2)(x - 2)$
31. $(3x + y)(3x + y)$
33. $(x + y)(x + y + 2)$
34. $(x - y)(x - y - 3)$
35. $(x + y + 1)(x + y - 1)$
37. $(x + 2)(y + 3)$
38. $(x - 1)(y - 2)$
39. $(x + 1)(x - 1)(x + 2)$
41. $(x + y + z)(x + y - z)$
42. $(x + 2y + 1)(x + 2y - 1)$
43. $(x + y + z)(x - y - z)$
45. $(x + 1)(x + 1)(x + 1)$
46. $(x - 2)(x - 2)(x - 2)$

REVIEW EXERCISES 1 (page 42)

1. False
2. True
3. $\{3, 4\}$
5. $\{1, 2, 3, 4, 5\}$
6. $\{3, 5\}$
7. $\{0, 2, -1\}$
9.

10.

11. $z + xy$
13. $x + y$
14. $(1)(x + y)$
15. Associative
17. Commutative, associative
18. Distributive, associative
19. -48
21. -28

22. 8

23. -21

25. \$195

26. 100 feet

27. $81x^8y^4$

29. $-x^4y^2 + xy^4$

30. $x^5y^6 + x^3y^7$

31. $-x$

33. $-6x^2$

34. $-3x^2 + 12x$

35. $x^4y^2 - z^6$

37. $x^3 - 9x^2 + 27x - 27$

38. $x^3 + 12x^2y + 48xy^2 + 64y^3$

39. $2x^3 - x^2y - 5xy^2 + 3y^3$

41. $x^2 - 9x - 16$

42. $x^4 + 8x^3y + 24x^2y^2 + 32xy^3 + 16y^4$

43. $3x^2y(y^3 - 2x)$

45. $(2x + y)(4x^2 - 2xy + y^2)$

46. $(x - 3y)(x^2 + 3xy + 9y^2)$

47. $2x^2(2x + 1)(2x - 1)$

49. $x(x - 4)(x^2 + 4x + 16)$

50. $(x^2 + 9)(x + 3)(x - 3)$

51. $(x - 5y)(x + y)$

53. $(4x - 3y)(3x - 4y)$

54. $(x + 2)(x - 2)(x + 1)(x - 1)$

55. $2x(x - 4y)(x + y)$

57. $(x + y + 4)(x + y - 4)$

58. $(x - 1)(x - 1)(x - 1)$

EXERCISES 2.1   (*page 53*)

1. $\dfrac{x}{2y^2}$

2. $\dfrac{-3y}{4x^2}$

3. $\dfrac{3y}{x}$

5. $\dfrac{-2x^3}{3}$

6. $\dfrac{1}{x^2}$

7. $\dfrac{x + 3}{x + 2}$

9. $\dfrac{x + 3}{2x + 1}$

10. $\dfrac{3x - 1}{2x + 1}$

11. $\dfrac{x - 3}{x - 2}$

13. $\dfrac{-x}{x + 2}$

14. $\dfrac{-x}{y}$

15. $\dfrac{1}{x^2 - xy + y^2}$

17. $\dfrac{x^2 - 2x + 4}{x + 2}$

18. $\dfrac{1}{x - 2}$

19. $\dfrac{y + 3}{y - 1}$

21. $\dfrac{-3x^2}{2}$

22. $\dfrac{2x}{y}$

23. $\dfrac{1}{2xy}$

25. $\dfrac{3xy}{2}$

26. $\dfrac{-1}{2x^2}$

27. $-xy^4$

29. $\dfrac{x + 1}{x + 2}$

30. $\dfrac{1}{x + 2}$

31. $\dfrac{2x + y}{x + 2y}$

33. $\dfrac{(x - 1)(x - 2)}{x}$

34. $2y$

35. x

37. $\dfrac{x+2}{x-2}$

38. 1

39. $(x-1)(x-2)$

EXERCISES 2.2 (*page 61*)

1. $\dfrac{2}{x}$

2. $\dfrac{4}{x}$

3. $\dfrac{x-2}{5}$

5. x

6. $x+3$

7. $\dfrac{x^2+4x-2}{x^2}$

9. $\dfrac{y^2-xy+2}{2xy}$

10. $\dfrac{-y^2+4xy+3}{3xy}$

11. $\dfrac{y^3+x^2y}{x^3}$

13. $\dfrac{2x^2+x-2}{x(x+2)}$

14. $\dfrac{2x^2-3}{x(x-3)}$

15. $\dfrac{x^2}{x-y}$

17. $\dfrac{x+5}{(x-1)(x+1)}$

18. $\dfrac{-3x+2}{(x+2)(x-2)}$

19. $\dfrac{-3}{(x+1)(x+2)}$

21. $\dfrac{1}{xy}$

22. $\dfrac{x}{2x-1}$

23. $\dfrac{1}{x}$

25. $\dfrac{x+2y}{x-y}$

26. $\dfrac{x+2y}{x-2y}$

27. $\dfrac{x-2y}{3x}$

29. $\dfrac{2x}{(x+1)^2(x-1)}$

30. $\dfrac{x^2}{(x-2y)^3}$

31. $\dfrac{x^2-2}{x^2(x+2)^2}$

33. 2

34. 2

35. $\dfrac{2}{x}$

37. $\dfrac{-1}{x}$

38. $\dfrac{1}{x+3}$

39. $x+1$

EXERCISES 2.3 (*page 69*)

1. $\dfrac{x-y}{x}$

2. $\dfrac{x+3}{x+4}$

3. $\dfrac{-x}{y^2z}$

5. $\dfrac{x-2}{x-7}$

6. $\dfrac{2x(x+y)}{y(x-y)}$

7. $\dfrac{1}{x}$

9. $\dfrac{1}{x^2 + 2x + 4}$ **10.** $(x - 2)(x + 1)$

11. $2x^2 - 3x + 4 + \dfrac{1}{x + 1}$ **13.** $x^2 + 3x + 1 + \dfrac{-3}{x - 3}$

14. $3x^3 + 4x^2 + 8x + 3 + \dfrac{6}{x - 2}$ **15.** $x - 2 + \dfrac{-1}{x^2 + 1}$

17. $x^2 + 2x - 2$ **18.** $x^2 - x + 2$

19. $x^3 + 2x + 1$ **21.** $x^2 + xy - 3y^2$

22. $x^2 - 3xy + 3y^2$ **23.** $3x^2 - xy + 2y^2$

25. $(x - 2)(x + 1)(x - 4)$ **26.** $(x + 2)(x + 3)(x - 1)$

27. $(x + 3y)(2x + y)(x - y)$ **29.** $(x - 1)(x^4 + x^3 + x^2 + x + 1)$

30. $(x + y)(x^4 - x^3y + x^2y^2 - xy^3 + y^4)$ **31.** $\dfrac{1}{x - 3}$

33. $\dfrac{-1}{xy}$ **34.** $\dfrac{1}{3x}$

35. $\dfrac{x + 2}{x}$ **37.** $\dfrac{x - y}{x + y}$

38. $\dfrac{x - 1}{y}$ **39.** $\dfrac{x + 2y}{x - y}$

EXERCISES 2.4   (page 75)

1. 1 **2.** $\frac{1}{5}$

3. $\frac{1}{9}$ **5.** $-\frac{1}{16}$

6. $-\frac{1}{36}$ **7.** $\frac{1}{25}$

9. $\frac{3}{2}$ **10.** -5

11. $-\frac{1}{25}$ **13.** $\frac{1}{81}$

14. $-\frac{1}{16}$ **15.** $\dfrac{2}{x^3}$

17. $\dfrac{-1}{xy}$ **18.** $\dfrac{-1}{x^3}$

19. $\dfrac{1}{x^4}$ **21.** $\dfrac{-1}{x^2}$

22. $\dfrac{1}{x^2y^2}$ **23.** $\dfrac{1}{x^2}$

25. x^2 **26.** $\dfrac{1}{x^6}$

27. $\dfrac{x}{y^2}$ **29.** $\dfrac{3}{x^3}$

30. $\dfrac{x^2}{y}$ **31.** $x^4 + x^2$

33. x^8 **34.** $\dfrac{1}{x^3}$

35. $\dfrac{x^2}{y^4}$

37. $\dfrac{2}{xy}$

38. $\dfrac{y}{x}$

39. $\dfrac{y^2}{x}$

41. $\dfrac{y^5}{x^2}$

42. $\dfrac{y^2}{x^4}$

43. $\dfrac{1}{x^2y^5}$

45. x^3y^6

46. xy

47. $\dfrac{x^2}{y^2}$

49. $\dfrac{x^2 + 1}{x^2}$

50. $x + 1$

51. $\dfrac{1}{x}$

53. $(3.16) \cdot 10^4$

54. $(5.2) \cdot 10^{-5}$

55. $(4.5) \cdot 10^{-3}$

57. $8 \cdot 10^3$

58. $6 \cdot 10^{-7}$

59. $(1.5) \cdot 10^{-1}$

EXERCISES 2.5 (*page 81*)

1. $6\sqrt{2}$

2. $-5\sqrt{3}$

3. -14

5. 30

6. $48\sqrt{7}$

7. $6\sqrt{3}$

9. $-30\sqrt{3}$

10. $30\sqrt{30}$

11. $7\sqrt{2}$

13. $-7\sqrt{5}$

14. $17\sqrt{3}$

15. 0

17. $3 + 2\sqrt{3}$

18. $-2 + \sqrt{6}$

19. $10 - 2\sqrt{10}$

21. $9 + 5\sqrt{3}$

22. $1 + 3\sqrt{5}$

23. $5 - \sqrt{3}$

25. 20

26. 48

27. $9 + 4\sqrt{5}$

29. $14 - 4\sqrt{6}$

30. $30 + 12\sqrt{6}$

31. 1

33. -41

34. 39

35. $x^2\sqrt{y}$

37. $4x$

38. $6x^2$

39. xy^2

41. $5\sqrt{x}$

42. $\sqrt{2x}$

43. $xy - \sqrt{xy}$

45. $x - y^2$

46. $x^2y - x$

47. $x^2 + 2x\sqrt{y} + y$

49. $2|x|$

50. $|xy|$

51. x^2

53. $|x + y|$

54. $|x^3 - 2|$

EXERCISES 2.6 (*page 87*)

1. 3

2. -4

3. $-2\sqrt[3]{3}$

5. -5

6. $2\sqrt[3]{6}$

7. $4\sqrt[3]{3}$

9. x^2

10. $-x\sqrt[3]{x^2}$

11. $-x\sqrt[3]{y}$

13. xy

14. xy^2

15. $-x^2y\sqrt[3]{x}$

17. $\dfrac{x\sqrt{x}}{5y}$

18. $\dfrac{x}{y^2}$

19. $\dfrac{3}{x}$

21. $\dfrac{2}{x}$

22. $\dfrac{-x\sqrt[3]{x}}{y}$

23. $\dfrac{\sqrt[3]{x}}{y}$

25. $2\sqrt{5}$

26. $\sqrt{3}$

27. $\dfrac{\sqrt{6x}}{3}$

29. $\dfrac{\sqrt{2x}}{xy}$

30. $\dfrac{\sqrt{6y}}{3xy}$

31. $2\sqrt[3]{4}$

33. $\dfrac{\sqrt[3]{12xy}}{2y}$

34. $\sqrt[3]{xy^2}$

35. $-1 + \sqrt{2}$

37. $-2 - \sqrt{10}$

38. $8 - 3\sqrt{7}$

39. $\dfrac{2 + \sqrt{6}}{2}$

41. $\sqrt{x} - 3$

42. $\sqrt{x} + 1$

43. $x(\sqrt{x} - \sqrt{y})$

EXERCISES 2.7 (*page 93*)

1. 6

2. -3

3. $-\sqrt{6}$

5. 3

6. -2

7. -4

9. $\sqrt[3]{12}$

10. $-\sqrt[4]{20}$

11. 27

13. -32

14. 9

15. $\frac{1}{3}$

17. $-\frac{1}{2}$

18. $\frac{1}{8}$

19. $\frac{1}{8}$

21. 15

22. -2

23. Not real

25. -64

26. 1

27. 0

29. 1

30. -1

31. $\frac{1}{2}$

33. 2

34. $\frac{1}{3}$

35. $\frac{1}{4}$

37. 4

38. $\frac{1}{6}$

39. $\frac{8}{27}$

41. $x^{3/2}$

42. $x^{2/3}$

43. $x^{3/4}$

45. $x^{2/3}$

46. $x^{1/4}$

47. x^6

49. $x^2 + x$

50. $x^3 - y$

51. $x^{2/3} - 2x^{1/3}y^{2/3} + y^{4/3}$

53. $x^2 y$

54. $x^2 y$

55. $xy^{3/2}$

57. $\dfrac{y^{2/3}}{x^{1/3}}$

58. $\dfrac{1}{y^{1/2}}$

59. $x^{1/2}y$

REVIEW EXERCISES 2 (*page 94*)

1. $\dfrac{x^2 - 2x + 4}{(x^2 + 4)(x - 2)}$

2. $\dfrac{-3}{2y}$

3. $\dfrac{3(x + y)}{x - y}$

5. $\dfrac{-3x^2}{4y}$

6. $\dfrac{-x^4}{y^3 z^5}$

7. $\dfrac{y^2}{x^2}$

9. $\dfrac{x - 2}{x + 3}$

10. $\dfrac{5x^2 + 4xy - 2y^2}{x(x + 2y)}$

11. $\dfrac{x^2 + y^2}{x - y}$

13. $\dfrac{x^2 + 8}{(x + 2)(x - 2)(x + 1)}$

14. $\dfrac{x^2 + 1}{(x - 1)(x^2 + x + 1)}$

15. $\dfrac{x^2 + y^2}{xy(x - y)}$

17. $\dfrac{1}{(x + 2y)^2}$

18. $\dfrac{x + 1}{x - 1}$

19. $x^3 + x^2 - 3x + 2$

21. $\dfrac{x + 2y}{x}$

22. $2x^2 - 1$

23. $xy^2 - x^4$

25. $\dfrac{y^3}{x}$

26. $\dfrac{y^2}{x^2 z^4}$

27. $\dfrac{y^3 z^4}{x^3}$

29. $2x^2 + 4x + 9 + \dfrac{9}{x - 2}$

30. $(x + 2)(x^4 - 2x^3 + 4x^2 - 8x + 16)$

31. $-14\sqrt{10}$

33. $4\sqrt{5}$

34. $\sqrt{3} + \sqrt{2}$

35. $24 + 7\sqrt{10}$

37. $x^2 y\sqrt{y}$

38. $xy\sqrt{y} - y\sqrt{x}$

39. $-2xy^2\sqrt[3]{2x^2}$

41. $\dfrac{2\sqrt{6xy}}{y}$

42. $\dfrac{\sqrt[3]{6x^2 y}}{2xy}$

43. $2 - \sqrt{3}$ **45.** $x^2 |y^3|$

46. $x + y$ **47.** $\frac{1}{36}$

49. $\frac{1}{16}$ **50.** $\frac{1}{27}$

51. 5   **53.** -8

54. $\frac{1}{9}$ **55.** $\frac{1}{16}$

57. $x^{1/12}$ **58.** $xy^{1/3}$

59. $xy^3 + x^2 y$

EXERCISES 3.1 (*page 103*)

1. $\{4\}$ **2.** $\{-2\}$

3. $\{-3\}$ **5.** $\{-\frac{2}{3}\}$

6. $\{4\}$ **7.** $\{\frac{5}{3}\}$

9. $\varnothing$ **10.** R

11. $\{-2\}$ **13.** $x = \dfrac{c - b}{a}$

14. $x = \dfrac{a - c}{b}$ **15.** $x = \dfrac{ab - c}{a}$

17. $v = \dfrac{h + at^2}{t}$ **18.** $h = \dfrac{S - \pi r^2}{2\pi r}$

19. $n = \dfrac{L - a + d}{d}$ **21.** $3\frac{1}{2}$ pounds

22. 170 items   **23.** $3\frac{1}{3}$ seconds

25. 28 cubic inches   **26.** $4\frac{4}{5}$ pounds

27. $\frac{17}{3}$ **29.** 8 fish

30. 62 games   **31.** 14 centimeters by 28 centimeters

33. 15 seconds   **34.** 45 miles per hour

35. 120 miles per hour   **37.** 6 miles per hour

38. 25 seconds

EXERCISES 3.2 (*page 110*)

1. $\{7\}$ **2.** $\{-2\}$

3. $\{-\frac{14}{5}\}$ **5.** $\{\frac{5}{3}\}$

6. $\{-\frac{5}{6}\}$ **7.** $\{\frac{9}{2}\}$

9. $\{\frac{13}{2}\}$ **10.** $\{-\frac{13}{5}\}$

11. $\{-9\}$ **13.** $x = \dfrac{bc}{a}$

14. $x = bc - a$ **15.** $x = \dfrac{b + c^2}{a}$

17. $h = \dfrac{3V}{\pi r^2}$

18. $v = \dfrac{2s - gt^2}{2t}$

19. $b = \dfrac{2A - Bh}{h}$

21. 30°

22. $4000

23. $5\frac{1}{6}$ meters per second

25. $13,000

26. $12,000 at 10%; $20,000 at 6%

27. $15,000 at 7%; $25,000 at 9%

29. 300 milliliters

30. 24 milliliters

31. 520 grams

33. 360 persons

34. 13 quarters; 19 dimes

35. 24 pounds

EXERCISES 3.3 (page 117)

1. $\{2\}$

2. $\{-3\}$

3. $\{-1\}$

5. $\{4\}$

6. $\{7\}$

7. $\{-\frac{1}{3}\}$

9. $\{-4\}$

10. $\{3\}$

11. $\varnothing$

13. $\{-8\}$

14. $\{\frac{1}{2}\}$

15. $\{-\frac{1}{4}\}$

17. $\{7\}$

18. $\{-6\}$

19. $\{\frac{2}{3}\}$

21. $x = \dfrac{ab}{a^2 - 1}$

22. $x = \dfrac{-b}{a - b}$

23. $x = \dfrac{b + bc}{a + c}$

25. $s = \dfrac{r}{r - 1}$

26. $t = \dfrac{rs}{s - r}$

27. $r = \dfrac{st + t}{1 - s}$

29. 12 ohms

30. 2

31. $1\frac{2}{3}$ miles per hour

33. 6 hours

34. $10\frac{1}{2}$ minutes

35. $2\frac{2}{5}$ hours

EXERCISES 3.4 (page 124)

1. $\{2, 3\}$

2. $\{-4, 2\}$

3. $\{0, \frac{1}{3}\}$

5. $\{-3, \frac{1}{2}\}$

6. $\{-\frac{1}{3}, \frac{1}{2}\}$

7. $\{-1, 3\}$

9. $\{1\}$

10. $\{-4\}$

11. $\{-4, 1\}$

13. $\{1, -\frac{2}{3}\}$

14. $\{-1, -\frac{1}{2}\}$

15. $\{1, \frac{1}{2}\}$

17. $\{-1, 8\}$

18. $\{-3, 1\}$

19. $\{4\}$

21. $x = 0; x = -\dfrac{b}{a}$

22. $x = 4a; x = -a$

23. $x = a; x = -\dfrac{a}{3}$

25. 2 seconds

26. 5 seconds

27. 3 amperes

29. $3\frac{1}{2}$ inches by $5\frac{1}{2}$ inches

30. 12 feet

31. 8 centimeters by 6 centimeters

33. 10 miles per hour

34. 9 miles per hour

35. 6 minutes

EXERCISES 3.5 *(page 132)*

1. $\left\{\dfrac{\sqrt{11}}{2}, -\dfrac{\sqrt{11}}{2}\right\}$

2. $\left\{\dfrac{1}{\sqrt{3}}, \dfrac{-1}{\sqrt{3}}\right\}$

3. $\left\{\dfrac{4}{\sqrt{7}}, \dfrac{-4}{\sqrt{7}}\right\}$

5. $\{0\}$

6. $\varnothing$

7. $\{3 + \sqrt{7}, 3 - \sqrt{7}\}$

9. $\left\{\dfrac{-5 + \sqrt{29}}{2}, \dfrac{-5 - \sqrt{29}}{2}\right\}$

10. $\left\{\dfrac{7 + \sqrt{61}}{2}, \dfrac{7 - \sqrt{61}}{2}\right\}$

11. $\varnothing$

13. $\{1 + \sqrt{\frac{5}{3}}, 1 - \sqrt{\frac{5}{3}}\}$

14. $\{-2 + \sqrt{\frac{13}{2}}, -2 - \sqrt{\frac{13}{2}}\}$

15. $\{\frac{1}{2}, -3\}$

17. $\left\{\dfrac{-5 + \sqrt{17}}{2}, \dfrac{-5 - \sqrt{17}}{2}\right\}$

18. $\left\{\dfrac{-1 + \sqrt{13}}{2}, \dfrac{-1 - \sqrt{13}}{2}\right\}$

19. $\left\{\dfrac{7 + \sqrt{41}}{4}, \dfrac{7 - \sqrt{41}}{4}\right\}$

21. $\left\{\dfrac{2 + \sqrt{14}}{5}, \dfrac{2 - \sqrt{14}}{5}\right\}$

22. $\left\{\dfrac{4 + \sqrt{2}}{7}, \dfrac{4 - \sqrt{2}}{7}\right\}$

23. $\{\frac{3}{2}, -\frac{1}{3}\}$

25. $\{-2 + \sqrt{3}, -2 - \sqrt{3}\}$

26. $\{1 + \sqrt{2}, 1 - \sqrt{2}\}$

27. $\left\{\dfrac{-4 + 2\sqrt{19}}{5}, \dfrac{-4 - 2\sqrt{19}}{5}\right\}$

29. $x = \dfrac{\pm c}{\sqrt{a - 1}}$

30. $x = \dfrac{\pm b}{\sqrt{b^2 - a^2}}$

31. $x = \dfrac{y \pm \sqrt{y^2 + 2y}}{2}$

33. $r = \dfrac{s \pm \sqrt{s^2 - 4s}}{2}$

34. $s = \dfrac{\pm r}{\sqrt{r - 1}}$

35. $\dfrac{5\sqrt{5}}{2}$ seconds; approximately 5.59 seconds

37. $\dfrac{-5 + 5\sqrt{33}}{2}$ centimeters by $\dfrac{5 + 5\sqrt{33}}{2}$ centimeters; approximately 11.9 centimeters by 16.9 centimeters

38. $3 + \sqrt{30}$ inches by $5 + \sqrt{30}$ inches; approximately 8.48 inches by 10.48 inches

39. $25 - 5\sqrt{13}$ feet; approximately 6.97 feet

EXERCISES 3.6 (*page 138*)

1. $\{2\}$

2. $\{\frac{1}{2}\}$

3. $\{0, \frac{3}{2}\}$

5. $\varnothing$

6. $\varnothing$

7. $\{3\}$

9. $\{-1\}$

10. $\{-3\}$

11. $\{9\}$

13. $\{1\}$

14. $\{3\}$

15. $\{\frac{1}{2}\}$

17. $\{-\frac{2}{9}\}$

18. $\{-1, -\frac{7}{4}\}$

19. $\{4\}$

21. $\{7\}$

22. $\{2\}$

23. $\{-2\}$

25. $\{26\}$

26. $\{5\}$

27. $\{-\frac{3}{4}\}$

29. $\{4\}$

30. $\{2\}$

31. $\{14\}$

33. $\{8, -8\}$

34. $\{0, -64\}$

35. $x = \dfrac{y^2 + 4}{2y}$

37. $t = \dfrac{1}{\sqrt{s^2 - 1}}$

38. $r = \dfrac{t^2}{2t - 1}$

39. 8 items

EXERCISES 3.7 (*page 142*)

1. $\{4\}$

2. $\{-2\}$

3. $\{-\frac{1}{2}\}$

5. $\{\sqrt[3]{2}\}$

6. $\{-\sqrt[3]{3}\}$

7. $\{0, 4, -4\}$

9. $\{0, -8\}$

10. $\{0, \frac{3}{2}\}$

11. $\{0, -1, -2\}$

13. $\{0, -3, \frac{1}{2}\}$

14. $\{0, -2, \frac{1}{3}\}$

15. $\{0, -1 + \sqrt{2}, -1 - \sqrt{2}\}$

17. $\{1, -1, 2, -2\}$

18. $\{1, -1, 3, -3\}$

19. $\{1, -1, \sqrt{3}, -\sqrt{3}\}$

21. $\{\sqrt{2}, -\sqrt{2}\}$

22. $\{\sqrt{3}, -\sqrt{3}\}$

23. $\{0, \frac{1}{4}, -\frac{1}{4}\}$

25. $\{\frac{1}{2}, -\frac{1}{2}\}$

26. $\{0, -\frac{3}{2}\}$

27. $\{0, 1, -1\}$

29. $\{0, \frac{1}{9}\}$

30. $\{0, -3\}$

31. $\{1, -1, -2\}$

33. $\{-1, \sqrt{2}, -\sqrt{2}\}$

34. $\{-2, \sqrt{5}, -\sqrt{5}\}$

35. $\{-1\}$

37. $\{8, 27\}$

38. $\{64, -8\}$

39. $\{81, 16\}$

41. $\{2, -2, \sqrt{3}, -\sqrt{3}\}$

42. $\left\{1, \dfrac{1}{\sqrt{2}}, -\dfrac{1}{\sqrt{2}}\right\}$

EXERCISES 3.8 (*page 147*)

1. $\{x : x < 3\}$

2. $\{x : x < 4\}$

3. $\{x : x > 2\}$

![number line, open circle at 2, shaded right]
　　2

5. $\{x : x < -1\}$

![number line, open circle at -1, shaded left]
　　-1

6. $\{x : x > 2\}$

![number line, open circle at 2, shaded right]
　　2

7. $\{x : x > 3\}$

![number line, open circle at 3, shaded right]
　　3

9. $\{x : x \geq 1\}$

![number line, closed circle at 1, shaded right]
　　1

10. $\{x : x \leq -2\}$

![number line, closed circle at -2, shaded left]
　　-2

11. $\{x : x \leq -1\}$

![number line, closed circle at -1, shaded left]
　　-1

13. $\{x : x > -\frac{1}{3}\}$

14. $\{x : x \leq \frac{3}{2}\}$

15. $\{x : x \leq \frac{5}{2}\}$

17. $\{x : x > 0\}$

18. $\{x : x < 0\}$

19. R

21. $\{x : x \geq -\frac{3}{2}\}$

22. $\{x : x < -\frac{4}{5}\}$

23. $\{x : x > \frac{1}{4}\}$

25. $\{x : x \geq 1\}$

26. $\{x : x > -1\}$

27. $\{x : -4 < x < -1\}$

![number line, open circles at -4 and -1, shaded between]
　　-4　　-1

29. $\{x : 0 \leq x < 2\}$

![number line, closed circle at 0, open circle at 2, shaded between]
　　0　　2

30. $\{x : -3 < x \leq 1\}$

![number line, open circle at -3, closed circle at 1, shaded between]
　　-3　　1

31. $\{x : -2 \leq x \leq 2\}$

![number line, closed circles at -2 and 2, shaded between]
　　-2　　2

33. $\{x : x < -1\} \cup \{x : x > 1\}$

![number line, open circles at -1 and 1, shaded outward]
　　-1　　1

34. $\{x : x \leq -2\} \cup \{x : x \geq 2\}$

![number line, closed circles at -2 and 2, shaded outward]
　　-2　　2

35. $\{x : -4 < x < 2\}$

37. $\{x : x < 1\} \cup \{x : x > 3\}$

38. $\{x : x < -5\} \cup \{x : x > 1\}$

39. $\{x : x \leq -1\} \cup \{x : x \geq 3\}$

41. $\{x : -3 \leq x \leq 0\}$

42. $\{x : x \leq \frac{1}{3}\} \cup \{x : x \geq 1\}$

43. $\varnothing$

45. $\frac{1}{2} < t < 2$

46. $68 < F < 86$

EXERCISES 3.9 (*page 152*)

1. $\{x : -3 < x < 0\}$

![number line, open circles at -3 and 0, shaded between]
　　-3　　0

2. $\{x : x < 0\} \cup \{x : x > 2\}$

3. $\{x : x < -2\} \cup \{x : x > 2\}$

5. $\{x : x < 0\} \cup \{x : x > 4\}$

6. $\{x : 0 < x < 3\}$

7. $\{x : -1 < x < 1\}$

9. $\{x : 3 \le x \le 5\}$

10. $\{x : -4 \le x \le 2\}$

11. $\{x : x \le -2\} \cup \{x : x \ge 3\}$

13. $\{x : 0 < x < \frac{1}{2}\}$

14. $\{x : -\frac{1}{3} < x < 0\}$

15. $\{x : -\frac{1}{3} < x < \frac{1}{3}\}$

17. $\{x : x < -3\} \cup \{x : x > \frac{1}{2}\}$

18. $\{x : -1 < x < -\frac{2}{3}\}$

19. $\{x : \frac{1}{2} < x < \frac{2}{3}\}$

21. $\{x : -5 < x < 5\}$

22. $\{x : x < -1\} \cup \{x : x > 1\}$

23. $\{x : x < -3\} \cup \{x : x > 3\}$

25. $\{x : x \le -\sqrt{3}\} \cup \{x : x \ge \sqrt{3}\}$

26. $\{x : -\sqrt{5} \le x \le \sqrt{5}\}$

27. $\{x : -\sqrt{\frac{7}{2}} \le x \le \sqrt{\frac{7}{2}}\}$

29. $\varnothing$

30. R

31. $\{x : 1 - \sqrt{2} < x < 1 + \sqrt{2}\}$

33. $\{x : x < -2 - \sqrt{3}\} \cup$
$\{x : x > -2 + \sqrt{3}\}$

34. $\{x : x < 2 - \sqrt{2}\} \cup$
$\{x : x > 2 + \sqrt{2}\}$

35. $\{x : x \le 3 - \sqrt{2}\} \cup$
$\{x : x \ge 3 + \sqrt{2}\}$

37. $\{x : 4 - \sqrt{6} \le x \le 4 + \sqrt{6}\}$

38. $\{x : x \le 3 - \sqrt{7}\} \cup$
$\{x : x \ge 3 + \sqrt{7}\}$

39. R

REVIEW EXERCISES 3 (*page 153*)

1. $\{\frac{1}{3}\}$

2. $\{-2\}$

3. $\left\{\dfrac{4 + \sqrt{37}}{3}, \dfrac{4 - \sqrt{37}}{3}\right\}$

5. $\{-12 + \sqrt{70}, -12 - \sqrt{70}\}$

6. $\{\frac{5}{6}, -\frac{9}{2}\}$

7. $\{\frac{4}{3}\}$

9. $\varnothing$

10. $\{7, -2\}$

11. $\{1, -1\}$

13. $\{2\}$

14. $\{-4\}$

17. $\{\frac{1}{2}\}$

19. $\{98\}$

22. $\{0, 1, -5\}$

25. $\{0, -1, -5\}$

27. $\{x : x \geq 2\}$

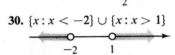

30. $\{x : x < -2\} \cup \{x : x > 1\}$

33. $\{x : x < 0\}$

35. $\{x : \frac{1}{3} < x < \frac{1}{2}\}$

38. $\{x : 1 - \sqrt{3} < x < 1 + \sqrt{3}\}$

41. $r = \dfrac{S - a}{S - b}$

43. $L = \dfrac{gP^2}{4\pi^2}$

46. 8 inches from the weight

49. 72 miles

51. $6\frac{2}{3}$ pounds of cashews; $13\frac{1}{3}$ pounds of peanuts

54. $2\frac{2}{3}$ hours

15. $\{3\}$

18. $\{-1\}$

21. $\left\{\dfrac{\sqrt[3]{3}}{2}\right\}$

23. $\{2, -2, \sqrt{6}, -\sqrt{6}\}$

26. $\{1, -1, 8, -8\}$

29. $\{x : 1 < x < 5\}$

31. $\{x : x < 0\} \cup \{x : x > 3\}$

34. R

37. $\{x : x < -\sqrt{5}\} \cup \{x : x > \sqrt{5}\}$

39. $t = \dfrac{A - P}{Pr}$

42. $R_1 = \dfrac{RR_2}{R_2 - R}$

45. 40 meters per second

47. \$13,000 at 10%; \$15,000 at 8%

50. 14 miles per hour

53. 20 hours

55. $20 + 10\sqrt{2}$ feet by $40 - 20\sqrt{2}$ feet; approximately 34.1 feet by 11.7 feet

EXERCISES 4.1 *(page 162)*

1.

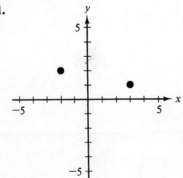

2.

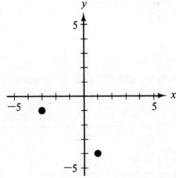

3.

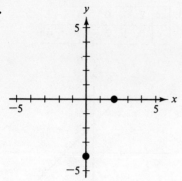

5.

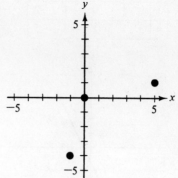

6.

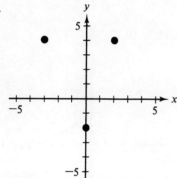

7.

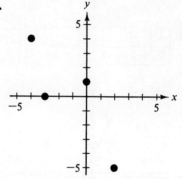

9.

x	2	1	0	−1	−2
y	3	2	1	0	−1

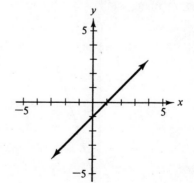

10.

x	2	1	0	−1	−2
y	1	0	−1	−2	−3

11.

x	2	1	0	−1	−2
y	3	1	−1	−3	−5

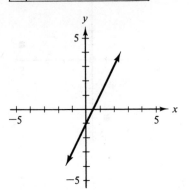

13.

x	2	1	0	−1	−2
y	0	1	2	3	4

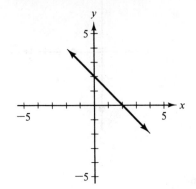

14.

x	2	1	0	−1	−2
y	−3	−1	1	3	5

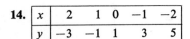

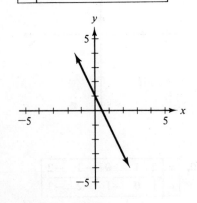

15. $(4, 0), (0, 2)$

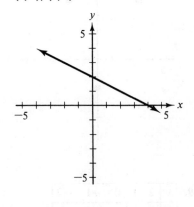

17. $(2, 0), (0, −6)$

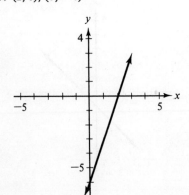

18. $(6, 0), (0, −3)$

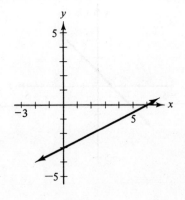

19. $(-3, 0), (0, 2)$

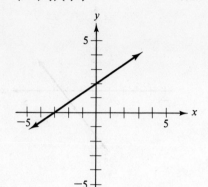

21. $(-4, 0), (0, -2)$

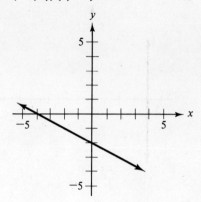

22. $(-1, 0), (0, -2)$

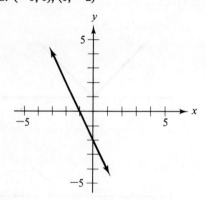

23.

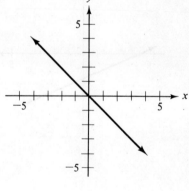

25.

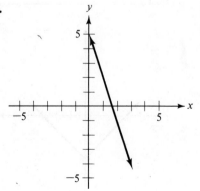

26.

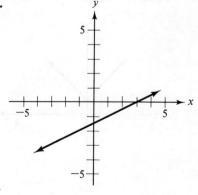

27.

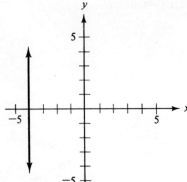

29.

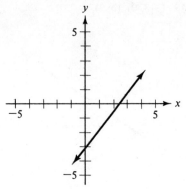

30.

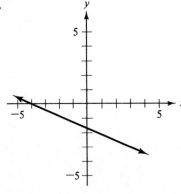

31.

x	3	2	1	0	−1	−2	−3
y	3	2	1	0	1	2	3

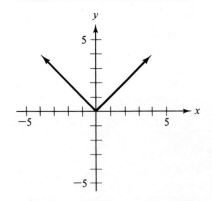

33.

x	3	2	1	0	−1	−2	−3
y	4	3	2	1	2	3	4

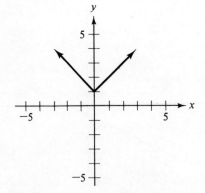

34.

x	3	2	1	0	−1	−2	−3
y	0	−1	−2	−3	−2	−1	0

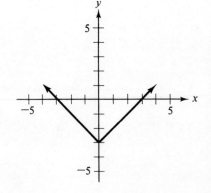

35.

x	3	2	1	0	−1	−2	−3
y	1	0	1	2	3	4	5

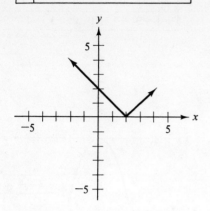

EXERCISES 4.2 (page 168)

1. $m = \frac{1}{2}$

2. $m = 3$

3. $m = -\frac{3}{4}$

5. $m = -2$

6. $m = -\frac{1}{2}$

7. Not defined

9. $y - 3 = 2(x - 2)$

10. $y - 4 = -3(x + 1)$

11. $y = -\frac{1}{2}(x + 5)$

13. $y + 2 = 0$

14. $x = 3$

15. $y = -x + 4$

17. $y = \frac{1}{3}x + \frac{11}{3}$

18. $y = -\frac{1}{2}x + \frac{7}{2}$

19. $x = 1$

21. $m = 2; b = -3$

22. $m = -\frac{1}{3}; b = 2$

23. $m = -\frac{3}{2}; b = -4$

25. $m = 0; b = \frac{1}{2}$

26. $m = 0; b = 0$

27. Slope is not defined; y-intercept does not exist.

29. $x - y = 2$

30. $x - 3y = 3$

31. $-2x + y = 4$

33. $x - 2y = 8$

34. $-2x + 3y = 9$

35. $2x + 3y = -6$

EXERCISES 4.3 (*page 177*)

1.

x	3	2	1	0	−1	−2	−3
y	9	4	1	0	1	4	9

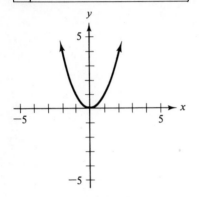

2.

x	3	2	1	0	−1	−2	−3
y	−9	−4	−1	0	−1	−4	−9

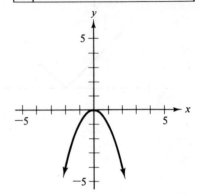

3.

x	3	2	1	0	−1	−2	−3
y	11	6	3	2	3	6	11

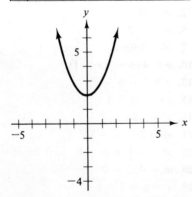

5.

x	3	2	1	0	−1	−2	−3
y	15	8	3	0	−1	0	3

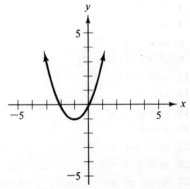

6.

x	3	2	1	0	−1	−2	−3
y	0	−2	−2	0	4	10	18

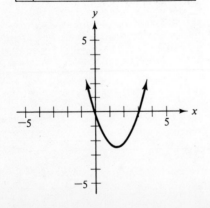

7.

x	3	2	1	0	−1	−2	−3
y	−3	2	5	6	5	2	−3

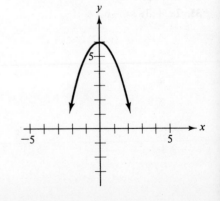

9.

x	3	2	1	0	−1	−2	−3
y	0	2	2	0	−4	−10	−18

10.

x	3	2	1	0	−1	−2	−3
y	−15	−8	−3	0	1	0	−3

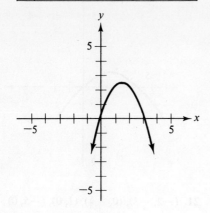

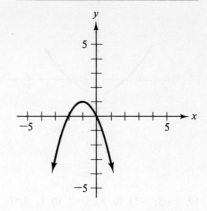

11. $(0, 4), (2, 0), (−2, 0)$

13. $(2, −4), (0, 0), (4, 0)$

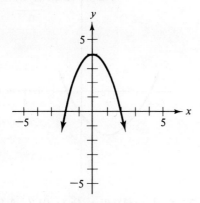

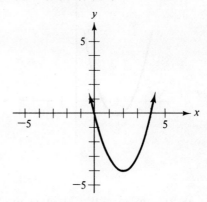

14. $(−2, −4), (0, 0), (−4, 0)$

15. $(1, 1), (0, 0), (2, 0)$

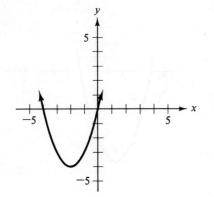

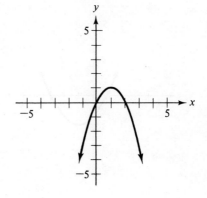

17. $(0, -1), (2, 0), (-2, 0)$

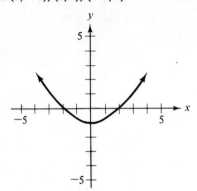

18. $(-2, 1), (0, 0), (-4, 0)$

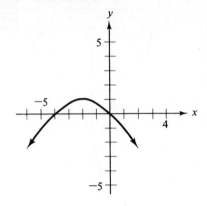

19. $(-3, -1), (0, 8), (-2, 0), (-4, 0)$

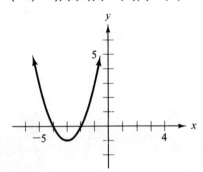

21. $(-2, -3), (0, -\frac{5}{3}), (1, 0), (-5, 0)$

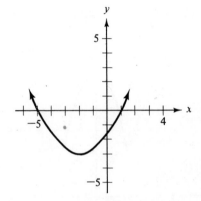

22. $(1, -2), (0, -\frac{3}{2}), (-1, 0), (3, 0)$

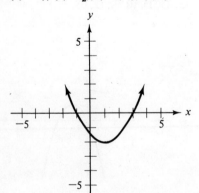

23. $(-\frac{3}{2}, -\frac{25}{4}), (0, -4), (1, 0), (-4, 0)$

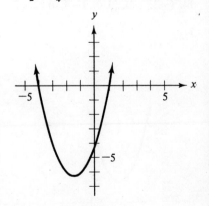

25. (−2, 1), (0, 5)

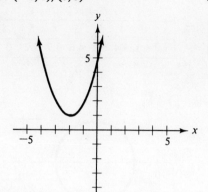

26. (2, 0), (0, −4)

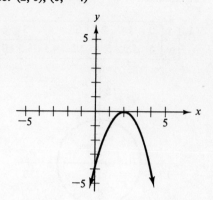

27. (4, −2), (0, 0), (0, −4)

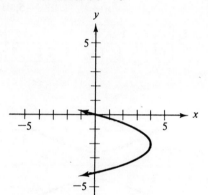

29. (−2, −1), (0, 1), (0, −3), (−$\frac{3}{2}$, 0)

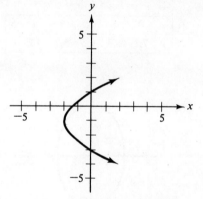

30. ($\frac{9}{4}$, 2), (0, 5), (0, −1), ($\frac{5}{4}$, 0)

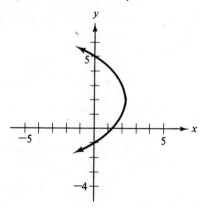

31. Revenue is $2500 if the price is $50.

33. 180 meters; 6 seconds

34. 24$\frac{1}{2}$ feet; 3$\frac{1}{2}$ seconds

EXERCISES 4.4 *(page 186)*

1.

x	0	1	2	3	4	5	6
y	6	5.9	5.7	5.2	4.5	3.3	0

2.

x	0	1	2	3	4	5	5.5
y	5.5	5.4	5.1	4.6	3.7	2.2	0

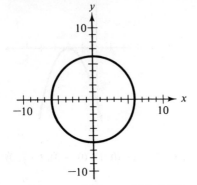

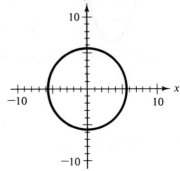

3.

x	0	1	2	3	4	5
y	7.1	6.9	6.5	5.7	4.2	0

5.

x	0	1	2	3	4	5
y	1	1.1	1.4	1.8	2.2	2.7

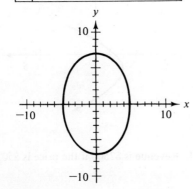

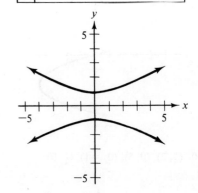

6.

x	2	3	4	5	6	7
y	0	3.2	4.9	6.5	8	9.5

7. $(\pm 8, 0), (0, \pm 4)$

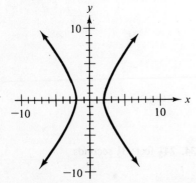

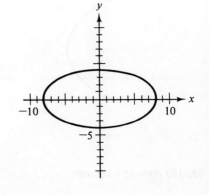

9. $(\pm\frac{9}{2}, 0), (0, \pm\frac{9}{2})$

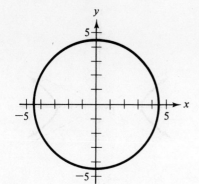

10. $(\pm3, 0), (0, \pm6)$

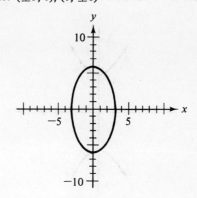

11. $(\pm\frac{10}{3}, 0), (0, \pm5)$

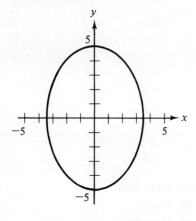

13. $y = \pm x; (\pm1, 0)$

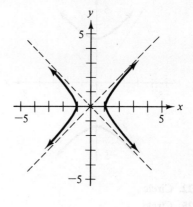

14. $y = \pm x; (0, \pm2)$

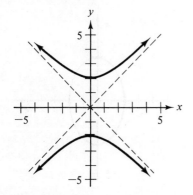

15. $y = \pm\frac{1}{2}x; (\pm4, 0)$

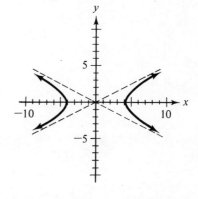

17. $y = \pm 2x$; $(0, \pm\sqrt{6})$

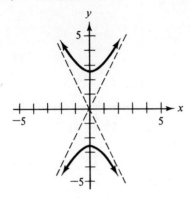

18. $y = \pm\frac{1}{2}x$; $(\pm, 3, 0)$

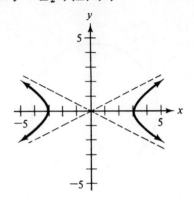

19. $y = \pm\frac{3}{2}x$; $(0, \pm 3)$

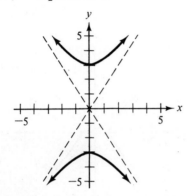

21. Ellipse

22. Circle

25. Circle

27. Parabola

30. Parabola

23. Hyperbola

26. Ellipse

29. Hyperbola

31. Ellipse; $(\pm 2, 0)$, $(0, \pm 3)$

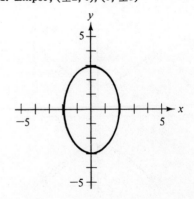

33. Hyperbola; $y = \pm x$; $(0, \pm 3)$

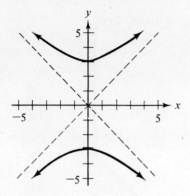

34. Ellipse; $(\pm 4, 0)$, $(0, \pm 8)$

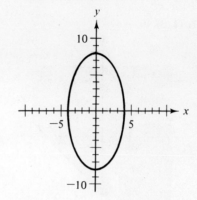

35. Hyperbola; $y = \pm\sqrt{2}\,x$; $(\pm 2, 0)$

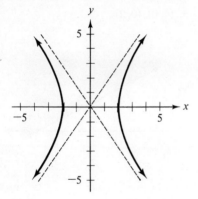

37. Ellipse; $(\pm 4, 0)$, $(0, \pm 2)$

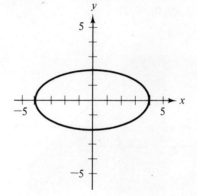

38. Hyperbola; $y = \pm x$; $(\pm\sqrt{3}, 0)$

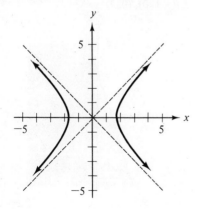

EXERCISES 4.5 *(page 192)*

1. (4, 0), (0, −4)

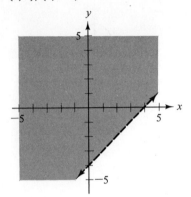

2. (1, 0), (0, −1)

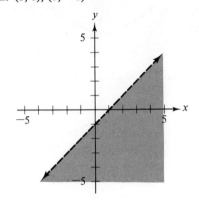

3. (2, 0), (0, 2)

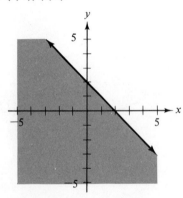

5. (4, 0), (0, 2)

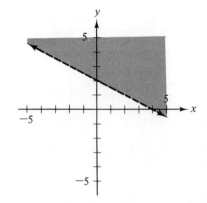

6. (1, 0), (0, 2)

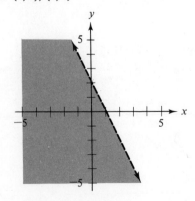

7. (−1, 0), (0, 3)

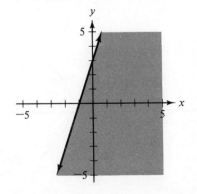

9. $(0, 0)$

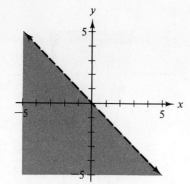

10. $(0, 0)$

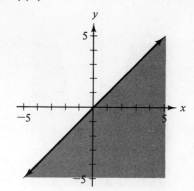

11. $(0, 0)$

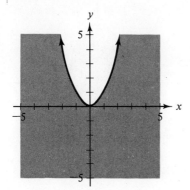

13. $(4, 0), (0, 2), (0, -2)$

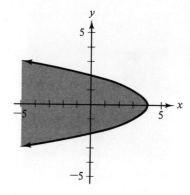

14. $(2, 0), (-2, 0), (0, 1)$

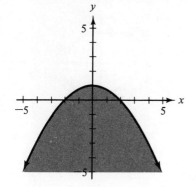

15. $(0, 0), (-2, 0)$

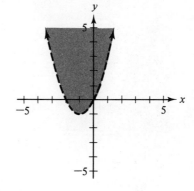

17. $(2, 0)$, $(-1, 0)$, $(0, -2)$

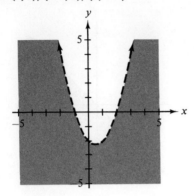

18. $(3, 0)$, $(-2, 0)$, $(0, -6)$

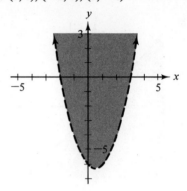

19. $(\pm 2, 0)$, $(0, \pm 2)$

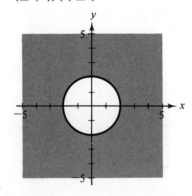

21. $(\pm 4, 0)$, $(0, \pm 8)$

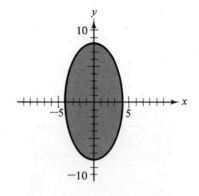

22. $(\pm 2, 0)$, $(0, \pm 3)$

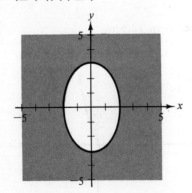

23. $(\pm \frac{5}{2}, 0)$, $(0, \pm 2)$

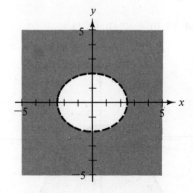

25. $(\pm 2, 0)$

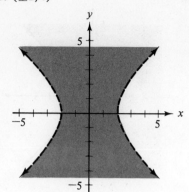

26. $(0, \pm 1)$

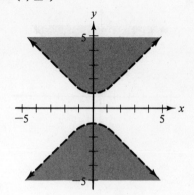

27.

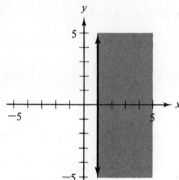

29.

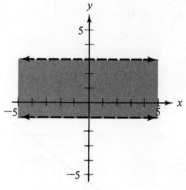

30.

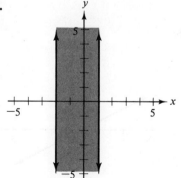

31.

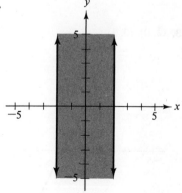

33.

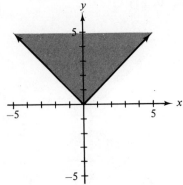

34.

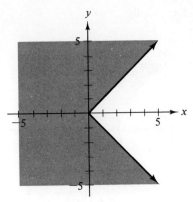

REVIEW EXERCISES 4 (*page 193*)

1. (4, 0), (0, −3)

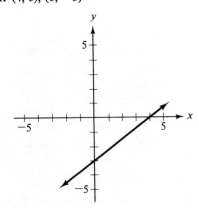

2. (−3, 0), (0, −2)

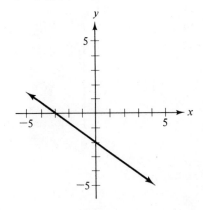

3. ($\frac{3}{2}$, 0), (0, 3)

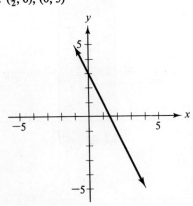

5.

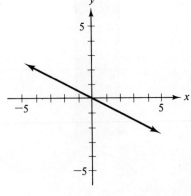

6.

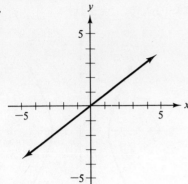

7.

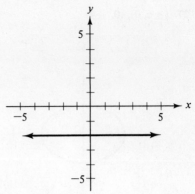

9. $m = -\frac{5}{4}$

10. $m = \frac{1}{2}$

11. $m = \frac{4}{3}; b = 2$

13. $-3x + y = 11$

14. $2x + 3y = 3$

15. $2x + y = 0$

17. $-x + 3y = 2$

18. $x = 0$

19. $(-3, 2)$

21. $(8, 128)$

22. $(-\frac{5}{2}, -\frac{21}{4})$

23. $(0, -4), (4, 0), (-4, 0)$

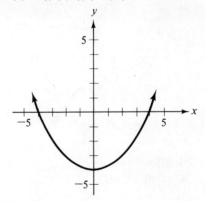

25. $(-4, -2), (0, 0), (0, -4)$

26. $(0, 0)$

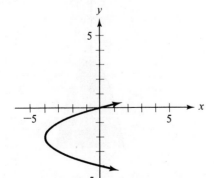

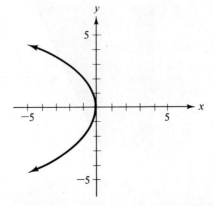

27. $(\pm 6, 0), (0, \pm 4)$

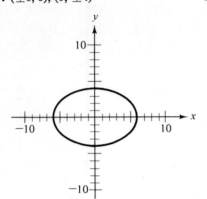

29. $(\pm 2, 0); y = \pm \frac{3}{2}x$

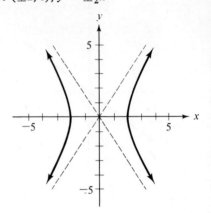

30. $(0, \pm 2); y = \pm 2x$

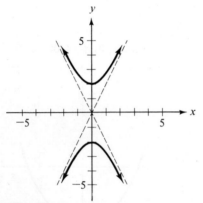

31. Circle

33. Hyperbola

34. Ellipse

35. $(1, 0), (0, -2)$

37. $(\pm 1, 0), (0, 1)$

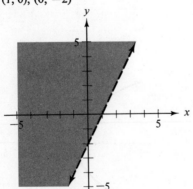

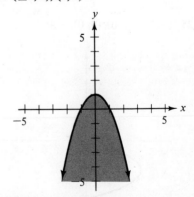

38. $(-1, 0), (0, \pm 2)$ **39.** $(\pm 4, 0), (0, \pm 4)$

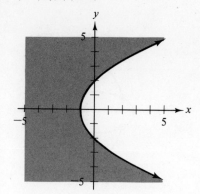   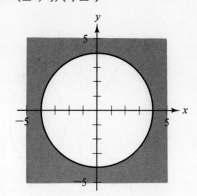

41.   **42.**

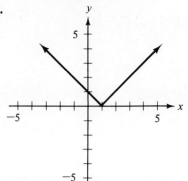   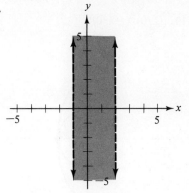

EXERCISES 5.1   (*page 201*)

1. $\{(1, 2)\}$ **2.** $\{(-1, 1)\}$

3. $\{(3, -2)\}$ **5.** $\{(4, 0)\}$

6. $\{(0, -2)\}$ **7.** $\{(\frac{1}{2}, \frac{3}{2})\}$

9. $\{(2, 5)\}$ **10.** $\{(2, -2)\}$

11. $\{(-3, 1)\}$ **13.** $\{(8, -12)\}$

14. $\{(11, 6)\}$ **15.** $\{(3, 3)\}$

17. $\{(3, 4), (3, -4), (-3, 4), (-3, -4)\}$ **18.** $\{(2, 1), (2, -1), (-2, 1), (-2, -1)\}$

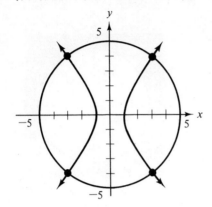

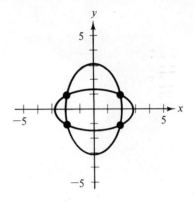

19. $\{(2, 0), (-2, 0)\}$ **21.** $\{(2, 2), (2, -2), (-2, 2), (-2, -2)\}$

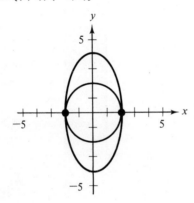

22. $\{(5, 0), (-5, 0)\}$

25. $\varnothing$; inconsistent

27. $\{(x, y): 2x - 3y = 4\}$; dependent

30. $\varnothing$; inconsistent

33. $7\frac{1}{2}$ miles per hour; $1\frac{1}{2}$ miles per hour

23. $\{(2, 3), (2, -3), (-2, 3), (-2, -3)\}$

26. $\{(x, y): x + 3y = 2\}$; dependent

29. $\{(0, 0)\}$; neither inconsistent nor dependent

31. 190 gallons skim milk; 10 gallons cream

34. $27\frac{1}{2}$ miles per hour; $22\frac{1}{2}$ miles per hour

EXERCISES 5.2 (*page 209*)

1. -1

3. 11

2. -4

5. 8

6. 0

7. $D = \begin{vmatrix} 3 & 5 \\ 4 & 7 \end{vmatrix}$ $D_x = \begin{vmatrix} 2 & 5 \\ 1 & 7 \end{vmatrix}$

$D_y = \begin{vmatrix} 3 & 2 \\ 4 & 1 \end{vmatrix}$

9. $D = \begin{vmatrix} 4 & -1 \\ 1 & -6 \end{vmatrix}$ $D_x = \begin{vmatrix} 0 & -1 \\ -3 & -6 \end{vmatrix}$

$D_y = \begin{vmatrix} 4 & 0 \\ 1 & -3 \end{vmatrix}$

10. $D = \begin{vmatrix} 1 & -2 \\ 3 & 4 \end{vmatrix}$ $D_x = \begin{vmatrix} 6 & -2 \\ -5 & 4 \end{vmatrix}$

$D_y = \begin{vmatrix} 1 & 6 \\ 3 & -5 \end{vmatrix}$

11. $\{(-\frac{2}{5}, \frac{3}{5})\}$

13. $\{(14, 5)\}$

14. $\{(-9, -14)\}$

15. $\{(0, \frac{3}{2})\}$

17. $\{(\frac{11}{5}, \frac{1}{5})\}$

18. $\{(-\frac{5}{7}, \frac{11}{7})\}$

19. $\{(\frac{1}{2}, -\frac{1}{2})\}$

21. $\{(\frac{2}{7}, -\frac{1}{14})\}$

22. $\{(\frac{12}{31}, \frac{20}{31})\}$

23. $\{(\frac{20}{7}, \frac{18}{7})\}$

25. $\{(\frac{1}{2}, -1)\}$

26. $\{(\frac{5}{3}, -\frac{5}{4})\}$

27. $\{(3, -\frac{3}{4})\}$

29. $\left\{\left(\frac{1}{2}, \frac{\sqrt{2}}{2}\right), \left(\frac{1}{2}, -\frac{\sqrt{2}}{2}\right),\right.$
$\left.\left(-\frac{1}{2}, \frac{\sqrt{2}}{2}\right), \left(-\frac{1}{2}, -\frac{\sqrt{2}}{2}\right)\right\}$

30. $\left\{\left(\frac{\sqrt{7}}{3}, \frac{\sqrt{5}}{3}\right), \left(\frac{\sqrt{7}}{3}, -\frac{\sqrt{5}}{3}\right),\right.$
$\left.\left(-\frac{\sqrt{7}}{3}, \frac{\sqrt{5}}{3}\right), \left(-\frac{\sqrt{7}}{3}, -\frac{\sqrt{5}}{3}\right)\right\}$

31. $D = 0$, $D_x = -2$; no pairs; inconsistent system

33. $D = 0$, $D_x = 0$; many pairs; dependent system

34. $D = 5$; one pair; independent, consistent system

35. 9 inches

37. 7.5 centimeters per second

38. Pipe A takes 12 minutes; pipe B takes 60 minutes.

EXERCISES 5.3 (*page 216*)

1. $\{(-3, 7)\}$

2. $\{(-4, 3)\}$

3. $\{(8, 6)\}$

5. $\{(1, 1), (-2, 4)\}$

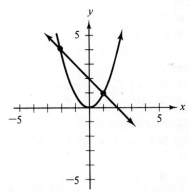

6. $\{(1, 2), (-1, -2)\}$ **7.** $\varnothing$

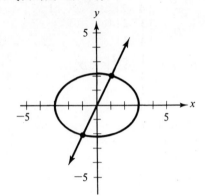

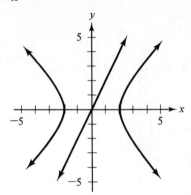

9. $\{(6, 2), (-6, -2)\}$

11. $\{(5, 9), (-1, -3)\}$

14. $\{(-1, -2), (6, \frac{1}{3})\}$

17. $\{(0, 0), (-1, -1)\}$

19. $\{(2, 2), (-3, 12)\}$

22. $\{(2, 4), (-2, 4), (\sqrt{15}, -7), (-\sqrt{15}, -7)\}$

25. $\{(2, 3), (-2, -3), (3, 2), (-3, -2)\}$

27. $\{(2\sqrt{2}, -\sqrt{2}), (-2\sqrt{2}, \sqrt{2})\}$

30. $\{(0, 0), (2, 8), (-2, -8)\}$

33. 12 inches by 16 inches

10. $\{(1, -2), (-1, 2)\}$

13. $\{(2, -3), (-\frac{3}{2}, 4)\}$

15. $\{(4, 16)\}$

18. $\{(0, 0), (\frac{1}{2}, -\frac{1}{2})\}$

21. $\{(2, 1), (2, -1), (-1, 2), (-1, -2)\}$

23. $\{(1, 1), (-\frac{7}{13}, -\frac{17}{13})\}$

26. $\{(2, -1), (-2, 1)\}$

29. $\{(0, 0), (1, 1), (-1, -1)\}$

31. $\{(0, 0), (2, 4), (-1, -2)\}$

34. $\sqrt{2}$ centimeters and $2\sqrt{2}$ centimeters

EXERCISES 5.4   (*page 222*)

1. $(2, 1, 1)$

3. $(-2, 2, 1)$

6. $(0, -\frac{2}{3}, \frac{1}{3})$

9. $(\frac{2}{5}, -\frac{3}{5}, \frac{1}{5})$

11. $(1, 1, 1)$

14. $(2, -1, 3)$

17. $(\frac{13}{12}, -\frac{1}{3}, \frac{7}{12})$

19. $(\frac{4}{11}, \frac{17}{11}, -\frac{8}{11})$

22. No solution

25. \$2000 at 5%; \$5000 at 8%; \$5000 at 10%

2. $(-1, 1, -1)$

5. $(\frac{1}{2}, \frac{3}{2}, -\frac{1}{2})$

7. $(2, -1, 1)$

10. $(-\frac{2}{3}, \frac{1}{3}, \frac{5}{3})$

13. $(3, 0, 2)$

15. $(1, -2, 1)$

18. $(\frac{47}{15}, \frac{19}{15}, -\frac{5}{3})$

21. Many solutions

23. No solution

26. $y = -x^2 + 3x - 1$

EXERCISES 5.5 (page 228)

1. $\begin{bmatrix} -1 & 2 & -3 & 2 \\ 1 & -1 & 2 & 0 \\ 2 & 0 & -1 & -2 \end{bmatrix}$

2. $\begin{bmatrix} 1 & -1 & 2 & 0 \\ -1 & 2 & -3 & 2 \\ -2 & 0 & 1 & 2 \end{bmatrix}$

3. $\begin{bmatrix} 1 & -1 & 2 & 0 \\ 0 & 1 & -1 & 2 \\ 2 & 0 & -1 & -2 \end{bmatrix}$

5. $\begin{bmatrix} 1 & -1 & 2 & 0 \\ -1 & 2 & -3 & 2 \\ 0 & 2 & -5 & -2 \end{bmatrix}$

6. $\begin{bmatrix} 2 & -3 & 5 & -2 \\ -1 & 2 & -3 & 2 \\ 2 & 0 & -1 & -2 \end{bmatrix}$

7. $x + 2y - z = 3$
$2x - y + 5z = 1$
$-x + y + 2z = 4$

9. $(1, 2, 1)$

10. $(1, -1, 1)$

11. $(-2, 2, 1)$

13. $(0, 1, -1)$

14. $(1, 0, 2)$

15. $(-2, -2, 2)$

17. $(1, -1, 1, 1)$

18. $(2, 0, 1, -1)$

19. $(-2, 1, 0, 2)$

EXERCISES 5.6 (page 236)

1. 11

2. -17

3. -5

5. $(\frac{3}{2}, -\frac{5}{8}, -\frac{7}{8})$

6. $(-\frac{2}{7}, \frac{3}{7}, \frac{6}{7})$

7. $(-1, 3, 2)$

9. -3

10. 6

11. 6

13. -7

14. 3

15. 16

17. 6

18. -10

19. -2

21. $D = 0$; $D_{x_1} = 0$; many solutions

22. $D = 0$; $D_{x_1} = 8$; no solution

REVIEW EXERCISES 5 (page 237)

1. $\{(-2, 2)\}$

2. $\{(5, -4)\}$

3. $\{(-\frac{2}{3}, -\frac{4}{3})\}$

5. $\{(3, 1)\}$

6. $\{(-2, 1)\}$

7. $\{(3, 2)\}$

9. $\{(\frac{26}{7}, -\frac{9}{7})\}$

10. $\{(\frac{5}{16}, -\frac{17}{16})\}$

11. $\{(-2, 6)\}$

13. $\{(12, -15)\}$

14. $\{(\frac{1}{2}, -1)\}$

15. $\{(2, -4), (5, 5)\}$

17. $\{(-3, 4), (5, 0)\}$

18. $\{(2, -1), (-8, -11)\}$

19. $\{(2\sqrt{3}, \sqrt{3}), (-2\sqrt{3}, -\sqrt{3})\}$

21. $(2, 1, -1)$

22. $(3, 1, -2)$

23. No solution

25. $(-2, 1, 2)$

27. 12

30. $\sqrt{3}$ centimeters by $2\sqrt{3}$ centimeters

26. $(2, 1, -1, 3)$

29. 56 milliliters of 10%; 24 milliliters of 30%

31. 150 feet; 50 feet per second

EXERCISES 6.1 (*page 248*)

1. Domain $= \{x : x \geq -2\}$; range $= \{1\}$; function

3. Domain $= \{x : x \leq 2\}$; range $= \{y : y \leq 3\}$; not a function

6. Domain $= R$; range $= \{y : y \leq 3\}$; function

9. Domain $= \{-3\}$; range $= R$; not a function

2. Domain $= \{2\}$; range $= \{y : y \geq -1\}$; not a function

5. Domain $= \{x : x \geq -3\}$; range $= R$; not a function

7. Domain $= \{x : -2 \leq x \leq 4\}$; range $= \{y : -2 \leq y \leq 3\}$; function

10. Domain $= R$; range $= \{2\}$; function

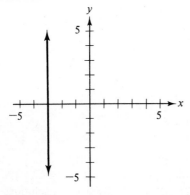

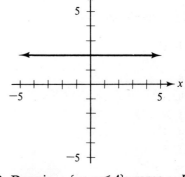

11. Domain $= R$; range $= R$; function

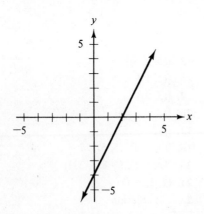

13. Domain $= \{x : x \leq 4\}$; range $= R$; not a function

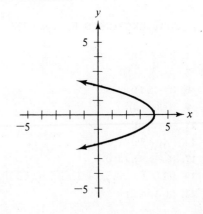

14. Domain $= R$; range $=$ $\{y : y \geq -4\}$; function

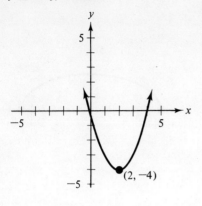

15. Domain $=$ $\{x : -2\sqrt{2} \leq x \leq 2\sqrt{2}\}$; range $= \{y : -4 \leq y \leq 4\}$; not a function

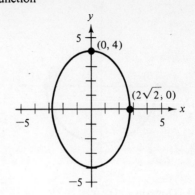

17. $y = \dfrac{3x - 6}{2}$; function

18. $y = 2 - |x|$; function

19. $y = \pm\sqrt{1 - x}$; not a function

21. $y = \sqrt[3]{x^2 - 1}$; function

22. $y = \sqrt[3]{x^2}$; function

23. $f(x) = \dfrac{-x + 4}{2}$

25. $f(x) = \dfrac{3}{x + 2}$

26. $f(x) = \dfrac{x}{x^2 - 2}$

27. $f(x) = \sqrt[3]{x - 2}$

29. R

30. R

31. $\{x : x \neq -3\}$

33. $\{x : x \geq -2\}$

34. $\{x : x \leq \frac{3}{2}\}$

35. $\{x : x \neq \pm 1\}$

37. R

38. R

39. Domain $= \{x : x \leq 1\}$; range $= \{y : y \geq 0\}$

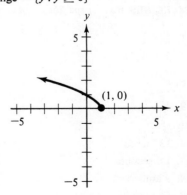

41. Domain $= \{x: -4 \leq x \leq 4\}$;
range $= \{y: -4 \leq y \leq 0\}$

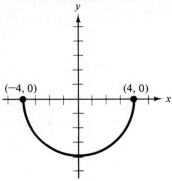

42. Domain $= \{x: -6 \leq x \leq 6\}$;
range $= \{y: 0 \leq y \leq 3\}$

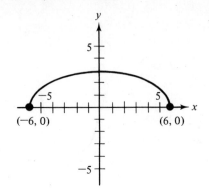

43. Domain $= \{x: x \leq -2\}$
$\cup \{x: x \geq 2\}$; range $= \{y: y \geq 0\}$

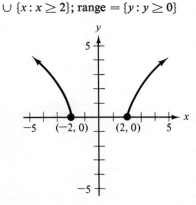

EXERCISES 6.2 (*page 255*)

1. $y = \frac{5}{2}x$

2. $y = \frac{9}{4}x^2$

3. $p = 3\sqrt{q}$

5. $r = \frac{3}{4}st$

6. $r = \dfrac{32\sqrt{s}}{t^2}$

7. 16

9. $\frac{32}{9}$

10. 3

11. $\frac{10}{3}$

13. 40 pounds per square inch

14. 13 inches

15. 180 meters

17. 1.6 seconds

18. 80 feet per second

19. 9 amperes

21. $67\frac{1}{2}$ candle power

22. $6\frac{3}{4}$ pounds

23. 24 cubic feet

25. 80 pounds

26. 4608 kilograms

EXERCISES 6.3 (*page 262*)

1. 4, 9, 14, 19; yes
2. 3, 1, −1, −3; yes
3. $1, \frac{1}{2}, \frac{1}{3}, \frac{1}{4}$, no
5. 1, 8, 27, 64; no
6. 1, 16, 81, 256; no
7. 2, 4, 8, 16; no
9. $a_n = 3n + 1$
10. $a_n = 2n + 3$
11. $a_n = -2n + 7$
13. $a_n = \frac{1}{2}n + \frac{1}{2}$
14. $a_n = -\frac{3}{2}n + \frac{15}{2}$
15. 74
17. −55
18. −76
19. 158
21. 10
22. 23
23. 27
25. 26
26. 19
27. 28
29. 110
30. −344
31. 363
33. 630
34. 420
35. 725
37. −375
38. −1275
39. 2475
41. 240,000
42. $253.25
43. $107,200
45. 5500
46. 6615

EXERCISES 6.4 (*page 268*)

1. 3, 9, 27, 81; yes
2. −2, −4, −8, −16; yes
3. 1, 2, 4, 8; yes
5. 2, −6, 18, −54; yes
6. $\frac{1}{2}, -1, 2, -4$; yes
7. $\frac{1}{2}, \frac{1}{4}, \frac{1}{8}, \frac{1}{16}$; yes
9. $b_n = 3^{n-1}$
10. $b_n = 2 \cdot 2^{n-1}$
11. $b_n = 2(-4)^{n-1}$
13. Not a geometric progression
14. $b_n = 16(-\frac{1}{2})^{n-1}$
15. $3 \cdot 2^8$
17. 3^{12}
18. $\dfrac{1}{2^8}$
19. 4^{12}
21. $-\dfrac{1}{2^{10}}$
22. $2 \cdot 3^{15}$
23. $2^{10} - 1$
25. $\dfrac{5^9 - 5}{2}$
26. $4^6 - 1$
27. $\dfrac{3^6 - 2^6}{2^5}$
29. $1 - 2^6$
30. $-\dfrac{3^6 + 3}{4}$
31. $18(\frac{3}{4})^5$ feet; approximately 4.27 feet
33. $4000 \cdot (1.05)^8$ dollars; approximately $5910
34. $100 \cdot (\frac{3}{4})^{12}$ grams; approximately 3.17 grams

35. $3600[1 - (\frac{5}{6})^8]$ dollars; approximately $2760

37. $5000(1.06)^{10}$ dollars; approximately $8950

38. $1000(1.04)^{14}$ dollars; approximately $1730

EXERCISES 6.5 (*page 274*)

1. $r = \frac{1}{3}$; limit is zero.

2. $r = \frac{3}{4}$; limit is zero.

3. $r = \frac{3}{2}$; divergent

5. $r = -2$; divergent

6. $r = -\frac{1}{2}$; limit is zero.

7. $r = -\frac{2}{3}$; limit is zero.

9. $\frac{3}{2}$

10. $\frac{1}{2}$

11. 3

13. $\frac{2}{3}$

14. $-\frac{2}{5}$

15. -1

17. 2

18. $\frac{4}{3}$

19. 36

21. $\frac{81}{4}$

22. $\frac{1}{3}$

23. Divergent

25. $\frac{7}{9}$

26. $\frac{3}{11}$

27. $\frac{15}{37}$

29. $\frac{7}{30}$

30. $\frac{19}{55}$

31. 210 centimeters

33. $2500

34. 40 feet

EXERCISES 6.6 (*page 279*)

1. $x^4 + 8x^3 + 24x^2 + 32x + 16$

2. $x^4 - 4x^3 + 6x^2 - 4x + 1$

3. $16x^4 - 32x^3 + 24x^2 - 8x + 1$

5. $x^8 + 4x^6 y + 6x^4 y^2 + 4x^2 y^3 + y^4$

6. $x^4 + 4x^3 y^3 + 6x^2 y^6 + 4xy^9 + y^{12}$

7. $x^6 + 6x^5 y + 15x^4 y^2 + 20x^3 y^3$

9. $x^8 - 8x^7 y + 28x^6 y^2 - 56x^5 y^3$

10. $x^9 - 9x^8 y + 36x^7 y^2 - 84x^6 y^3$

11. $x^{10} + 10x^9 y + 45x^8 y^2 + 120x^7 y^3$

13. $x^5 + 10x^4 + 40x^3 + 80x^2$

14. $x^6 + 6x^5 + 15x^4 + 20x^3$

15. $x^7 - 7x^6 + 21x^5 - 35x^4$

17. $x^{18} + 9x^{16} y + 36x^{14} y^2 + 84x^{12} y^3$

18. $x^{10} + 10x^9 y^2 + 45x^8 y^4 + 120x^7 y^6$

19. $32x^5 + 240x^4 + 720x^3 + 1080x^2$

21. $35x^3 y^4$

22. $-56x^3 y^5$

23. $126x^5 y^4$

25. $-80x^2$

26. $240x^2$

27. $\frac{5}{32}$

29. $\frac{8}{27}$

30. $\frac{96}{625}$

REVIEW EXERCISES 6 (*page 280*)

1. Domain $= R$; range $= \{y : y \leq 1\}$; function

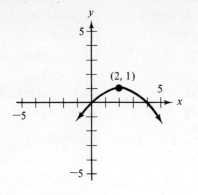

2. Domain $= \{x : -4\sqrt{2} \leq x \leq 4\sqrt{2}\}$; range $= \{y : -4 \leq y \leq 4\}$; not a function

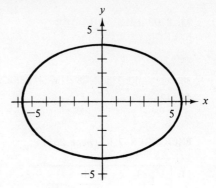

3. If $x = 0$, then $y = \pm 1$; not a function

5. $\{x : x \geq \frac{3}{4}\}$

6. $\{x : x \neq 0, x \neq -1\}$

7. Domain $= \{x : -2 \leq x \leq 2\}$; range $= \{y : 0 \leq y \leq 2\}$

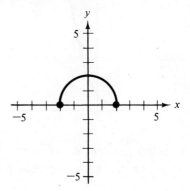

9. $y = \frac{75}{x^2}; \frac{75}{16}$

10. $r = \frac{1}{2}\sqrt{s}\, t^3$; 54

11. $7\frac{1}{2}$ inches

13. Arithmetic; $u_n = -3n + 15$; -45

14. Geometric; $u_n = 3 \cdot 2^{n-1}$; $3 \cdot 2^{15}$

15. Geometric; $u_n = 2(-3)^{n-1}$; $-2 \cdot 3^{17}$

17. Geometric; $u_n = (\frac{1}{8})(\frac{2}{3})^{n-1}$; $\frac{2^{13}}{3^{16}}$

18. Arithmetic; $u_n = \frac{1}{4}n - \frac{1}{12}$; $\frac{14}{3}$

19. $\frac{5^{20} - 1}{4}$

21. -1360

22. $\dfrac{2^{10}-1}{2^{10}}$

23. 1050

25. Series; divergent

26. Series; $\frac{5}{2}$

27. Sequence; 0

29. Series; $\frac{9}{40}$

30. Sequence; divergent

31. $10^3(\frac{4}{5})^{10}$ grams; approximately 107 grams

33. 8200 items

34. $\dfrac{10^2(1-0.8^{12})}{0.2}$ dollars; approximately \$466

35. $\frac{1}{22}$

37. $x^{12}+12x^{11}y+66x^{10}y^2+220x^9y^3$

38. $x^{13}-13x^{12}y+78x^{11}y^2-286x^{10}y^3$

39. $x^{10}-20x^9+180x^8-960x^7$

41. $126x^4y^5$

42. $\frac{15}{64}$

EXERCISES 7.1   (*page 288*)

1.

x	3	2	1	0	−1	−2	−3
y	27	9	3	1	$\frac{1}{3}$	$\frac{1}{9}$	$\frac{1}{27}$

2.

x	3	2	1	0	−1	−2	−3
y	$\frac{8}{27}$	$\frac{4}{9}$	$\frac{2}{3}$	1	$\frac{3}{2}$	$\frac{9}{4}$	$\frac{27}{8}$

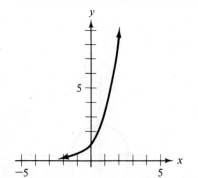

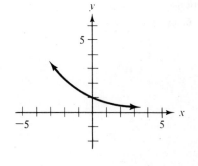

3.

x	3	2	1	0	−1	−2	−3
y	3.4	2.2	1.5	1	0.7	0.4	0.3

5.

x	3	2	1	0	−1	−2	−3
y	0.5	0.6	0.8	1	1.2	1.6	2.0

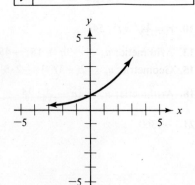

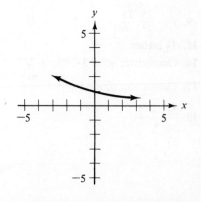

6.

x	3	2	1	0	−1	−2	−3
y	0.1	0.2	0.4	1	2.5	6.2	16

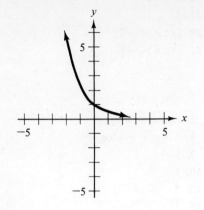

7.

x	3	2	1	0	−1	−2	−3
y	$\frac{1}{8}$	$\frac{1}{4}$	$\frac{1}{2}$	1	2	4	8

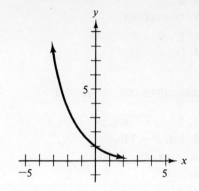

9. 4

10. 3

11. 9

13. 16

14. $\frac{1}{8}$

15. $\frac{1}{3}$

17. 3^x

18. 2^{2x}

19. 2^{5x}

21. 3^{2x-1}

22. 3^{x+1}

23. 2^{3x-2}

25. $\{4\}$

26. $\{-3\}$

27. $\{0\}$

29. $\{\frac{1}{3}\}$

30. $\{\frac{3}{2}\}$

31. $\{-\frac{1}{2}\}$

33. $\{\frac{4}{3}\}$

34. $\{\frac{1}{2}\}$

35. $\{1\}$

37. $\{3\}$

38. $\{10\}$

39. $\{-3\}$

EXERCISES 7.2 (page 295)

1. $f^{-1}(x) = x - 3$

2. $f^{-1}(x) = \frac{1}{2}x$

3. $f^{-1}(x) = \frac{1}{4}(1 - x)$

5. Not one-to-one

6. $f^{-1}(x) = \sqrt[3]{x - 1}$

7. $f^{-1}(x) = \frac{1}{8}x^3$

9. $x = 4^y$

10. $x = 10^y$

11. $x = \log_a z$

13. $x = e^r$

14. $x = \log_e z$

15. $x = \dfrac{\log_b c}{a}$

17. $\{16\}$

18. $\{1\}$

19. $\{4\}$

21. $\{8\}$

22. $\{4\}$

23. $\{\frac{1}{3}\}$

25. 3

26. 4

27. 1   **29.** $\frac{3}{2}$

30. $\frac{2}{3}$ **31.** $-\frac{4}{3}$

33. 0   **34.** 1

35. Not defined   **37.** $\frac{4}{3}$

38. $\frac{4}{3}$ **39.** $\{x : x > -2\}$

41. $\{x : x < \frac{1}{2}\}$ **42.** $\{x : x > -\frac{2}{3}\}$

EXERCISES 7.3 (*page 301*)

1. $2 \log_b x + \log_b y$ **2.** $\log_b x + 3 \log_b y$

3. $\log_b x - 3 \log_b y$ **5.** $\frac{1}{2} \log_b x + \frac{1}{2} \log_b y$

6. $\frac{2}{3} \log_b x + \frac{1}{3} \log_b y$ **7.** 5

9. -2 **10.** 1

11. 6   **13.** 8

14. 13   **15.** 1

17. 16   **18.** 6

19. $\frac{3}{2}$ **21.** $\frac{10}{3}$

22. $-\frac{4}{3}$ **23.** $\frac{11}{2}$

25. $\{\frac{16}{3}\}$ **26.** $\{24\}$

27. $\{18\}$ **29.** $\{\frac{1}{2}\}$

30. $\{\frac{4}{3}\}$ **31.** $\{\frac{1}{3}\}$

33. $\{4\}$ **34.** $\{8\}$

35. 0.8   **37.** 1.5

38. -0.1 **39.** 0.6

EXERCISES 7.4 (*page 306*)

1. $\dfrac{\log 3}{\log 2} = 1.58$ **2.** $\dfrac{\log 2}{\log 5} = 0.431$

3. $\dfrac{\log 4 - \log 7}{\log 7} = -0.288$ **5.** $\dfrac{\log 5 - \log 2}{2 \log 5} = 0.285$

6. $\dfrac{\log 3 - \log 4}{3 \log 4} = -0.0692$ **7.** $\dfrac{\log 4}{\log 4 - \log 3} = 4.82$

9. $\dfrac{2 \log 2 + \log 6}{\log 6 - \log 2} = 2.89$ **10.** $\dfrac{\log 7 - \log 6}{\log 7 + \log 6} = 0.412$

11. $\dfrac{\log 3}{2 \log 3 + \log 5} = 0.289$ **13.** $\frac{1}{3} \ln 5 = 0.536$

14. $1 + \ln 2 = 1.69$ **15.** $\dfrac{-1 + \ln 3}{2} = 0.0493$

17. $-1 + \ln 2 = -0.307$ **18.** $\ln \frac{3}{2} = 0.405$

19. $-1 + \ln 3 = 0.0986$ **21.** $1 + e^2 = 8.39$

22. $\frac{1}{2}e^3 = 10.0$

23. $\frac{1}{e} = 0.368$

25. $\frac{1}{4}e^3 = 5.02$

26. $\frac{e^2 - 3}{3} = 1.46$

27. $\frac{1}{e-1} = 0.582$

29. $10^4 \cdot e^{0.9}$ dollars; approximately $24,600

30. $10^4 \cdot e^{-0.4}$ dollars; approximately $6703

31. $\frac{\ln 2}{0.07}$ years; approximately 9.90 years

33. $10^2 \cdot e^{-0.3}$ milligrams; approximately 74.1 milligrams

34. $\frac{\ln 2}{0.0003}$ years; approximately 2310 years

EXERCISES 7.5 (*page 311*)

1. 0.7973	**2.** 0.9708
3. 0.0128	**5.** 7.54
6. 3.14	**7.** 9.15
9. 2.7292	**10.** 1.2765
11. $0.8932 - 1$	**13.** 1.9717
14. 3.9263	**15.** $0.3522 - 2$
17. 3.8451	**18.** $0.4771 - 4$
19. $0.5441 - 5$	**21.** 22.4
22. 657	**23.** 1220
25. 0.0415	**26.** 0.981
27. 0.000350	**29.** 0.501
30. 0.0158	**31.** 0.00126
33. 5.19	**34.** 0.3324
35. $0.6902 - 1$	**37.** 2510
38. 1.7259	**39.** $0.8573 - 2$
41. 0.0518	**42.** 0.206
43. 0.655	

EXERCISES 7.6 (*page 316*)

1. 311	**2.** 206
3. 6.42	**5.** 42.5
6. 737,000	**7.** 5.21
9. 8.66	**10.** 0.0618
11. 0.0299	**13.** 0.882
14. 0.0768	**15.** 0.00147
17. 13.5	**18.** 1.81

19. $5740

22. 1720 pounds

21. 18,100 cubic centimeters

23. 2.19 seconds

EXERCISES 7.7 (*page 322*)

1. 0.8576

3. 0.4507

6. 2.6410

9. 4.133

11. 3.754

14. 61.33

17. $2054

19. 0.1659 gram

2. 0.9515

5. 1.7187

7. 0.9089 − 1

10. 8.524

13. 5187

15. 0.04467

18. 2,017,000

REVIEW EXERCISES 7 (*page 322*)

1.

x	4	2	0	−2	−4
y	9	3	1	$\frac{1}{3}$	$\frac{1}{9}$

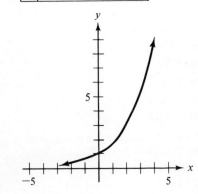

2.

x	2	1	0	−1	−2
y	$-\frac{1}{4}$	$-\frac{1}{2}$	−1	−2	−4

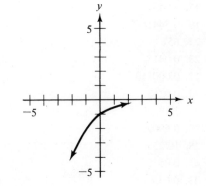

3. 4

6. {2}

9. $r = \dfrac{a^s}{t}$

11. {8}

14. $-\frac{2}{3}$

17. $3 \log_b x + 2 \log_b y$

19. $\frac{9}{2}$

22. {$\frac{1}{2}$}

5. {$\frac{1}{2}$}

7. $f^{-1}(x) = \frac{1}{4}(x - 3)$

10. $r = \log_a (t - s)$

13. $\frac{3}{2}$

15. $-\frac{1}{3}$

18. $\frac{1}{2} \log_b x - \frac{2}{3} \log_b y$

21. {3}

23. $\dfrac{\log 5 - 3 \log 2}{\log 2} = -0.678$

25. $\dfrac{1 + \ln 2}{3} = 0.564$

26. $-1 + \ln \frac{3}{2} = -0.595$

27. $e^{-2} = 0.135$

29. $4 \cdot 10^9 e^{0.8}$; approximately 8.90 billion

30. $20 \ln 2\%$; approximately 13.9%

31. Domain $= R$; range $= \{y : y > 0\}$

33. $0.6191 - 1$

34. 2.8722

35. 22.0

37. 1510

38. $0.9117 - 1$

39. 4.37

41. 0.201

42. 3.36

43. 2.9407

45. 2.727

46. 53.79

EXERCISES 8.1 (*page 329*)

1. $5 - 3i$

2. $2i$

3. 12

5. $-1 - 2i$

6. $2 - 7i$

7. $-2i$

9. $(1 + \sqrt{2}) + 2i$

10. $(1 + \sqrt{3}) - i$

11. $-3 + (1 - \sqrt{3})i$

13. $6 + 3i$

14. $-2 + 6i$

15. $-1 + 2i$

17. $1 + 3i$

18. $7 + i$

19. $5 + i$

21. $3 + 4i$

22. $2i$

23. $-8 - 6i$

25. 41

26. 13

27. 3

29. $-1 + 2\sqrt{2}\,i$

30. $2 + 2\sqrt{3}\,i$

31. $\frac{2}{5} - \frac{4}{5}i$

33. $\frac{3}{13} + \frac{2}{13}i$

34. $\frac{1}{5} + \frac{3}{5}i$

35. $1 + 2i$

37. i

38. $-4 - 2i$

39. 1

41. i

42. -1

43. $-2 + 2i$

EXERCISES 8.2 (*page 333*)

1. $7i$

2. $-6i$

3. $1 - 2\sqrt{2}\,i$

5. -6

6. -20

7. -4

9. $-24 + 12i$

10. $14 + 6i$

11. $-3 - 6i$

13. $1 + i$

14. $-1 + \sqrt{3}\,i$

15. $\frac{2}{3} - \frac{1}{3}\sqrt{5}\,i$

17. $\{3i, -3i\}$

18. $\{\frac{1}{2}i, -\frac{1}{2}i\}$

19. $\{-1 + 2i, -1 - 2i\}$

21. $\left\{\dfrac{3 + \sqrt{7}i}{4}, \dfrac{3 - \sqrt{7}i}{4}\right\}$

22. $\left\{\dfrac{-5 + \sqrt{23}i}{6}, \dfrac{-5 - \sqrt{23}i}{6}\right\}$

23. $\left\{\dfrac{-1 + 2i}{5}, \dfrac{-1 - 2i}{5}\right\}$

25. $\{0, 2i, -2i\}$

26. $\{0, -1 + i, -1 - i\}$

27. $\{1, -1, 3i, -3i\}$

29. $\{-2, 1 + \sqrt{3}i, 1 - \sqrt{3}i\}$

30. $\left\{3, \dfrac{-3 + 3\sqrt{3}i}{2}, \dfrac{-3 - 3\sqrt{3}i}{2}\right\}$

31. $\{2, -2, 2i, -2i\}$

33. $4, -2 + 2\sqrt{3}i, -2 - 2\sqrt{3}i$

34. $1, \dfrac{-1 + \sqrt{3}i}{2}, \dfrac{-1 - \sqrt{3}i}{2}$

35. $-3, \dfrac{3 + 3\sqrt{3}i}{2}, \dfrac{3 - 3\sqrt{3}i}{2}$

index